The Cognitive Therapeutics Method

Non-Pharmacological Approaches to Slowing the Cognitive and Functional Decline Associated with Dementia

---

edited by Samuel T. Gontkovsky, PsyD

All Rights Reserved. No part of this book may be used or reproduced in any matter without the written permission of the Publisher. Printed in the United States of America. For information address Home Care Press, 148 Hawthorne Avenue, Palo Alto, CA 94301.

ISBN 978-0-9857236-3-7

TABLE OF CONTENTS

CONTRIBUTORS

Anthony Andrews, MS
Nova Southeastern University, Center for Psychological Studies,
Fort Lauderdale, FL

Rebecca Fontanetta, MS
Nova Southeastern University, Center for Psychological Studies, Fort
Lauderdale, FL

Elkhonon Goldberg, PhD, ABPP-CN
New York University School of Medicine, Department of Neurology,
New York, NY
Fielding Graduate University, School of Psychology, Santa Barbara, CA

Charles J. Golden, PhD, ABPP-CP, CN
Nova Southeastern University, Center for Psychological Studies,
Fort Lauderdale, FL

Samuel T. Gontkovsky, PsyD
Home Care Assistance, Palo Alto, CA

Katherine Hickock, MA
Home Care Assistance, Palo Alto, CA

Deborah S. Hoffnung, PhD, ABPP-CN
Alegent Creighton Health, Omaha, NE

Lisa Lashley, PsyD
Nova Southeastern University, Center for Psychological Studies,
Fort Lauderdale, FL

Kelly McCormick, BS
Home Care Assistance, Palo Alto, CA

Josh Mervis, BA
New York State Psychiatric Institute, Columbia University Medical Center,
New York, NY

Timothy I. Michaels, BA
Research Foundation for Mental Hygiene, The Nathan S. Kline Institute for Psychiatric Research, Orangeburg, NY
Manhattan Psychiatric Center, Psychopharmacology Research Program, New York, NY

Robert M. Nevels, PhD
The Counseling Center, Ridgeland, MS

Aaron W. Powell, PhD
Home Care Assistance, Palo Alto, CA

Joseph J. Ryan, PhD, ABPP-CN
University of Central Missouri, Department of Psychological Science, Warrensburg, MO

Sara L. Schara McAnulty, PhD
The Rehab Center, Charlotte, NC

Scott W. Sumerall, PhD
Eastern Kansas Veterans Affairs Healthcare System, Leavenworth, KS

R. Lauren Whitehead, PsyD, JD
Nova Southeastern University, Center for Psychological Studies, Fort Lauderdale, FL

Kimberly R. Willis, PT, DPT
Saint Dominic Medical Center, Jackson, MS

CHAPTER 1

Understanding Dementia and Its Causes

Timothy I. Michaels, Josh Mervis, Samuel T. Gontkovsky, and Elkhonon Goldberg

Dementia is a general term corresponding to a number of heterogeneous signs and symptoms associated with cognitive decline. Although this term is quite often used incorrectly by the general public to refer to a single disease or thought to be an inevitable part of normal aging, dementia refers to declines in cognitive ability severe enough to interfere with daily functioning that can have myriad causes. However, the general public frequently misunderstands the concept of dementia. Laypersons oftentimes equate dementia with Alzheimer's disease (AD), believing the two to be interchangeable, or contrast the two, asking the question, "Does this person have Alzheimer's disease or dementia?" Rather, the term "dementia" signifies a cluster of cognitive and functional symptoms that represents a decline from an individual's premorbid capabilities. To say a person has dementia is analogous to simply saying that a person is sick, or ill. When someone is ill, healthcare professionals must look for the underlying cause of this illness. For example, consider that an illness may be due to an allergy, disease, or infection. An infection may be viral or bacterial. A viral infection may occur in the respiratory system or the gastrointestinal system. When a person presents to a physician as sick, a systematic process ensues in which the physician examines signs and symptoms of the illness to rule out some causes and eventually reach a determination as to the etiology. A similar process takes places when an individual presents to a physician with disturbances of cognition (e.g., attention, memory, language, visual-spatial perception, executive functioning, etc.). The clinician must consider the specific combination of signs and symptoms. Other issues to be considered include but are not limited to whether the initial onset of problems occurred rapidly or slowly, whether deficits have remained stable or progressively worsened over time, whether difficulties have become worse, and whether comorbid health/medical issues may be related to these new symptoms. This task is complex and generally requires a lengthy and time-consuming clinical evaluation, often involving multiple healthcare professionals across disciplines and myriad diagnostic tools.

Though describing the entire process that comprises a comprehensive examination for dementia is beyond the scope of this chapter, the reader is referred to the bibliography for additional information on this specific topic. The purpose of this chapter is to clarify the meaning of the term dementia, provide a basic overview for diagnosing and classifying dementia, and describe the main neurological diseases/disorders that may result in dementia. With respect to the latter objective, an emphasis will be placed on explaining the distinct manifestations of the cognitive and behavioral issues associated with each of these neurological conditions that may underlie dementia.

Diagnosing and Classifying Dementia

While recent advancements in clinical and translational research have greatly improved our understanding of the pathophysiology of dementia, accurate differential diagnosis still can be challenging. Although post-mortem brain autopsy remains the most definitive means for diagnostic confirmation, it is now widely recognized that the major causes of dementia have unique pathophysiology that manifest through clearly distinguishable clinical presentations (Lichtenberg, Murman, & Mellow, 2003). Accurate diagnosis is critical, as it provides patients with a clearer understanding of prognosis, establishes expectations of disease course, and provides clinicians with the information necessary for conceptualization and development of a treatment plan.

Dementia diagnosis is a multidisciplinary effort requiring the expertise of neuropsychologists, neurologists, and in some instances, radiologists and nuclear medicine specialists. Lichtenberg et al. (2003) provide a series of clinical practice guidelines for optimizing the diagnostic process that include the accurate assessment of cognitive deficits, collection of important medical and psychosocial information, and careful neurological examination. Well-trained, experienced neuropsychologists should complete cognitive assessments with the use of psychometrically valid tools. Cutoff scores should be interpreted in the context of available norms for patient sociodemographic information including gender, education, age, ethnicity, and literacy. Whenever possible, self-report data should be confirmed through additional, corroborating sources, such as partners or adult children (Lichtenberg et al., 2003). Timing of dementia onset is especially important in distinguishing Lewy body disease from Parkinson's disease dementia, as clinical symptoms overlap significantly. However, cognitive decline precedes symptoms of parkinsonism in Lewy body disease and often occurs many years later in the cases of Parkinson's disease dementia (Robillard, 2007). Careful neurological examination and laboratory tests can rule out dementia due to cerebrovascular disease, mass lesions, or hydrocephalus. When economically and practically feasible, brain imaging can provide convergent evidence for conclusively diagnosing dementia etiology (Lichtenberg et al., 2003). In certain cases, such as the diagnosis of dementia due to Creutzfeldt-Jakob disease, data garnered from diagnostic tools such as electroencephalography (EEG) and magnetic resonance imaging (MRI) reveal distinct biomarkers that greatly strengthen diagnostic accuracy (Haïk et al., 2000; Meissner et al., 2004).

Diagnosis can be especially difficult when clinical data suggest overlapping pathology or suggest signs of another neurological or psychiatric condition. In as many as two-thirds of AD cases, patients present with a co-morbid condition (Lim et al., 1999). In some instances, diagnostic specificity can be obtained through additional, extensive neuropsychological testing or through the identification of biomarkers via neuroimaging. Mixed dementia (MD), the presentation of more than one concurrent dementia (often the co-occurrence of both vascular dementia and AD) can be especially challenge for clinicians to diagnose. Vascular pathology is not uncommon in AD, and many neuropsychological deficits common to AD can be present in patients with subcortical vascular dementia (Graham, Emery, & Hodges, 2004). Some researchers have suggested that differentiation can be achieved through adopting extensive cognitive assessments that are sensitive enough to distinguish between subtle differences in recognition memory and verbal fluency (Tierney et al., 2001). In order to firmly establish MD, clinicians must fully understand subtle differences in the cognitive impairment profile while also taking into account neuroimaging data, including the presence and location of white matter lesions (Lichtenberg et al., 2003).

Recent advancements in radiology and nuclear medicine have facilitated the increased use of neuroimaging techniques in the differential diagnosis of dementia. Positron emission tomography (PET) not only has allowed clinicians to detect in vivo amyloid beta plaques but also has aided in identifying disease pathophysiology (Laforce Jr. & Rabinovici, 2011). When used in combination with computed tomography and functional MRI, PET imaging can facilitate the investigation of structural abnormalities secondary to dementia etiology and can provide an accurate anatomical substrate for evaluating functional activity. Through measuring cerebral glucose metabolism and employing the use of tracers sensitive to different neurotransmitter systems, PET imaging can readily distinguish between dementia due to Alzheimer's disease, Lewy body dementia, and frontotemporal dementia (Berti, Pupi, & Mosconi, 2011). Current research is exploring the possibility of utilizing PET in the early detection of cognitive decline prior to the onset of dementia (Burke et al., 2011).

The diagnosis of less severe forms of cognitive impairment may help identify those at high risk for conversion to dementia, thereby providing a means for the development of prophylactic treatment (Alzheimer's Association, 2013). Mild cognitive impairment (MCI) refers to the presentation of measurable cognitive impairments (most often deficits in memory) beyond those associated with normal aging that are less pronounced then those required for establishing a diagnosis of dementia (Petersen et al., 1999). Patients with MCI exhibit cognitive deficits without a corresponding change or deterioration in daily functioning. Deficits may be so slight that they are not noticed even by individuals close to the patient, such as family and friends (Gontkovsky, Johnson, Johnson, & Sarafan, 2012). Although the criteria for diagnosing MCI only recently have been codified in the Fifth Edition of the Diagnostic and Statistical Manual of Mental Disorders (American Psychiatric Association, 2013), it can be readily distinguished from normal aging and full-on dementia through clinical scales, neuropsychological testing, and neuroimaging (Grundman et al., 2004). Conversion rates from MCI to AD range from approximately 25% to 50%, although the pattern and type of MCI (i.e., amnesiac and nonamnesiac) do not necessarily predict the development of different forms of dementia (Fischer et al., 2007). Clinicians and researchers also have suggested the possibility of an even milder form of MCI, referred to as subjective cognitive complaint or subjective cognitive impairment (SCI). Patients with SCI report cognitive decline despite neuropsychological testing that suggests normal cognitive functioning. In contrast to MCI, patients with SCI exhibit little or no cognitive impairment across multiple cognitive domains (Stewart, 2012). SCI itself is a controversial diagnosis, as it relies almost entirely on self-report data, and it remains unclear as to whether or to what degree this form of impairment is related to the later development of MCI or dementia. Yet, it is difficult to improve early detection and increase public awareness of the risk for dementia without acknowledging the importance of objective complaints from patients and their caregivers.

Advancements in clinical assessment, cognitive psychology, and neuroimaging have greatly enhanced scientific understanding of the many different causes of dementia, thereby improving clinicians' ability to make specific and accurate diagnoses. This provides patients with a more informed understanding of prognosis and expected disease course while allowing clinicians to develop individualized treatment plans. In moving towards the classification of dementia through differences in pathophysiology rather than differences in clinical presentation, it is anticipated that future treatment options will become increasingly tailored to disease etiology and atypical variations between individuals. Such an approach could be especially helpful in further elucidating the role of genetic and environmental factors in modifying disease course. It also could help determine those at risk for developing dementia through the identification of biomarkers that correspond to clinical signs and quantifiable measures of cognitive decline.

Primary Neurological Diseases/Disorders that Underlie Dementia

As mentioned previously, there are a number of neurological diseases and disorders that are associated with chronic and progressive dementia. This section will describe the most common causes of irreversible dementia, with an emphasis on the distinct cognitive and behavioral characteristics of each.

Alzheimer's Disease (AD)

Alzheimer's disease is the leading cause of dementia. Although statistics vary to some extent, studies consistently suggest that AD is responsible for more than half of all cases of dementia. According to recent statistics reported by the Alzheimer's Association (2013), AD accounts for an estimated 60% to 80% of dementia cases and is the sixth leading cause of death in the United States. The etiology of AD remains unknown, but advancing age is the primary risk factor for developing this condition. Associations have been reported to exist between Alzheimer's disease and various other medical conditions, including head trauma, cardiovascular disease, hypertension, hyperthyroidism, obesity, and diabetes mellitus (Miller & Boeve, 2009; Vignini et al., 2013); however, results are not entirely consistent and the implications of these relationships remain unclear. Although there is a genetic component to AD, data from the MacArthur Research Network on Successful Aging Community Study suggests that non-genetic factors appear to account for two-thirds of the formula for how long and how well individuals live. In this light, the importance of lifestyle choices in the prevention of Alzheimer's disease is underscored (Small & Vorgan, 2011).

Neuropathological changes firmly associated with AD include the aggregation of amyloid beta in extracellular plaques, accumulation of hyperphosphorylated tau proteins in intraneuronal neurofibrillary tangles, and synaptic and neuronal degeneration (Blennow, de Leon, & Zetterberg, 2006; Zetterberg & Blennow, 2013). Interestingly, the presence of these brain abnormalities does not necessarily translate directly into cognitive problems. In other words, studies have found that individuals may exhibit these same pathological brain changes that are associated with AD without ever developing dementia.

The typical presentation of Alzheimer's disease is characterized by an insidious onset and gradual, but progressive, worsening of symptoms over time. Initial cognitive issues usually involve short-term memory problems and word-finding difficulties. Remote memory generally remains relatively intact until the later stages of the disease process. As a result, individuals with AD may remember where they were born, describe events from their early adult years, such as work experiences and family vacations, but may be unable to recall what they had for breakfast that day. As the disease progresses, cognitive deficits may come to include the use of incorrect words when speaking, referred to as paraphasic errors, as well as executive problems involving impaired reasoning and judgment. Attention/concentration abilities generally remain relatively well preserved early in the disease process; however, all domains of cognitive functioning eventually will be compromised to some extent by the end stages of the disease (Golden, Zillmer, & Spiers, 1992).

In the earlier stages of AD, diagnosed individuals may remain conversant and exhibit an appropriate range of social skills, which oftentimes may mask subtle disturbances of cognition. Physical abilities also usually remain intact initially. As cognitive abilities, in particular visual-spatial perception skills, deteriorate over time, individuals with AD may begin to have difficulties integrating visual and motor functions and are at an increased risk for falls. The disparity between the cognitive and physical deficits associated with AD illustrates why individuals with this disease have not uncommonly been found wandering through neighborhoods lost and confused. Nevertheless, as with cognitive functions, many physical abilities are also detrimentally affected in the end stages of the illness, due to severe neuropathological changes. For example, individuals may become incontinent or lose the ability to swallow and/or speak.

Persons diagnosed with AD may also experience a range of psychiatric and behavioral disturbances. Apathy, agitation, fear, anger, and depression are not uncommon during the earlier stages of the condition. As the brain continues to undergo pathological changes and individuals progress further in the disease process, delusions and hallucinations may occur and often involve a paranoid ideation.

Vascular Dementia (VaD)

Vascular Dementia (VaD) refers to several types of dementia that result from diseases of brain vasculature. VaD is the second most common form of dementia after AD (Battistin & Cagnin, 2010), with an overall prevalence estimated at 6-12 cases per 1,000 persons (Hébert & Brayne, 1995). The rate of VaD increases linearly with age (prevalence rates double every 5.3 years) with a rate of 14 to 16.3 per 100 for those age 80 years and older (Jorm & Jolley, 1998). The high prevalence of VaD is due, in part, to the large risk of stroke and heart disease in the elderly and the increasing number of adults living past age 85 years (Román, 2003). Disease duration is approximately five years, and survival rates are generally lower for VaD than AD (Hébert & Brayne, 1995). The risk for dementia doubles for stroke survivors following a single stroke (Kokmen, Whisnant, O'Fallon, Chu, & Beard, 1996); one in three patients who suffer from recurrent strokes are likely to develop dementia (Pendlebury & Rothwell, 2009). VaD is more common in men than women and is more prevalent in Asian, Black, and Hispanic populations than in Caucasian populations (Román, 2003). Although historically VaD has been underdiagnosed, clinicians are increasingly aware of the devastating impact of cerebrovascular and cardiovascular damage on cognition and daily functioning.

Stroke, also referred to as cerebrovascular accident (CVA), is the most common cause of VaD and falls into the two categories of ischemic and hemorrhagic. Ischemic strokes occur upon blockage of blood flow to the brain and can be caused by either a blood clot (thrombosis) or by arterial blockage (arterial embolism). Hemorrhagic strokes result from the occurrence of hemorrhages, or internal bleeding, in the brain. Strokes often lead to tissue death in the brain region deprived of oxygen (a lesion known as an infarction), although the location and extent of such damage is highly variable. It is important to distinguish between infarctions as a result of a single major CVA and those following several major CVAs, as well as those that occur from the disseminated proliferation of numerous transient ischemic attacks or smaller strokes. These different patterns of stroke result in different pathological presentations and thereby result in different forms of vascular dementia. Risk factors for stroke include diabetes mellitus, hypertension, atrial fibrillation, elevated plasma homocysteine, lipid disorders, and smoking (Sahathevan, Brodtmann, & Donnan, 2012). Although these factors have been shown to have a cumulative effect in the risk for development of AD, this does not appear to be the case in VaD (Sahathevan et al., 2012). While some studies have concluded that pre-stroke cognitive functioning is associated with the development of VaD (Savva et al., 2010), this finding remains controversial.

VaD also can be cardiogenic in origin, although the relationship between cardiovascular disease and cognitive functioning only recently has begun to receive attention by researchers and clinicians. Congestive heart failure increases the risk of stroke and of cerebral hypoperfusion, a condition in which the brain receives an insufficient supply of oxygen in the blood. Given increasing rates of heart disease in the United States, cardiogenic causes of dementia may become more common, and therefore, it is important for clinicians to identify the signs and symptoms of VaD following a cardiovascular incident.

The diagnosis of VaD can be difficult for clinicians, as cognitive symptoms may appear similarly to other forms of dementia and are not always readily apparent immediately following signs of a stroke. In many instances, the symptoms of VaD are actually attributable to AD or mixed dementia, but this is only discovered upon post-mortem examination (Nolan, Lino, Seligmann, & Blass, 1998). Differences between established clinical guidelines for VaD can further complicate the process, with sources recommending different approaches for confirming evidence of stroke and providing different definitions of cognitive impairment. Among these competing guidelines, the National Institute of Neurological Disorders and Stroke Association Internationale de Recherche et L'Ensignment en Neurosciences (NINDS-AIREN) criteria are perhaps the most useful, as they provide specific guidance on different forms of stroke in terms of both etiology and location of lesions, requirements for the diagnosis of dementia, and the important information about the relationship between the two (Román, 2003).

The NINDS-AIREN criteria classify VaD among six different sub-types. Multi-infarct dementia (MID) is defined by the onset of cognitive impairment upon the occurrence of several strokes and is more commonly found in older patients. Patients who experience left hemispheric strokes and those who have had hypoxic or ischemic complications following a stroke are at an increased risk for developing MID. Strategic infarct dementia occurs after a single cerebrovascular incident and includes several sub-types that differ in stroke location and the nature of associated cognitive impairment. Approximately 25% of patients who experience a stroke in the posterior cerebral artery (PCA) develop VaD. PCA stroke can lead to damage to the ventral-medial temporal lobe, occipital structures, and thalamus causing cognitive impairment in verbal memory, visuospatial memory, and even episodic anterograde amnesia. A stroke in the anterior cerebral artery often results in medial frontal lobe lesions, with patients exhibiting anterograde amnesia as well as deficits in executive functioning (Román, 2003). Patients with subcortical damage to the basal ganglia and thalamus often present with cognitive impairment in attention, motivation, executive functioning,

11

and memory. Patients with damage to the inferomedial frontal cortex following a single lacunar stroke often exhibit sudden impairment in attention and memory in addition to other symptoms of frontal lobe dysfunction (Pantoni & García, 1997). Binswanger's disease and CADASIL are subacute forms of VaD, in which symptoms of cognitive impairment appear well after the cerebrovascular or cardiovascular incident and are characterized by chronic and progressive cognitive decline. Symptoms include deficits in executive functioning, mood changes, motor impairment, parkinsonian features, and pseudobulbar palsy (Román, 2003).

Despite the heterogeneity of cerebrovascular sources of VaD and the potential for lesions to impact almost any aspect of cognition, deficits in executive functioning are the hallmark clinical presentation of cognitive impairment in patients with VaD (Cummings, 1994). In contrast to the clinical presentation of AD, memory deficits do not present as early and are not as severe in VaD. Executive functioning deficits include difficulties in planning, abstraction, conceptual flexibility, and monitoring complex goal-directed behavior (Fuster, 2000). Executive deficits typically arise due to the disruption of frontal cortico-subcortical pathways that link the frontal lobes to the striatum, substantia nigra, and thalamus. Damage to these circuits also can result in behavioral abnormalities such as mood and personality changes and impulsive and uninhibited behavior. In assessing cognitive functioning in patients with VaD, clinicians often utilize neuropsychological batteries that are especially attuned to evaluate executive functioning (Hachinski et al., 2006; Norris, MacNeill, & Haines, 2003).

Unlike AD, the proximal causes of VaD are well understood and are among the most common causes of mortality in the United States. Although the risk factors for stroke and cardiovascular disease are numerous, many are already the focus of large public health initiatives. A targeted effort at treating the distal and preventive risk factors for cerebrovascular and cardiovascular conditions will be critical in reducing the high prevalence of vascular dementia.

Frontotemporal Dementia (FTLD)

Frontotemporal lobar degeneration (FTLD) refers to a group of neurodegenerative disorders characterized by atrophy of the frontal and temporal lobes and the clinical presentation of changes in behavior and language. Frontotemporal dementia (FTD) is the most prevalent form of FTLD and is primarily associated with behavioral symptoms, while progressive nonfluent aphasia (PNFA) and semantic dementia (SD) are characterized by language impairment. FTD is the second most common type of presenile dementia after Alzheimer's disease and accounts for 5% to 15% of all dementia diagnoses (Wang, Shen, & Chen, 2012). FTD occurs equally in men and women, with an incidence rate of 15 per 100,000 in those 45 years to 64 years and a rate of 3.8 per 100,000 for those between 70 years and 79 years (Rosso et al., 2003). Some patients with FTD later develop motor neuron disease (FTD-MND), and there is some overlap in the clinical presentation of FTD and other motor diseases, such as corticobasal degeneration (CBD) and progressive supranuclear palsy. The symptoms of FTD progress rapidly and eventually lead to severe deteriorations in cognitive functioning; patients typically survive 2-10 years and eventually require 24-hour care (Kertesz, 2004). Although genetic mutations account for as much as one-third of FTD cases, the majority of presentations occur sporadically. Current research on disease etiology focuses on similarities in the genetic susceptibility and clinical presentation of FTD with neuropsychiatric conditions, such as schizophrenia (Harciarek, Malaspina, Sun, & Goldberg, 2013). Limitations in fully understanding disease etiology present many challenges in the prevention, clinical management, and treatment of FTD.

Although frontal and temporal lobe atrophy are the core features of FTD, patterns of neuroanatomical involvement variy significantly among patients. This is due, in part, to the different genetic mutations underlying the disorder, which include the tau gene (MAPT), the progranulin gene (PGRN), and the C90RF72 gene (Wider, Dickson, Rademakers, & Wszolek, 2010). Cortical degeneration is often categorized based on the presence of either tau-positive pathology (FTD-T, due to mutations in the tau gene) or the identification of ubiquitin-positive inclusions (FTD-U, often caused by PGRN and VCP mutations). The accumulation of tau proteins in neurons results in spherical aggregations known as Pick bodies, and therefore, this specific form of FTD often is referred to as Pick's Disease. Tau-positive patients have significant cortical atrophy in the frontal and parietal regions and symmetrical medial temporal and orbitofrontal atrophy, while patients with PGRN mutation have asymmetric fronto-temporoparietal atrophy (Rohrer & Warren, 2011). In patients with PGRN mutations, atrophy also occurs in the caudate nucleus, medial thalamus, substantia nigra, and hippocampus. A neucleotide repeat in the C9ORF72 gene has been associated with a unique pattern of frontal lobe atrophy and may significantly explain rates of both FTD and amyotrophic lateral sclerosis in patients of European descent.

The clinical presentation of FTLD is strongly associated with the underlying brain areas affected in each condition; FTD primarily affects the frontal lobes, PNFA impacts the left posterior frontal regions, and SD leads to deterioration in the left temporal lobe. Although typically atrophy of specific regions results in a unique clinical presentation, behavioral, and language symptoms often overlap making an initial diagnosis difficult. A sudden change in behavior may suggest a FTD phenotype, yet the development of language impairment may suggest SD or PNFA. Similarly, it is difficult to establish clinical criteria that can accurately distinguish the genetically-determined forms of FTD from one another (Wider et al, 2010). FTLD is highly dynamic, and therefore, it is important for clinicians to constantly reassess patients' symptoms regularly, as diagnosis can change through the course of the disease.

The onset of FTD may appear suddenly, yet it may progress gradually and is often marked by a dramatic change in character and social behavior. Patients often are emotionally inappropriate, display a lack of sympathy and empathy, and exhibit radical changes in affect. Impulsive and inappropriate behaviors are markedly increased in patients with FTD; some even develop changes in eating habits, such as binge eating. Other symptoms include repetitive behaviors (i.e. motor perseveration) and altered response to sensory stimuli, such as reduced pain response (Neary, Snowden, & Mann, 2005). FTD patients with the PGRN mutation present with significant language difficulty, and parkinsonism symptoms are much more likely in PGRN mutation carriers compared to MND carriers (Wider et al., 2010). Hallucinations have been reported in 30% of patients with the PGRN mutation (Le Ber et al., 2007).

The dominant feature of PNFA is nonfluent aphasia, in which patients exhibit difficulty in speech production. This can include articulatory breakdown, difficulty producing certain sounds, difficulty in using the correct word tense, and mixing up word order. At later stages of the disease, patients often become mute, and some develop behavioral symptoms similar to FTD. Some patients develop akinesia (i.e., loss of voluntary movement) as well as rigidity and tremors. In contrast to PNFA, patients with SD are able to retain word fluency and speech production but are unable to comprehend the meaning of words and recognize common objects. Patients are able to read out loud and take dictation but are unable to understand content. Prosopagnosia, the inability to recognize faces, can develop in some cases, and in later stages of the disease parkinsonism symptoms such as akinesia, rigidity, and tremor are evident.

Cognitive impairment in FTD is characterized by deficits in executive functions, including difficulties in planning, judgment, and problem solving. Deficits in attention and response inhibition can be evident during neuropsychological testing and may impair overall performance on cognitive tasks. In contrast to the cognitive profile of patients with Alzheimer's disease, FTD patients often perform relatively well on memory tasks. For instance, upon reproducing figures from memory, patients with FTD exhibit some difficulty due to poor organization, but spatial orientation and visual memory remain relatively intact (Thompson, Stopford, Snowden, & Neary, 2005). Social cognition and emotional processing are markedly impaired, as patients often have difficulty inferring what other people feel or think. This finding is consistent across different forms of FTD, including patients with restricted orbitofrontal atrophy in whom social cognition is particularly impaired while aspects of executive dysfunction may be less pronounced.

Parkinson's Disease (PD) and Lewy Body Dementia (LBD)

Parkinson's Disease (PD) is a chronic and progressive degenerative disorder that affects movement and cognition. Prevalence of the disease is estimated to be approximately 1 or 2 people out of 1000 (Bartels & Leenders, 2009); in 2005 there were an estimated 4.1 to 4.6 million people with PD, with these numbers expected to reach 8.7 to 9.3 million by 2030 (Dorsey et al., 2007). PD afflicts subcortical areas in the basal ganglia. Significant emphasis is placed on abnormalities of the substantia nigra and subsequent degeneration of dopaminergic neurons projecting to the striatum at a rate of several times the norm for healthy aging. Additional degeneration of the dopaminergic neurons is present in the ventral tegmental area, especially in some patients who progress to later dementia

(Torack & Morris, 1988) and those who are depressed. Cognitive functioning in Parkinson's disease is moderated by the health of these and other areas in the fronto-striatal dopaminergic pathways (Kehagia, Barker, & Robbins, 2010). Lewy bodies, round compact masses of proteins (predominantly alpha-synuclein), are another marker of the disease when present in the substantia nigra. They are seen with normal aging, in people with AD, or in those with non-PD progressive neurodegenerative disorder, such as Pick's disease, CBD, and, when cortical, are notable features of Lewy body dementia (LBD). Non-motor symptoms in PD are correlated with the progression of Lewy body development, though the motor symptoms of PD will not show until sufficient degradation of key dopaminergic areas has occurred (Chaudhuri & Schapira, 2009). Recent scholarly attention has focused on the putamen and caudate nucleus as being particularly affected in PD.

The disease often begins with subtle motor symptoms, such as limb or hand weakness, soft voice, or diminished facial expression. Symptoms can be so subtle at the beginning that they are often ignored and only recalled once a diagnosis is made. The typical presentation of PD includes resting tremors (nonvoluntary), which can disappear during sleep, bradykinesia (slowness of movements; Lees, Hardy, & Revesz, 2009), and rigidity in movements caused by increased muscle tone. The tremor experienced by patients with PD when sitting still will disappear when executing purposeful movements, though some patients have difficulty initiating movement and must consciously think of the actual movement in order to start. Patients often have a stooped posture, walk with small, shuffling steps, and struggle with turning while ambulating. Also evident are step-like rotational movements, referred to as cogwheel rigidity, as well as "masked facies," an emotionless quality to the face that looks masklike. Dysarthria, a weakness or slowing of muscles involved in speech, can make communication difficult, with patients sometimes struggling to speak at audible volumes.

There appear to be subgroups of PD patients, separated into those with minimal, specific, or generalized cognitive deficits. Motor impairments and fatigue can make assessing cognitive deficits difficult with individuals with PD, as testing participation often requires fine motor skills and lengthy sessions. Additionally, when patients have lateralized physical symptoms, as is the classic presentation (Bartels & Leenders, 2009), their cognitive deficits may be more related to the contralateral part of the brain as where the symptoms occur. In PD, asymmetrical involvement of the fronto-striatal brain circuitry seems to suggest that those who have dysfunction in the left frontal lobe (patients with physical symptoms that are more lateralized to the right side of the body) may be more likely to progress to later dementia (Varanese, Perfetti, Mason, Di Rocco, & Goldberg, 2010). A left-sided onset and left-handedness, as well as early disease onset, is associated with longer survival and greater mobility in PD (Munhoz et al., 2013). It has been suggested that in right-hand individuals, right-side dominance of physical symptoms is more common (van der Hoorn, Bartels, Leenders, & de Jong, 2011), though other researchers have found right-sided and left-sided asymmetry of symptoms more evenly distributed (Djaldetti, Ziv, & Melamed, 2006; Yust-Katz, Tesler, Treves, Melamed, & Djaldetti, 2008).

Patients with PD primarily experience deficits in executive functioning, memory, and mood. Visuospatial deficits have also been noted in PD, with some researchers suggesting that such difficulties may be secondary to the executive problems, especially those in changing mental set. Another possible explanation is that PD does not present uniformly among patients, and variance in deficits creates different clinical pictures. In patients without a co-occurring dementia, individuals may have difficulty with spatial orientation or judgment. Executive functioning deficits include task switching, formation of concepts, as well as other abilities requiring internal initiation. Deficits in this area also include difficulty with recalling words associated with a particular letter (i.e., fluency), but not so in naming objects presented to them, as seen in patients with AD. Language difficulties have been noted in PD, as well, particularly affecting articulation of speech. Patient can experience difficulty with rapid clusters of speech or unwanted repetition of phrase. Memory problems also have been noted, affecting recall more than recognition. Procedural learning may suffer. As the disease progresses, any new learning that requires motor skills will be deficient.

Depression may be present in patients with PD, with estimated prevalence being approximately 25% (Riedel et al., 2010). Other researchers suggest reevaluating this estimate because the rates of depressive symptoms are much higher than the rates of diagnosed major depression (McDonald, Richard, & DeLong, 2003), while others estimate over 70% of PD patients have some kind of neuropsychiatric symptoms (Riedel et al., 2010). Since

many symptoms of depression are the same as or similar to symptoms of
PD, including fatigue, movement issues, and loss of appetite, depression can
be challenging to diagnose in this population (Ryder et al., 2002). Also, the
degree of non-motor symptom severity has been associated with poorer quality
of life in PD patients (Santos-García & de la Fuente-Fernández, 2013).

PD patients with dementia and LBD patients have widespread
cortical atrophy; whereas, patients with PD and no dementia have primarily
frontal lobe atrophy (Burton, McKeith, Burn, Williams, & O'Brien, 2004).
LBD also is associated with pathological brainstem changes that are similar
to those in PD (Thompson & Vinters, 2012). Generally speaking, LBD is
thought to occur when a toxic level of combined pathologies, including
cortical Lewy bodies, is reached, as some of these pathologies overlap with
PD (Burn, 2004). Community prevalence of LBD is estimated at 8% of
dementia cases (Stevens et al., 2002). Early in the disease process, patients
with LBD may suffer falls, variation in cognitive functioning, temporary loss
of consciousness (syncope), hallucinations, and symptoms of parkinsonism
(Gontkovsky et al., 2012; Hanson & Lippa, 2009). Early LBD without
other comorbid disorders is characterized less by memory deficits and more
by attentional, executive, and visuospatial impairments. Distinguishing PD
from LBD is debated, as some researchers believe they are not distinct
diagnostic entities. A distinction, however, is sometimes made as follows: if
movement deficits precede cognitive deficits, a PD diagnosis is made;
whereas, the opposite presentation is labeled as LBD. Research with PD
patients found that 78% eventually developed dementia, with some LBD
symptoms and widespread cortical Lewy bodies confirmed through autopsy,
which has been interpreted as LBD and PD that progress to dementia being
on a spectrum of disease involving Lewy bodies and other common pathologies
(McKeith & Mosimann, 2004; Tsuboi & Dickson, 2005).

Recent work has identified an association between prefrontal and
temporal cortical thinning with depression in LBD as well as in AD
(Lebedev et al., 2013). This work suggests that depression in mild dementia
might be due to degeneration of brain circuitry implicated in other
disorders, and, noting that antidepressants are not often effective in this
group, researchers suggest exploring other means of handling depression in
this population, especially via non-pharmacological treatments (see Chapter 8).
Currently, new diagnostic procedures have been identified to differentiate

LBD from AD, including sympathetic skin response and heart rate variability (Negami, Maruta, Takeda, Adachi, & Yoshikawa, 2013). Additionally, imaging that examines the health of the cardiac sympathetic nervous system has been used to differentiate LBD from other neurodegenerative disorders resulting in cognitive impairment. Recent work found that smoking and education level, while important factors in AD and PD, are not associated with LBD risk; depression and low-caffeine intake, however, may increase risk of AD, PD, and most prominently LBD (Camacho et al., 2013). These new developments in identifying the disorder might be fruitful sources for further research into LBD.

Mixed Dementia

Mixed dementia (MD) is the term given to the concurrent presentation of AD, VaD, FTD, or LBD, which may be present together in any possible combination. One area of study is co-occurring AD and VaD, as the brain pathologies associated with both disorders, amyloid beta plaques and neurofibrillary tangles in AD and infarction and ischemia in VaD, often occur together and interact in ways that mutually contribute to cognitive decline (Langa, Foster, & Larson, 2004). Autopsy studies have found vascular pathologies in 24% to 28% of AD cases (Gearing et al., 1995; Massoud et al., 1999), a criteria for diagnosing MD consisting of AD and VaD. In this case, there is some conceptualization of VaD and AD as two points on a spectrum, with this specific presentation of MD a gradient between the poles (Schreiter Gasser, Rousson, Hentschel, Sattel, & Gasser, 2008).

Though MD is thought to be the most common type of dementia by some researchers (Korczyn & Vakhapova, 2007; Zekry, Hauw, & Gold, 2002), other researchers call into question the validity of MD as a diagnosis. Some suggest that MD may be either AD with co-morbid cerebrovascular disease or that the vascular component of MD is primary to the AD element (Meguro, Tanaka, Nakatsuka, Nakamura, & Satoh, 2012). Issues related to study design, diagnostic criteria, and sociocultural factors, however, contribute to the variety of MD cases observed in many studies (Zekry et al., 2002). The heterogeneity of dementia causes and combined effects of different brain lesions contribute to uncertainties in diagnosis and research of MD. The cognitive profile of MD consisting of AD and VaD can appear similar to AD, but with MD patients showing greater deficits in global cognition, visuoconstruction, and attention (Dong et al., 2013).

Multiple Sclerosis (MS)

Multiple sclerosis (MS) is an inflammatory and degenerative neurological disorder characterized by the destruction of the insulating covers, or myelin sheath, of nerve cells in the brain and spinal cord. Demyelization impairs the transmission of nerve impulses and can lead to axonal and cortical damage (Hulst & Geurts, 2011, Trapp et al., 1998). MS can take on many different forms, resulting in a high variability of clinical symptoms between individuals and ranging from language and motor difficulties to physical impairment and psychiatric illness. The disease affects approximately 2.0-2.5 million people worldwide (World Health Organization, 2008) and is considered the most common form of non-traumatic neurological illness in young and middle aged adults (Compston & Coles, 2002). MS predominantly affects individuals of northern European decent, is more common in females, and typically presents around age 30, although diagnosis in children and older adults can occur (Beatty, 2008; Milo & Kahana, 2010). Patients with MS are at an increased risk of developing depression, anxiety, and other psychological conditions (Feinstein, DeLuca, Baune, Filippi, & Lasseman, 2013). MS is a leading cause of disability in middle-aged adults (World Health Organization, 2008), leading to a severe decline in mobility, daily functioning, and quality of life.

Although the specific etiology of MS is not fully understood, it is considered an autoimmune disorder in which the nervous system attacks the myelin sheath, a lipid-rich layer around the axon of a neuron that facilitates the conduction of electrical signaling. Attacks can occur through the destruction of oligodendrocytes, the cells that produce and maintain myelin sheath, or through neuronal inflammation, in which the body's T cells pass through the blood-brain barrier, recognize myelin as foreign, and attack the myelin (Compston & Coles, 2002). As nerve cells become unable to repair damaged myelin, large lesions develop around axons leading to broader cortical damage. Susceptibility for MS is associated with a complex interaction of genetic and environmental factors. Although the disease has a higher occurrence rate in families (15%) and monozygotic twins (35%), genetic studies have yet to identify promising candidate genes (Compston & Coles, 2002). Despite a higher prevalence of MS in Europeans, population-based studies have struggled to explain the global distribution and historical development of MS (Milo & Kahana, 2010). Current research centers on the role of environmental risk factors, such as viral infection, vaccination, and climate on disease susceptibility (Marrie et al., 2008).

While the clinical presentation of MS can include a set of common symptoms that reflect broad impairment in neuronal signaling (e.g., fatigue, changes in sensory and pain perception, and movement difficulty), most patients present with a diverse set of symptoms that reflect the underlying functional anatomy of localized impaired regions. Damage to the brainstem can result in balance problems, impaired speech, and swallowing difficulties, while damage to the spinal cord can cause stiffness, spasms, bladder dysfunction, and incontinence (Compston & Coles, 2002). The clinical course of MS is difficult to predict, with some patients experiencing isolated attacks (relapsing-remitting MS) and others developing new symptoms over time (progressive MS). Symptoms may worsen over the course of several days followed by a period of improvement or may gradually worsen over time. Relapse may be sudden and unpredictable or can be triggered by seasonal change, stress, or viral infection (Milo & Kahana, 2010).

Cognitive impairment is one of the most common consequences of MS, with a prevalence rate of 65% to70% (Chiaravalloti, Stojanovic-Radic, & DeLuca, 2013). Overall cognitive ability often is impacted, with many patients exhibiting a statistically significant decrease in Full scale IQ from pre-illness levels (Ryan, Gontkovsky, Kreiner, & Tree, 2012). The specific presentation of cognitive difficulties varies significantly among patients, in part due to differences in the location and the extent of MS lesions. Impairment has been well documented in a number of cognitive domains, including attention (Janculjak, Mubrin, Brinar, & Spilich, 2002; Paul, Beatty, Schneider, Blanco, & Hames, 1998), working memory (Chiaravalloti et al., 2013; Fera et al., 2013; Lengenfelder, Chiaravalloti, Ricker, & DeLuca, 2003), executive functioning (Arnett et al., 1997; Owens, Denney, & Lynch, 2013), learning and episodic memory (DeLuca, Barbieriberger, & Johnson, 1994, DeLuca, Gaudino, Diamond, Christodoulou, & Engel, 1998; Thorton, Raz, & Tucke, 2002) processing speed (Archibald & Fisk, 2000; Aupperle, Beatty, Shelton, & Gontkovsky, 2002; Diamond, DeLuca, Kim, & Kelley, 1997) and social cognition (Banati et al., 2010; Ouellet et al., 2010; Pottgen, Dziobek, Reh, Heesen, & Gold, 2013). Although there is no standard profile of cognitive impairment in MS, patients typically experience difficulties in more than one area, as impairment in one domain, such as processing speed, may underscore difficulties in executive function and learning. Cognitive impairment is further exacerbated by physical symptoms of fatigue, pain, and motor difficulties, which can prove challenging in accurately assessing and treating the cognitive issues in patients with MS.

Memory deficits in MS appear to be driven by diffuse demyelination across the neocortex and the resulting disruption in communication between large-scale brain networks (Charil et al., 2003). Working memory difficulties are well established in MS through several modalities including behavioral, neuroimaging, and clinical neuropsychology studies. Patients do not perform as well as healthy controls on an array of cognitive tasks (Grigsby, Kaye, & Busenbark, 1994; Lengenfelder et al., 2003); this has been consistently replicated in both visual and auditory tasks (Chiaravalloti et al., 2013). Although patients struggle to learn new information and maintain short-term information, the retrieval of well-learned information is generally preserved (Lengenfelder et al., 2003). Episodic memory deficits are less common in MS but appear to be more prevalent in those with the relapsing-remitting form of the disease (Fera et al., 2013). For some patients, MS can stimulate compensatory hyperactivation of the hippocampal system, leading to relatively well-preserved episodic memory (Hulst & Geurts, 2011). Current research suggests that variations in the rate of episodic memory impairment in MS patients may be due to genetic differences in neuroplasticity (Fera et al., 2013).

Patients with MS exhibit deficits both in attention processing and across many areas of executive function. Difficulties in attention are common and perhaps one of the earliest neuropsychological indicators of cognitive decline (Feinstein et al., 2013). Despite broad frontal lobe pathology in MS, difficulties in executive function vary significantly between individuals with conflicting reports on the extent and nature of such impairment (Foong et al., 1997). This may be due to differences in the form of MS examined (relapsing-remitting versus progressive forms), variation in the focal region of MS lesions, as well as individual differences in cognitive reserve. Despite these differences, impairments in problem solving and planning appear to be the most prevalent form of executive dysfunction across all forms of MS. Patients may exhibit difficulties in abstract reasoning on tasks (Rao, Hammeke, & Speech, 1987) and require more time to find the correct solution when presented with planning tasks.

In many respects, processing speed may be seen as one of the primary sources of cognitive impairment in MS. While it often is difficult to measure processing speed given the confound of comorbid impairment in other domains (e.g., working memory, learning, and planning), information processing is a critical and sensitive indicator of brain dysfunction in patients with MS (Gontkovsky & Beatty, 2006). Reduced processing speed is evident early in the disorder and continues to decline as the disease progresses (Archibald & Fisk, 2000). Difficulties in processing speed often underlie other neurocognitive deficits observed in patients with MS, including difficulties in learning new information (Chiaravalloti et al., 2013) and planning (Owens et al., 2013). It therefore is critical for clinicians and researchers alike to understand the specific nature and extent of processing speed impairment in patients with MS, especially when present alongside other cognitive deficits. The development of new treatments to specifically address deficits in processing speed has recently received new emphasis in the literature, as this may be one of the most promising areas for preserving patients' current level of daily functioning (Kalmar, Gaudino, Moore, Halper, & DeLuca, 2008).

Despite only recently receiving significant attention in research, deficits in social cognition are an especially important component of cognitive impairment in MS that may help promote the development of new treatments that the increase patients' quality of life. Compared to healthy individuals, patients with MS have difficulty in emotion recognition and in understanding the emotions and mental states of others (Theory of Mind, ToM; Henry et al., 2009; Henry et al., 2011). These deficits are not secondary to other neuropsychological difficulties and are present even in the early stages of the disease (Pottgen et al., 2013). Some patients with MS develop neuropsychiatric symptoms that can further exacerbate social cognition deficits. MS patients with a distinct lesion pattern involving the bilateral medial inferior regions, bilateral inferior parietal regions, and brainstem regions can develop pseudobulbar affect (PBA), a condition in which individuals experience involuntary episodes of crying and laughing that are incongruent with their subjective mood state (Ghaffar, Chamelian, & Feinstein, 2008). Deficits in social cognition as well as the development of neuropsychiatric symptoms, such as PBA, may help to explain the high occurrence of interpersonal difficulties and social withdrawal in patients with MS; such situations lead to a general decline in quality of life and increase the risk for depression and other psychological illnesses. Given the positive role of social support and interpersonal relationships in improving quality of life in MS patients (Schwartz & Frohner, 2005), deficits in social cognition are an important consideration for the development of future treatment interventions.

Conclusion

In this chapter, we have discussed several different brain disorders leading to a level of cognitive impairment referred to as dementia. Overall, these diseases are highly comorbid; this presents an intriguing and challenging clinical picture, in terms of classifying and diagnosing the diseases. As noted by Lichtenberg et al. (2003), clinicians must weigh information received from cognitive profiles and neuroimaging, making diagnoses from multi-modal information, with nascent technologies furthering the ability, in some cases, to definitively diagnose while a patient is alive. Accurate diagnoses provide the patient and those close to them with a better understanding of what to expect as the disease progresses. Perhaps just as importantly, diagnostic accuracy and specificity gives the clinician as much information as possible on which to base the development of individual treatment plans.

Non-pharmacological treatments for dementia seek to approach the disorder from multiple perspectives, working with lifestyle or behavioral interventions. These treatments can be used to address the disease as a whole or a particular symptom, but it is essential to involve patients in the conversation both for purposes of feedback, as treatment must often be individualized, as well as the preservation of dignity for ethical reasons (Robinson et al., 2007). Researchers have suggested that efforts to evaluate the efficacy of non-pharmacological treatments might focus on the manner in which interventions target motivation and utilization of the patient's remaining functions (Yamaguchi, Maki, & Yamagami, 2010). Several non-pharmacological interventions for cognitive enhancement have shown greater effect than the corresponding pharmaceutical options, though some of these treatments are still controversial (Dresler et al., 2012). As research continues to provide new insights into these diseases, new possibilities for non-pharmacological treatments will arise to address behavioral and cognitive symptoms, with hope to improve the lives of patients and their families.

References

Alzheimer's Association. (2013). Alzheimer's disease facts and figures. *Alzheimer's and Dementia, 9*, 208-245.

American Psychiatric Association. (2013). *Diagnostic and statistical manual of mental disorders* (5th ed.). Washington, DC: American Psychiatric Publishing.

Archibald, C. J., & Fisk, J. D. (2000). Information processing efficiency in patients with multiple sclerosis. *Journal of Clinical and Experimental Neuropsychology, 22*, 686-701.

Arnett, P. A., Rao, S. M., Grafman, J., Bernardin, L., Luchetta, T., Binder, J. R., & Lobeck, L. (1997). Executive functions in multiple sclerosis: An analysis of temporal ordering, semantic encoding, and planning abilities. *Neuropsychology, 11*, 535-544.

Aupperle, R. L., Beatty, W. W., Shelton, F. D., & Gontkovsky, S. T. (2002). Three screening batteries to detect cognitive impairment in multiple sclerosis. *Multiple Sclerosis, 8*, 382-389.

Banati, M., Sandor, J., Mike, A., Illes, E., Bors, L., Feldmann, A., Herold, R., & Illes, Z. (2010). Social cognition and Theory of Mind in patients with relapsing-remitting multiple sclerosis. *European Journal of Neurology, 17*, 426-433.

Bartels, A. L., & Leenders, K. L. (2009). Parkinson's disease: The syndrome, the pathogenesis and pathophysiology. *Cortex, 45*, 915-921.

Battistin, L., & Cagnin, A. (2010). Vascular cognitive disorder. A biological and clinical overview. *Neurochemical Research, 35*, 1933-1938.

Beatty, W. W. (2008). Assessment for rehabilitation of patients with multiple sclerosis. In S. T. Gontkovsky & C. J. Golden (Eds.), *Neuropsychology within the inpatient rehabilitation environment* (pp. 99-131). Hauppauge, NY: Nova Science.

Berti, V., Pupi, A., & Mosconi, L. (2011). PET/CT in diagnosis of dementia. *Annals of the New York Academy of Sciences, 1228*, 81-92.

Blennow, K., de Leon, M. J., & Zetterberg, H. (2006). *Alzheimer's disease. Lancet, 368*, 387-403.

Burke, J. F., Albin, R. L., Koeppe, R. A., Giordani, B., Kilbourn, M. R., Gilman, S., & Frey, K. A. (2011). Assessment of mild dementia with amyloid and dopamine terminal positron emission tomography. *Brain, 134*, 1647-1657.

Burn, D. J. (2004). Cortical Lewy body disease. *Journal of Neurology, Neurosurgery, and Psychiatry, 75*, 175-178.

Burton, E. J., McKeith, I. G., Burn, D. J., Williams, E. D., & O'Brien, J. T. (2004). Cerebral atrophy in Parkinson's disease with and without dementia: A comparison with Alzheimer's disease, dementia with Lewy bodies and controls. *Brain, 127*(Pt. 4), 791-800.

Camacho, V., Estorch, M., Marquié, M., Domènech, A., Flotats, A., Fernández, A., Duch, J., Geraldo, L. L., Deportos, J., Artigas, C., Lleó, I., & Carrió, I. (2013). Utility of early imaging of myocardial innervation scintigraphy in the diagnosis of Lewy body dementia. *Revista Española de Medicina Nuclear e Imagen Molecular, 32*, 77-80.

Charil, A., Zijdenbos, A. P., Taylor, J., Boelman, C., Worsley, K. J., Evans, A. C., & Dagher, A. (2003). Statistical mapping analysis of lesion location and neurological disability in multiple sclerosis: Application to 452 patient data sets. *Neuroimage, 19*, 532-544.

Chaudhuri, K. R., & Schapira, A. H. V. (2009). Non-motor symptoms of Parkinson's disease: Dopaminergic pathophysiology and treatment. *Lancet Neurology, 8*, 464-474.

Chiaravalloti, N. D., Stojanovic-Radic, J., & DeLuca, J. (2013). The role of speed versus working memory in predicting learning new information in multiple sclerosis. *Journal of Clinical and Experimental Neuropsycholoaly, 35*, 180-191.

Compston A., & Coles A. (2002). Multiple sclerosis. *Lancet, 359*, 1221-1231.

Cummings, J. L. (1994). Vascular subcortical dementia: *Clinical aspects. Dementia, 5*, 177-180.

DeLuca, J., Barbieri-Berger, S., & Johnson, S. K. (1994). The nature of memory impairments in multiple sclerosis - acquisition versus retrieval. *Journal of Clinical and Experimental Neuropsychology, 16*, 183-189.

DeLuca, J., Gaudino, E. A., Diamond, B. J., Christodoulou, C., & Engel, R. A. (1998). Acquisition and storage deficits in multiple sclerosis. *Journal of Clinical and Experimental Neuropsychology, 20*, 376-390.

Diamond, B. J., DeLuca, J., Kim, H. J., & Kelley, S. M. (1997). The question of disproportionate impairments in visual and auditory information processing in multiple sclerosis. *Journal of Clinical and Experimental Neuropsychology, 19*, 34-42.

Djaldetti, R., Ziv, I., & Melamed, E. (2006). The mystery of motor asymmetry in Parkinson's disease. *Lancet Neurology, 5*, 796-802.

Dong, Y., Gan, D. Z. Q., Tay, S. Z., Koay, W. I., Collinson, S. L., Hilal, S., Venketasubramanian, N., & Chen, C. (2013). Patterns of neuropsychological impairment in Alzheimer's disease and mixed dementia. *Journal of the Neurological Sciences, 333*, 5-8.

Dorsey, E. R., Constantinescu, R., Thompson, J. P., Biglan, K. M., Holloway, R. G., Kieburtz, K., Marshall, F. G., Ravina, B. M., Schifitto, G., Siderowf, A., & Tanner, C. M. (2007). Projected number of people with Parkinson disease in the most populous nations, 2005 through 2030. *Neurology, 68*, 384-386.

Dresler, M., Sandberg, A., Ohla, K., Bublitz, C., Trenado, C., Mroczko-Wasowicz, A., Kühn, S., & Repantis, D. (2012). Non-pharmacological cognitive enhancement. *Neuropharmacology, 64*, 529-543.

Feinstein, A., DeLuca, J., Baune, B. T., Filippi, M., & Lasseman, H. (2013). Cognitive and neuropsychiatric disease manifestations in MS. *Multiple Sclerosis and Related Disorders, 2*, 4-12.

Fera, F., Passamonti, L., Cerasa, A., Gioia, M. C., Liguori, M., Manna, I., Valentino, P., & Quattrone, A. (2013). The BDNF Val[66]Met polymorphism has opposite effects on memory circuits of multiple sclerosis patients and controls. *PloS One, 8(4)*, e61063. doi: 10.1371/journal.pone.0061063.

Fischer, P., Jungwirth, S., Zehetmayer, S., Weissgram, S., Hoenigschnabl, S., Gelpi, E., Krampla, W., & Tragl, K. H. (2007). Conversion from subtypes of mild cognitive impairment to Alzheimer dementia. *Neurology, 68*, 288-291.

Foong, J., Rozewicz, L., Quaghebeur, G., Davie, C. A., Kartsounis, L. D., Thompson, A. J., Miller, D. H., & Ron, M. A. (1997). Executive function in multiple sclerosis: The role of frontal lobe pathology. *Brain, 120*, 15-26.

Fuster, J. M. (2000). Executive frontal functions. *Experimental Brain Research, 133*, 66-70.

Gearing, M., Mirra, S. S., Hedreen, J. C., Sumi, S. M., Hansen, L. A., & Heyman, A. (1995). The Consortium to Establish a Registry for Alzheimer's Disease (CERAD). Part X. Neuropathology confirmation of the clinical diagnosis of Alzheimer's disease. *Neurology, 45*, 461-466.

Ghaffar, O., Chamelian, L., & Feinstein, A. (2008). Neuroanatomy of pseudobulbar affect: A quantitative MRI study in multiple sclerosis. *Journal of Neurology, 255*, 406-412.

Golden, C. J., Zillmer, E., & Spiers, M. (1992). Neuropsychological assessment and intervention. Springfield, IL: Charles C. Thomas. Gontkovsky, S. T., & Beatty, W. W. (2006). Practical methods for the clinical assessment of information processing speed. *International Journal of Neuroscience, 116*, 1317-1325.

Gontkovsky, S. T., Johnson, K. N., Johnson, J. J., & Sarafan, L. (2012). *Mind over gray matter: A new approach to dementia care.* Palo Alto, CA: Home Care Press.

Graham, N. L., Emery, T., & Hodges, J. R. (2004). Distinctive cognitive profiles in Alzheimer's disease and subcortical vascular dementia. *Journal of Neurology, Neurosurgery and Psychiatry, 75*, 61-71.

Grigsby, J., Kaye, K., & Busenbark, D. (1994). Alphanumeric sequencing: A report on a brief measure of information-processing used among persons with multiple sclerosis. *Perceptual and Motor Skills, 78,* 883-887.

Grundman, M., Petersen, R. C., Ferris, S. H., Thomas, R. G., Aisen, P. S., Bennett, D. A., Foster., N. L., Jack, C. R. Jr., Galsko, D. R., Doody, R., Kaye, J., Sano, M., Mohs, R., Gauthier, S., Kim, H. T., Jin, S., Schultz, A. N., Schafer, K., Mulnard, R., van Dyck, C. H., Mintzer, J., Zamrini, E. Y., Cahn-Weiner, D., Thal, L. J., & Alzheimer's Disease Cooperative Study. (2004). Mild cognitive impairment can be distinguished from Alzheimer disease and normal aging for clinical trials. *Archives of Neurology, 61,* 59-66.

Hachinski, V., Iadecola, C., Petersen, R. C., Breteler, M. M., Nyenhuis, D. L., Black, S. E., Powers, W. J., DeCarli, C., Merino, J. G., Kalaria, R. N., Vinters, H. V., Holtzman, D. M., Rosenberg, G. A., Wallin, A., Dichgans, M., Marler, J. R., & Leblanc, G. G. (2006). National Institute of Neurological Disorders and Stroke-Canadian Stroke Network vascular cognitive impairment harmonization standards. *Stroke, 37,* 2220-2241.

Haïk, S., Brandel, J. P., Sazdovitch, V., Delasnerie-Laupretre, N., Peoc'h, K., Laplanche, J. L., Privat, N., Duychaerts, C., Kemeny, J. L., Kopp, N., Laquerriere, A., Mohr, M., Deslys, J. P., Dormont, D., & Hauw, J. J. (2000). Dementia with Lewy bodies in a neuropathologic series of suspected Creutzfeldt-Jakob disease. *Neurology, 55,* 1401-1404.

Hanson, J. C., & Lippa, C. F. (2009). Lewy body dementia. *International Review of Neurobiology, 84,* 215-228.

Harciarek, M., Malaspina, D., Sun, T., & Goldberg, E. (2013). Schizophrenia and frontotemporal dementia: Shared causation? *International Review of Psychiatry, 25,* 168-177.

Hébert, R. & Brayne, C. (1995). Epidemiology of vascular dementia. *Neuroepidemiology, 14,* 240-257.

Henry, J. D., Phillips, L. H., Beatty, W. W., McDonald, S., Longley, W. A., Joscelyne, A., & Rendell, P. G. (2009). Evidence for deficits in facial affect recognition and theory of mind in multiple sclerosis. *Journal of the International Neuropsychological Society, 15,* 277-285.

Henry, A., Tourbah, A., Chaunu, M. P., Rumbach, L., Montreuil, M., & Bakchine, S. (2011). Social cognition impairments in relapsing-remitting multiple sclerosis. *Journal of the International Neuropsychological Society, 17,* 1122-1131.

Hulst, H. E., & Geurts, J. J. G. (2011). Gray matter imaging in multiple sclerosis: What have we learned? *BMC Neurology, 11,* 153: doi:10.1186/1471-2377-11-153.

Janculjak, D., Mubrin, Z., Brinar, V., & Spilich, G. (2002). Changes of attention and memory in a group of patients with multiple sclerosis. *Clinical Neurology and Neurosurgery, 104,* 221-227.

Jorm, A. F., & Jolley, D. (1998). The incidence of dementia: A meta-analysis. *Neurology, 51,* 728-733.

Kalmar, J. H., Gaudino, E. Z., Moore, N. B., Halper, J., & DeLuca, J. (2008). The relationship between cognitive deficits and and everyday functioning activities in multiple sclerosis. *Neuropsychology, 22,* 442-449.

Kehagia, A. A., Barker, R. A., & Robbins, T. W. (2010). Neuropsychological and clinical heterogeneity of cognitive impairment and dementia in patients with Parkinson's disease. *Lancet Neurology, 9,* 1200-1213.

Kertesz, A. (2004). Frontotemporal dementia/Pick's disease. *Archives of Neurology, 61,* 969-971.

Kokmen, E., Whisnant, J. P., O'Fallon, W. M., Chu, C. P., & Beard, C. M. (1996). Dementia after ischemic stroke: A population-based study in Rochester, Minnesota (1960-1984). *Neurology, 46,* 154-159.

Korczyn, A. D., & Vakhapova, V. (2007). The prevention of the dementia epidemic. *Journal of the Neurological Sciences, 257,* 2-4.

Laforce, R. Jr., & Rabinovici, G. D. (2011). Amyloid imaging in the differential diagnosis of dementia: Review and potential clinical applications. *Alzheimer's Research and Therapy, 3*(6), 31. doi: 10.1186/alzrt93.

Langa, K. M., Foster, N. L., & Larson, E. B. (2004). Mixed dementia: Emerging concepts and therapeutic implications. *JAMA, 292*, 2901-2908.

Lebedev, A. V., Beyer, M. K., Fritze, F., Westman, E., Ballard, C., & Aarsland, D. (2013). Cortical changes associated with depression and antidepressant use in Alzheimer and Lewy body dementia: An MRI surface-based morphometric study. *American Journal of Geriatric Psychiatry*, pii: S1064-7481(13)00122-X. doi:10.1016/j.jagp.2013.02.004.

Le Ber, I., van der Zee, J., Hannequin, D., Gijselinck, I., Campion, D., Puel, M., Laquerrie, A., De Pooter, T., Camuzat, A., Van den Broeck, M., Dubois, B., Sellal, F., Lacomblez, L., Vercelletto, M., Thomas-Anterion, C., Michel, B. F., Golfier, V., Didic, M., Salachas, F., Duyckaerts, C., Cruts, M., Verpillat, P., Van Broeckhoven, C., Brice, A., & French Research Network on FTD/FTD-MND. (2007). Progranulin null mutations in both sporadic and familial frontotemporal dementia. *Human Mutation, 28*, 846-855.

Lees, A. J., Hardy, J., & Revesz, T. (2009). Parkinson's disease. *Lancet, 373*, 2055-2066.

Lengenfelder, J., Chiaravalloti, N. D., Ricker, J. H., & DeLuca, J. (2003). Deciphering components of impaired working memory in multiple sclerosis. *Cognitive and Behavioral Neurology, 16*, 28-39.

Lichtenberg, P. A., Murman, D. L., & Mellow, A. M. (Eds.). (2003). Handbook of dementia: *Psychological, neurological and psychiatric aspects.* Hoboken, NJ: John Wiley & Sons.

Lim, A., Tsuang, D., Kukull, W., Nochlin, D., Leverenz, J., McCormick, W., Bowen, J., Teri, L., Thompson, J., Peskind, E. R., Raskind, M., & Larson, E. B. (1999). Clinico-neuropathological correlation of Alzheimer's disease in a community-based case series. *Journal of the American Geriatrics Society, 47*, 564-569.

Marrie, R., Horwitz, R., Cutter, G., Tyry, T., Campagnolo, D., & Vollmer, T. (2008). Comorbidity, socioeconomic status and multiple sclerosis. *Multiple Sclerosis, 14*, 1091-1098.

Massoud, F., Devi, G., Stern, Y., Lawton, a, Goldman, J. E., Liu, Y., Chin, S. S., & Mayeux, R. (1999). A clinicopathological comparison of community-based and clinic-based cohorts of patients with dementia. *Archives of Neurology, 56,* 1368-1373.

McDonald, W. M., Richard, I. H., & DeLong, M. R. (2003). Prevalence, etiology, and treatment of depression in Parkinson's disease. *Biological Psychiatry, 54,* 363-375.

McKeith, I. G., & Mosimann, U. P. (2004). Dementia with Lewy bodies and Parkinson's disease. *Parkinsonism and Related Disorders, 10*(Suppl. 1), S15-S18.

Meguro, K., Tanaka, N., Nakatsuka, M., Nakamura, K., & Satoh, M. (2012). Vascular lesions in mixed dementia, vascular dementia, and Alzheimer disease with cerebrovascular disease: the Kurihara Project. *Journal of the Neurological Sciences, 322,* 157-160.

Meissner, B., Kortner, K., Bartl, M., Jastrow, U., Mollenhauer, B., Schroter, A., Finkenstaedt, M., Windl, O., Poser, S., Kretzschmar, H. A., & Zerr, I. (2004). Sporadic Creutzfeldt-Jakob disease: Magnetic resonance imaging and clinical findings. *Neurology, 63,* 450-456.

Miller, B. L., & Boeve, B. F. (2009). *The behavioral neurology of dementia.* New York: Cambridge University Press.

Milo, R., & Kahana, E. (2010). Multiple sclerosis: Geoepidemiology, genetics and the environment. Autoimmunity Reviews, 9, A387-A394

Munhoz, R. P., Espay, A. J., Morgante, F., Li, J-Y., Teive, H. A., Dunn, E., Gallin, E., & Litvan, I. (2013). Long-duration Parkinson's disease: Role of lateralization of motor features. *Parkinsonism and Related Disorders, 19,* 77-80.

Neary, D., Snowden, J., & Mann, D. (2005). Frontotemporal dementia. *Lancet Neurology, 4,* 771-780.

Negami, M., Maruta, T., Takeda, C., Adachi, Y., & Yoshikawa, H. (2013). Sympathetic skin response and heart rate variability as diagnostic tools for the differential diagnosis of Lewy body dementia and Alzheimer's disease: A diagnostic test study. *BMJ Open, 3*(3), pii: e001796. doi: 10.1136/bmjopen-2012-001796.

Nolan, K. A., Lino, M. M., Seligmann, A. W., & Blass, J. P. (1998). Absence of vas¬cular dementia in an autopsy series from a dementia clinic. *Journal of the American Geriatrics Society, 46*, 596-604.

Norris, M. P., MacNeill, S. E., & Haines, M. E. (2003). Psychological and neuropsychological   aspects of vascular and mixed dementia. In P. A. Lichtenberg, D. L. Murman, & A. M. Mellow (Eds.), *Handbook of dementia: Psychological, neurological and psychiatric aspects* (pp.173-195). Hoboken, NJ: John Wiley & Sons.

Ouellet, J., Scherzer, P. B., Rouleau, I., Metras, P., Bertrand-Gauvin, C., Djerroud, N., Boisseau, E., & Duquette, P. (2010). Assessment of social cognition in patients with multiple sclerosis. *Journal of the International Neuropsychological Society, 16*, 287-296.

Owens, E. M., Denney, D. R., & Lynch, S. G. (2013). Difficulties in planning among patients with multiple sclerosis: A relative consequence of deficits in information processing speed. *Journal of the International Neuropsychological Society, 19*, 613-620.

Pantoni, L., & García, J. H. (1997). Cognitive impairment and cellular/vascular changes in the cerebral white matter. *Annals of the New York Academy of Sciences, 826*, 92-102.

Paul, R. H., Beatty, W. W., Schneider, R., Blanco, C., & Hames, K. (1998). Impairments of attention in individuals with multiple sclerosis. *Multiple Sclerosis, 4*, 433-439.

Pendlebury, S. T., & Rothwell, P. M. (2009). Prevalence, incidence, and factors associated with pre-stroke and post-stroke dementia: A systematic review and meta-analysis. *Lancet Neurology, 8*, 1006-1018.

Petersen, R.C., Smith, G.E., Waring, S.C., Ivnik, R.J., Tangalos, E.G. & Kokmen, E. (1999). Mild cognitive impairment: Clinical characterization and outcome. *Archives of Neurology, 56,* 760-760.

Pottgen, J., Dziobek, I., Reh, S., Heesen, C., & Gold, S. M. (2013). Impaired social cognition in multiple sclerosis. *Journal of Neurology, Neurosurgery and Psychiatry, 84,* 523-528.

Román, G. C. (2003). Neurological aspects of vascular dementia: Basic concepts, diagnosis, and management. In P. A. Lichtenberg, D. L. Murman, & A. M. Mellow (Eds.), *Handbook of dementia: Psychological, neurological and psychiatric aspects* (pp.149-171). Hoboken, NJ: John Wiley & Sons.

Rao, S. M., Hammeke, T. A., & Speech, T. J. (1987). Wisconsin Card Sorting Testperformance in relapsing remitting and chronic progressive multiple sclerosis. *Journal of Consulting and Clinical Psychology, 55,* 263-265.

Riedel, O., Klotsche, J., Spottke, A., Deuschl, G., Förstl, H., Henn, F., Heuser, I., Oertel, W., Reichmann, H., Riederer, P., Trenkwalder, C., Dodel, R., & Wittchen, H-U. (2010). Frequency of dementia, depression, and other neuropsychiatric symptoms in 1,449 outpatients with Parkinson's disease. *Journal of Neurology, 257,* 1073-1082.

Robillard, A. (2007). Clinical diagnosis of dementia. *Alzheimer's and Dementia, 3,* 292-298.

Robinson, L., Hutchings, D., Dickinson, H. O., Corner, L., Beyer, F., Finch, T., Hughes, J., Vanoli, A., Ballard, C., & Bond, J. (2007). Effectiveness and acceptability of non-pharmacological interventions to reduce wandering in dementia: A systematic review. *International Journal of Geriatric Psychiatry, 22,* 9-22.

Rohrer, J. D. & Warren, J. D. (2011). Phenotypic signatures of genetic frontotemporal dementia. *Current Opinion in Neurology, 24,* 542-549.

Rosso, S. M., Donker Kaat. L., Baks, T., Joosse, M., de Koning, I., Pijnenburg, Y., de Jong D., Dooijes, D., Kamphorst, W., Ravid, R., Niermeijer, M. F., Verheij, F., Kremer, H. P., Scheltens, P., van Duijn, C.

M., Heutink, P., & van Swieten, J. C. (2003). Frontotemporal dementia in The Netherlands: Patient characteristics and prevalence estimates from a population-based study. *Brain, 12*(Pt. 9), 2016-2022.

Ryan, J. J., Gontkovsky, S. T., Kreiner, D. S., & Tree, H. A. (2012). Wechsler Adult Intelligence Scale-Fourth Edition performance in relapsing-remitting multiple sclerosis. *Journal of Clinical and Experimental Neuropsychology, 34*, 571-579.

Ryder, K. A., Gontkovsky, S. T., McSwan, K. L., Scott, J. G., Bharucha, K. J., & Beatty, W. W. (2002). Cognitive function in Parkinson's disease: *Association with anxiety but not depression. Aging, Neuropsychology, and Cognition, 9*, 77-84.

Sahathevan, R., Brodtmann, A., & Donnan, G. A. (2012). Dementia, stroke, and vascular risk factors: *A review. International Journal of Stroke, 7*, 61-73.

Santos-García, D., & de la Fuente-Fernández, R. (2013). Impact of non-motor symptoms on health-related and perceived quality of life in Parkinson's disease. *Journal of the Neurological Sciences, 332*, 136-140.

Savva, G. M., Stephan, B. C. M., & the Alzheimer's Society Vascular Dementia Systematic Review Group. (2010). Epidemiological studies of the effect of stroke on incident dementia: *A systematic review. Stroke, 41*, E41-E46.

Schreiter Gasser, U., Rousson, V., Hentschel, F., Sattel, H., & Gasser, T. (2008). Alzheimer disease versus mixed dementias: An EEG perspective. *Clinical Neurophysiology, 119*, 2255-2259.

Schwartz, C., & Frohner, R. (2005). Contribution of demographic, medical, and social support variables in predicting the mental health dimension of quality of life among people with multiple sclerosis. *Health and Social Work, 30*, 203-212.

Small, G., & Vorgan, G. (2011). *The Alzheimer's prevention program: Keep your brain healthy for the rest of your life*. New York: Workman.

Stevens, T., Livingston, G., Kitchen, G., Manela, M., Walker, Z., & Katona, C. (2002). Islington study of dementia subtypes in the community. *British Journal of Psychiatry, 180*, 270-276.

Stewart, R. (2012). Subjective cognitive impairment. *Current Opinion in Psychiatry, 25*, 445-450.

Thompson, J. C., Stopford, C. L., Snowden, J. S., & Neary, D. (2005). Qualitative neuropsychological performance characteristics in frontotemporal dementia and Alzheimer's disease. *Journal of Neurology, Neurosurgery and Psychiatry, 76*, 920-927.

Thompson, P. M., & Vinters, H. V. (2012). Pathologic lesions in neurodegenerative diseases. *Progress in Molecular Biology and Translational Science, 107*, 1–40.

Thornton, A. E., Raz, N., & Tucke, K. A. (2002). Memory in multiple sclerosis: Contextual encoding deficits. *Journal of the International Neuropsychological Society, 8*, 395-409.

Tierney, M. C., Black, S. E., Szalai, J. P., Snow, W. G., Fisher, R. H., Nadon, G., & Chui, H. C. (2001). Recognition memory and verbal fluency differentiate probable Alzheimer disease from subcortical ischemic vascular dementia. *Archives of Neurology, 58*, 1654-1659.

Torack, R. M., & Morris, J. C. (1988). The association of ventral tegmental area histopathology with adult dementia. *Archives of Neurology, 45*, 497-501.

Trapp, B. D., Peterson, J., Ransohoff, R. M., Rudick, R., Mork, S., & Bo, L. (1998). Axonal transection in the lesions of multiple sclerosis. *New England Journal of Medicine, 338*, 278-285.

Tsuboi, Y., & Dickson, D. W. (2005). Dementia with Lewy bodies and Parkinson's disease with dementia: Are they different? *Parkinsonism and Related Disorders, 11*(Suppl. 1), S47-S51.

van der Hoorn, A., Bartels, A. L., Leenders, K. L., & de Jong, B. M. (2011). Handedness and dominant side of symptoms in Parkinson's disease. *Parkinsonism and Related Disorders, 17*, 58-60.

Varanese, S., Perfetti, B., Mason, S., Di Rocco, A., & Goldberg, E. (2010). *Lateralized profiles of frontal lobe dysfunction in Parkinson's disease.* Paper presented at 7th International Congress on Mental Dysfunctions and Other Non-motor Features in Parkinson's Disease and Related Disorders, Barcelona, Spain.

Vignini, A., Giulietti, A., Nanetti, L., Raffaelli, F., Giusti, L., Mazzanti, L., & Provinciali, L. (2013). Alzheimer's disease and diabetes: New insights and unifying therapies. *Current Diabetes Reviews, 9,* 218-227.

Wang, X., Shen, Y., & Chen, W. (2012) Progress in frontotemporal dementia research. *American Journal of Alzheimer's Disease and Other Dementias, 28,* 15-23.

Wider, C. W., Dickson, D. W., Rademakers, R. & Wszolek, Z. K. (2010). Frontotemporal dementia. In A. H. V. Schapira, A. E. T. Lang, & S. Fahn (Eds.), *Blue books of neurology: Movement disorders 4* (pp. 397-416). Philadelphia: Saunders.

World Health Organization (2008). *Atlas: Multiple sclerosis resources in the world. WHO Library Cataloguing-in-Publication Data.* Geneva: World Health Organization.

Yamaguchi, H., Maki, Y., & Yamagami, T. (2010). Overview of non-pharmacological intervention for dementia and principles of brain-activating rehabilitation. *Psychogeriatrics, 10,* 206-213.

Yust-Katz, S., Tesler, D., Treves, T. A., Melamed, E., & Djaldetti, R. (2008). Handedness as a predictor of side of onset of Parkinson's disease. *Parkinsonism and Related Disorders, 14,* 633-635.

Zekry, D., Hauw, J-J., & Gold, G. (2002). Mixed dementia: epidemiology, diagnosis, and treatment. *Journal of the American Geriatrics Society, 50,* 1431-1438.

Zetterberg, H., & Blennow, K. (2013). Biomarker evidence for uncoupling of amyloid build-up and toxicity in Alzheimer's disease. *Alzheimer's and Dementia, 9,* 459-462.

Bibliography

Beaumont, J. G. (2008). *Introduction to neuropsychology* (2nd ed.). New York: Guilford Press.

Compston, A., McDonald, I. R., Noseworthy, J., Lassman, H., Miller, D. H., Smith, K. J., Wekerle, H. & Confavreux, C. (Eds.). (2005). *McAlpine's multiple sclerosis* (4th ed.). London: Churchill Livingston.

Kaufman, D. M., & Milstein, M. J. (2013). *Kaufman's clinical neurology for psychiatrists* (7th ed.). Philadelphia: Saunders.

Weiner, W. J., Goetz, C. G., Shin, R. K., & Lewis, S. L. (Eds.). (2010). *Neurology for the non-neurologist* (6th ed.). Philadelphia: Lippincott Williams & Wilkins.

CHAPTER 2

Pharmacological Treatment of Dementia: Do Medications Work?

Robert M. Nevels and Samuel T. Gontkovsky

Presently, there exists no cure for the various chronic and neurodegenerative conditions described in Chapter 1, such as Alzheimer's disease (AD) and frontotemporal lobar degeneration, which cause dementia. In this light, medical treatment revolves primarily around behavioral and pharmacological interventions to address the multitude of symptoms associated with this condition. Medications targeted specifically to the cognitive sequelae of dementia attempt to slow the progression of deterioration over time in order to allow individuals to experience a greater level of independence and higher quality of life for as long as possible. Drugs also may be prescribed to assist in managing the many behavioral and emotional problems, such as agitation or aggression and anxiety or depression, which are commonly seen in individuals with dementia (see Chapter 8). Finally, medications are used to treat directly the symptomatology related to the underlying causes of the dementia. For example, a person who has developed dementia as a result of Parkinson's disease likely will be undergoing pharmacological intervention to address the many motor disturbances, such as tremors, that are present with this condition.

The purpose of this chapter is to review the primary pharmacological agents prescribed by health care professionals for individuals who have been diagnosed with dementia. We will discuss the various classes of medications used in treatment of dementia and its associated symptoms, specifying the principal drugs in each class and describing their indications, efficacy, and some of the common side effects that may be of concern. The chapter will conclude with a brief overview of examples of medications used in the treatment of various non-cognitive symptoms associated with some of the underlying diseases that may cause dementia as well as a discussion of other promising pharmacological options for the treatment of dementia.

Current Pharmacology in Alzheimer's Disease

Presently, no medication can prevent, halt, or reverse the progressive mental deterioration associated with neurodegenerative dementia. At best, medications may function to slow cognitive decline for a period of time. The pharmacotherapy of dementia, to date, has been targeted at preventing nerve cell destruction and has been influenced significantly by the *cholinergic deficiency hypothesis* of the etiology of Alzheimer's disease (Diamond, 2009; Julien, Advokat, & Comaty, 2011; Stahl, 2013). This deficit is thought to occur through the gradual destruction of cholinergic neurons and a significant decrease in the neurotransmitter acetylcholine, which facilitates the formation of new memories. Excessive accumulation of amyloid beta plaques impinge upon neural membranes causing the collapse and entanglement of tau proteins in the microtubules. Small clumps of amyloid beta may block neural signaling at synapses. Plaques and clumps also may activate immune system cells that trigger inflammation and devour disabled cells. Cellular tangles prevent nurturance, repair, and maintenance of organelles, such as mitochondria that function to provide cellular energy. Other neurotransmitters and neurohormones, including norepinephrine, serotonin, and somatostatin (growth hormone) are decreased; glutamate levels are elevated, and inflammation with increased microglia scavenging and cytokine production occurs; axonal myelin is damaged, neural cells die, and dead cells become debris for the formation of more plaques. Granulovacuolar degeneration, the accumulation of large, double membrane-bound bodies similar to autophagic organelles (e.g., macrophages) occurs within certain neurons during AD and other adult-onset dementias and is seen in the pyramidal cells of the hippocampus, a sign of a marked cholinergic deficit (Funk, Mrak, & Kuret, 2011). Most of this, however, is hypothetical and drugs (e.g., tarenflurbil, a gamma-secretase modulator) that have targeted plaque formations, including vaccines against plaques, have not been successful in phase III clinical trials (Green et al., 2009).

Cholinesterase Inhibitors

The first-line class of pharmacotherapy agents used in the treatment of dementia, particularly in suspected AD, is the acetylcholinesterase inhibitors, or cholinesterase inhibitors (ChEIs) for short. ChEIs work by inhibiting acetylcholinesterase, the main enzyme that breaks down and deactivates acetylcholine (ACh), an important neurotransmitter necessary for muscle movement, gastrointestinal, urinary functioning and, in the brain, memory formation. As many dementias progress, especially AD, acetylcholine nerve cells (cholinergic neurons) in critical brain regions appear to undergo rapid and accelerating cell death. This process is called apoptosis and is characterized as "cellular suicide" because it is genetically programmed to occur under circumstances involving inflammatory brain injury or disease. A decreasing number of cholinergic neurons leads to decreasing acetylcholine nerve signaling and results in a markedly decreased and continued decreasing capacity for formation of new memories (Stahl, 2013).

In 1993, tacrine (Cognex) became the first ChEI approved by the Food and Drug Administration (FDA) for treating Alzheimer's disease. Data that tacrine was an effective treatment for AD was derived from two well-controlled clinical investigations in patients with probable mild to moderate AD. In the first study, 468 patients were randomized to groups comparing treatment with placebo and 20, 40, and 80 mg daily of tacrine for 12 weeks (Farlow et al., 1992) Statistically significant differences were detected for the tacrine groups on measures of cognitive functioning as well as clinician-rated and caregiver-rated measures of global functioning. Improvements in functioning began appearing at six weeks and continued out to 12 weeks, with improvement being dose-related and significant. Comparison of 80 mg per day dosing with placebo showed significant improvement on all measures for the tacrine-treated patients as compared with the placebo-treated patients.

The second study was 30 weeks in duration and involved 663 patients randomized to a placebo and three drug groups (Knopman et al., 1996). The daily dose of tacrine was increased at six-week intervals, starting with the 40 mg per day dose. At the end of the study, comparisons between placebo, 80, 120, and 160 mg per day were possible. Patients in the 160 mg per day group received that dose for the final 12 weeks of the study; those in the 120 mg per day group received that dose for 18 weeks. Statistically significant drug versus placebo differences were found on measures of cognition and daily functioning for the 80 and 120 mg per day groups at 18 weeks and for the 120 and 160 mg per day groups at 30 weeks. Of the 663 patients who entered the study, 653 patients were included in an intent-to-treat (ITT) analysis. Only 263 patients, however, had evaluable data at 30 weeks. The results of the ITT analysis revealed significant dose-response trends and between-group differences on cognitive and daily functioning measures. In evaluable patients, statistically significant dose-dependent differences were observed on measures of cognition and functioning. Because 390 patients failed to complete 30 weeks of tacrine treatment, however, each patient's last on-study value was used in the ITT analysis. Study results confirmed tacrine's effectiveness; however, all groups, even those showing initial improvement, deteriorated with time. Age, gender, and other patient baseline characteristics did not predict clinical outcome. The ITT analysis found 23% and 42% of evaluable-patients treated with tacrine, respectively, were rated as improved on the measure of daily overall functioning compared with 17% and 18% of placebo patients, respectively. Tacrine-treated patients were withdrawn from the study because of asymptomatic liver transaminase elevations (28%) and gastrointestinal complaints (16%).

A meta-analysis of 12 trials of tacrine treatment with a total of 1984 patients with Alzheimer's disease (Qizilbash et al., 1998) found cognitive performance, measured by the Mini-Mental State Examination (MMSE; Folstein, Folstein, & McHugh, 1975), significantly better in patients receiving tacrine than in patients receiving placebo by 0.62 points at 12 weeks. Scores on the MMSE range from 0-30, with higher scores indicating better cognitive functioning. Similar untreated patients would be expected to deteriorate by 0.50 to 1.00 points on the MMSE during a period of 12 weeks; therefore, the progress of patients in this study on tacrine would be predicted to have a range between an improvement of 0.12 and a deterioration of 0.38 points. Fifty-eight percent more tacrine-treated than placebo-treated patients were found to be improved on the measure of clinician ratings. The behavioral scale of the test used to determine an overall assessment of AD also showed a significant difference in favor of tacrine; however, this small difference only represents a 1.2% difference, on average, between tacrine-treated and placebo-treated patients. Improvement on a scale measuring progressive deterioration, largely an index of functional skills involving activities of daily living, was not significant. Eventually, the modest treatment benefits coupled with the need for frequent dosing, high rates of increased transaminase levels and possible liver damage, and the availability of newer and more effective ChEIs with fewer side effects rendered tacrine less attractive than initially thought, and the drug was discontinued in the U.S. (Julien et al., 2011).

The first post-tacrine cholinesterase inhibitor to be developed was donepezil (Aricept), which is approved to treat all stages of AD and remains the first line ChEI. It has an oral bioavailability of 100%, easily crosses the blood-brain barrier, and can be dosed once per day given its elimination half-life of 70 hours (Janicak, Marder, & Pavuluri, 2011). Clinical trials demonstrated significant improvements in cognitive and overall functioning in people receiving Aricept compared with those receiving a placebo, with fewer adverse effects than with Cognex. For example, 80% of Aricept patients participating in a 24-week study suffered no cognitive decline compared with 57% of patients taking a placebo. Improvement was greater with higher doses; 54% of the patients taking 10 mg of Aricept improved slightly in cognitive functioning compared to 38% taking 5 mg and 27% taking the placebo (Rogers, Farlow, Doody, Mohs, & Friedhoff, 1998). In a multinational study involving 818 patients, individuals who took both 5 and 10 mg per day of Aricept showed statistically significant improvements in cognitive and global function compared to those receiving a placebo; treatment-associated changes also were observed in functional skills (Burns et al., 1999). The results of this study confirmed that donepezil was effective and well tolerated in treating the symptoms of mild to moderately severe AD.

In 2010, based on the results of a study of 1,467 people with moderate to severe AD, the FDA approved a 23 mg dose of Aricept to be taken once per day (Farlow et al., 2010). The 23 mg dose improved cognitive functioning significantly more than the 10 mg dose, although it did not show improvement in overall functioning. Overall functioning was defined as cognitive functioning in addition to the ability to perform activities of daily living, which traditionally covers several functional domains. The between-group difference in outcomes between donepezil 23 mg per day and 10 mg per day was not significant.

Increased side effects, including bleeding and weight loss, occur with the 23 mg dose compared to the 10 mg dose, although some side effects improve after a few weeks. A generic orally disintegrating donepezil tablet has been approved for patients who have difficulty swallowing, and a transdermal patch also is available.

Rivastigmine (Exelon) is approved for mild to moderate AD. In four placebo-controlled clinical trials with a total of 3,900 people, Exelon patients had significantly better scores on standard tests of cognitive function than patients taking a placebo. In one of these trials involving 725 AD patients, 24% of participants taking Exelon demonstrated significant improvements in cognitive function over 26 weeks compared to 16% taking a placebo (Etemad, Anand, & Hartman, 2001). One supposed possible advantage of rivastigmine is its inhibition of both acetylcholinesterase and butylcholinesterase, which also degrades acetylcholine (Stahl, 2013). Studies have not revealed significantly different outcomes for rivastigmine, however, compared to other ChEIs (Janicak et al., 2011).

A 13.3 mg per day transdermal patch (Exelon Patch) was approved by the FDA in late June of 2013 for an expanded indication for the rivastigmine transdermal system to include treating patients with severe AD. This approval means that it is the only transdermal therapy approved for use in all stages of AD. The patch already had received approval for patients with mild to moderate AD, as well as for patients with mild to moderate dementia associated with Parkinson's disease. Approval for use in severe AD was based on the ACTION (ACTivities of Daily Living and CognitION in Patients with Severe Dementia of the Alzheimer's Type) study, a randomized, double-blind trial comparing the 13.3 mg per day dose patch with the lower 4.6 mg per day dose. The higher-dose patch demonstrated statistically significant improvement across several measures of cognition and daily living skills in patients with severe AD at 24 weeks. The most common side effects were application site erythema (redness and rash), falls, insomnia, nausea/vomiting, diarrhea, and weight loss; the side effects were observed in a higher percentage of patients treated with the higher 13.3 mg per day dose (Novartis Pharmaceuticals, 2013).

The newest cholinesterase inhibitor is galantamine (Razadyne, previously named Reminyl), which is approved to treat mild to moderate Alzheimer's disease. Approval was based on data from four placebo-controlled clinical trials with over 2,650 people (Brodaty et al., 2005; Raskind, Peskind, Wessel, & Yuan, 2000; Rockwood, Mintzer, Truyen, Wessel, & Wilkinson, 2001; Wilcock, Lilienfeld, & Gaens, 2000). Patients taking Razadyne scored better on measures of cognitive performance and daily functioning than people taking a placebo. Burns and colleagues (2009), however, found that galantamine improved cognitive functioning but not functioning related to activities of daily living.

Although ChEIs can improve patients' current functioning, they do not prevent the eventual deterioration that occurs in AD and other dementias. In some patients, they slow or delay cognitive impairment and are most effective in mild to moderate dementia, though donepezil offers some relief in severe dementia. It is recommended that individuals with AD start on ChEIs immediately following diagnosis, as the medication appears to have better effects earlier in the disease process. Some patients do well, others have some beneficial responses, and many appear to have little or no positive response. On average, improvement is very modest and lasts for approximately 6-12 months (Diamond, 2009; Julien et. al., 2011).

The most common adverse effects of cholinesterase inhibitors are nausea, vomiting, loss of appetite, weight loss, and diarrhea. Some patients have experienced shortness of breath and pain. Further, patients taking ChEIs for dementia have a significantly higher risk of falls and bradycardia; all side effects should be considered before initiating cholinesterase inhibitor therapy.

Statistical Significance Versus Clinical Significance

A general issue that has arisen in many of the meta-analyses of the effectiveness of ChEIs is whether the differences between statistical significance and clinical significance are of practical significance (Lanctôt, Rajaram, & Herrmann, 2009). The ChEIs and memantine (discussed below) have demonstrated statistically significant improvements in research outcomes, including cognitive and behavior when compared with placebo, but how do these improvements translate in a clinical setting? Hogan (2007) cautioned that many reported results from randomized, controlled trials may be statistically significant but have not been proven to be clinically relevant. In order to avoid an exaggeration of results, he recommends reporting effect sizes, number of patients not treated, and/or setting minimum score changes for labeling participants as responders. Otherwise, positive results found thus far for the ChEIs have been very modest, at best, and generally are experienced by patients during the first year of treatment. Thereafter, the efficacy of ChEIs declines progressively and disappears entirely after two to three years (Mancuso, Siciliano, Barone, Butterfield, & Preziosi, 2011).

In this light, the FDA in early 2010 criticized two Aricept television commercials, describing them as "deceptive," "misleading," and "not supported by the available research data." In a letter dated February 3, 2010 to Eisai Company and Pfizer, co-marketers for the drug Aricept, the FDA stated the television commercials imply that as a result of taking Aricept an individual's neurocognitive and functional status may be completely restored to normal. The FDA went on to point out that respected clinical trials of Aricept have indicated only a small degree of improvement in some subjects taking donepezil and that in others there has been no measurable improvement, whatsoever. The FDA requested that the advertisements in question be pulled from television (Food and Drug Administration, 2010; The Elder Care Team, 2013).

Glutamate Receptor Antagonists

The single non-cholinesterase inhibitor approved to prevent or attenuate neurodegeneration, memory loss, and clinical deterioration of dementia is the N-methyl-D-aspartate (NMDA) glutamate receptor antagonist, memantine (Namenda), which has a low to moderate, noncompetitive affinity for the NMDA receptor and has been demonstrated to be effective in moderate to severe AD (Aarsland et al., 2009). Glutamate is excitatory and glutamatergic overactivity at NMDA receptors results in excitotoxicity and damage to glutamate and other transmitter releasing neurons (glutamatergic neurons also co-release glycine along with glutamate); excitotoxicity also occurs at other glutamate receptors, especially the α-amino-3-hydroxy-5-methyl-4-isoxazolepropionic acid (AMPA) receptors, which work in tandem with NMDA receptors. As the major central nervous system excitatory neurotransmitter, glutamate mediates NMDA receptor activity associated with two primary and opposing functions: 1) facilitation of the long-term potentiation of learning/memory (discussed further in Chapter 3), and 2) the initiation of apoptosis, or programmed cell death, as a result of excitotoxicity from overstimulation of the NMDA receptors, which leads to excessive calcium ion influx though NMDA-gated calcium channels. As noted, this is a co-linked process involving the AMPA glutamate receptors, which reside in close proximity to the NMDA receptors on the cell membrane.

Winblad and Poritis (1999) evaluated memantine treatment for AD in a long-term care setting. In a placebo-controlled trial, 166 patients who met diagnostic criteria for dementia, obtained MMSE scores of less than 10, and met specified criteria for severe deterioration were selected to receive either memantine 10 mg per day (half the current recommended dosage) or a placebo. Administering 10 mg per day of memantine for 12 weeks, statistically significant improvements in global and functional parameters were seen on a clinician-rated scale of global functioning. Scores on a geriatric behavioral rating scale, however, were not statistically significant. It also was found that treated patients needed less nursing care due to improved functioning. Though no improvements were noted on the behavioral rating scale, global, and functional improvements supported memantine's value as a potential pharmacological agent for patients with moderate to severe AD.

A study was conducted in an outpatient setting (Reisberg et al., 2003) using similar selection criteria and also satisfying diagnostic criteria of the National Institute of Neurologic and Communicative Disorders and Stroke and the Alzheimer's disease and Related Disorders Association (NINCDS-ADRDA). In this study, memantine 10 mg twice daily was administered for 28 weeks to 181 patients at 32 treatment centers in the United States. Over the course of the trial, patients receiving memantine demonstrated statistically significant benefits compared to those on placebo on measures of cognition and activities of daily living but not on measures of behavioral and emotional functioning. These results confirmed the results of the previously described long-term care setting study and also demonstrated better cognitive outcomes for patients receiving memantine.

Memantine generally is well tolerated, with no significant differences in reported adverse events between treatment and placebo groups. Studies have demonstrated modest improvements with memantine in cognitive functioning in individuals with moderate-to-severe AD in addition to benefits on global assessments, functional ability, and behavioral symptoms. The clinical relevance of these improvements, however, remains unclear (Lanctôt et al., 2009; Wilcock, Ballard, Cooper, & Loft, 2008).

ChEIs + Memantine

The combining of ChEIs and memantine can been considered (Diamond, 2009). Because memantine targets glutamate and cholinesterase inhibitors target acetylcholine, combining memantine with ChEIs may be more effective than monotherapy. A random, double-blind, placebo-controlled trial using a combination therapy of memantine and donepezil was conducted with 404 outpatients already on donepezil for 24 weeks, with 322 patients completing the trial (Tariott et al., 2004). Study participants were required to have MMSE scores between 5 and 14 and to have a diagnosis of dementia, based on the NINCDS-ADRDA criteria. They also were at least 50 years of age and had neuroimaging results consistent with AD. All patients continued on donepezil treatment, with half being randomized to the addition of memantine and half to the addition of a placebo. At the trial's conclusion, statistically significant benefits supporting the donepezil/memantine combination were found on all primary and secondary outcome measures, involving cognitive, behavioral, and functional status. In another study investigating the memantine/donepezil combination (van Dyck et al., 2006), similar results were found. According to Mancuso et al. (2011), the clinical benefit of combined treatment with donepezil and memantine remains unclear.

Current Pharmacology in Other Dementias

There are no standard drug treatments for addressing the neurocognitive deficits associated with conditions other than AD that may lead to dementia, such as frontotemporal lobar degeneration and Lewy body disease. Most treatments are palliative or aimed at reducing risk factors for further brain damage. Some studies, however, have found that ChEIs and memantine can improve cognitive functioning and behavioral symptoms in patients with early vascular dementia (e.g., Tariott et al., 2004). Nevertheless, these same medications developed for slowing the cognitive deterioration associated with Alzheimer's disease often are prescribed for patients presenting with other chronic neurological conditions that result in neurocognitive decline.

Similar to AD, cholinergic deficits are found in patients with vascular dementia and Lewy body dementia (LBD). There is growing support for the use and effectiveness of ChEIs in these forms of dementias and, to date, there is no clear indication that their use should be managed differently from treatment using ChEIs in AD. The cholinergic deficit in LBD may be even larger than that in AD, and it is hypothesized that patients with LBD may have better responses to a ChEI than those with AD. As patients with LBD often tolerate antipsychotic medications poorly, ChEIs provide the most practical option for treating the neuropsychiatric symptoms found in DLB. Indeed, patients with LBD have demonstrated symptomatic improvement in behavioral and emotional symptoms, including apathy, delusions, and hallucinations following initiation of treatment with ChEIs (McKeith et al., 2000). There also seems to be a treatment effect of ChEIs in patients with mixed dementia, involving AD and cerebrovascular disease, as well as growing evidence of similar benefits in individuals with vascular dementia. Cholinergic structures are vulnerable to the ischemic changes in vascular dementia, which can lead to significant loss of cholinergic neural pathways, although rarely as great as that seen in AD. Donepezil and galantamine have been shown to have a significant effect on cognition and global functioning in vascular dementia, and estimated effect sizes are similar to those seen in the first trials for AD (Overshott & Burns, 2005).

Current Pharmacology for the Non-Cognitive Symptoms Associated with Dementia and the Underlying Conditions that Cause Dementia

As described in detail in Chapter 1, the term dementia signifies a cluster of cognitive and functional symptoms that represents a decline from an individual's premorbid capabilities, which may be due to one or more of several underlying disease processes. Many of the various medical conditions that may result in dementia often involve a range of non-cognitive symptoms, including physical complications and behavioral/emotional issues, which may be manifested even if patients never meet the diagnostic criteria for dementia. For example, not all individuals with Parkinson's disease develop dementia, although some may exhibit more subtle disturbances of cognition. Nevertheless, resting tremors, bradykinesia, and depression are likely to be present with this disease and to require intervention. Further, individuals with dementia may develop physical and behavioral/emotional symptoms, particularly in the later stages of illness secondary to deterioration of neurons, which are not part of the criteria for diagnosing the underlying disease process or the dementia but that may substantially affect daily functioning and thus require treatment. For example, individuals with in the later stages of Alzheimer's disease may develop delusions, urinary incontinence, and difficulties swallowing. There symptoms are not diagnostic of AD and may not have been present in the early stages of the disease but developed over time and require management, possibly with pharmacological intervention. A complete discussion of the medications used for these purposes is beyond the scope of this chapter; however, we will provide a brief review for illustrative purposes in order to communicate to the reader that these medications generally are targeting non-cognitive as opposed to cognitive symptoms.

Individuals with vascular dementia may have a host of other conditions, which are associated with vascular pathology. Common health issues associated with vascular dementia include hypertension (high blood pressure), hypercholesterolemia (elevated cholesterols levels), and/or diabetes mellitus. Patients with hyptertension, for example, may be being prescribed diuretics or beta blockers to address this concern. Although the treatment may have a secondary effect on cognition, the drug is targeted to address the primary issue of blood pressure.

Patients with Parkinson's disease often are being prescribed medication to address the motor symptoms associated with the condition. One commonly prescribed drug for this purpose is carbidopa/levodopa (Sinement). This medication often is effective for its intended goal of alleviating certain physical problems associated with Parkinson's disease but does not have direct effects on cognitive functioning.

As a final example in this regard, people with relapsing-remitting multiple sclerosis may be taking medications to reduce the intensity of or shorten the duration of relapses. Common medications for this purpose include interferon beta-1b (Betaseron) and natalizmab (Tysabri). Additionally, fatigue is a commonly experienced as a consequence of multiple sclerosis, affecting up to 92% of patients with this disorder according to self-report data (Beatty, 2008). Therefore, many individuals with this disease are prescribed medications, such as amantadine (Symmetrel) or modafinil (Provigil), to provide symptomatic relief. Again, the primary targets of these drugs are specific mechanisms of the underlying disease process or associated symptoms of the disease, respectively, as opposed to the cognitive deficits associated with dementia.

Both Chapters 1 and 8 discuss the various behavioral and emotional issues that may be associated with dementia, and Chapter 8 provides an overview of non-pharmacological approaches to managing these symptoms. From a medication standpoint, antidepressants, anxiolytics, hypnotic-sedatives, and other pharmacological agents may be useful in treating specific emotional symptoms and behavioral problems associated with AD and other neurodegenerative diseases. Depression, which often is associated with all dementias, generally is best treated with selective serotonin reuptake inhibitors (SSRIs) as opposed to tricyclic antidepressants (TCAs), the latter having anticholinergic effects that may result in numerous negative side effects, including increased confusion (Julien et al., 2011). For example, Reynolds and colleagues (2006), in a study of 116 elderly patients with major depression, found that a combination of interpersonal psychotherapy and paroxetine raised rates of remission from 35% to 58% and indicated that depression in the elderly may best be treated with a combination of an antidepressant and psychotherapy.

In addition to the possibility of increasing confusion, anticholinergic side effects, which tend to worsen as people age, may involve hyperthermia (increased body temperature), mydriasis (dilated pupils), photophobia (sensitivity to light), tachycardia (rapid heart rate), cycloplegia (loss of accommodation with blurred vision), urinary retention, constipation, diplopia (double vision), vasodilation, dry skin, and dry mouth. More worrisome, and related to dementia and psychiatric considerations, anticholinergic drugs can heighten the startle response as well as increase hallucinations and delusions, incoherent thought, illogical thinking, irritability, agitation, euphoria, dysphoria, and, less frequently, may result in seizures, coma, and death (Katzung, 2004; Preston, O'Neal, & Talaga, 2013). A recent study by Cai, Campbell, Khan, Callahan, and Boustani (2013) also found that medications with severe anticholinergic burden may be a risk factor for developing mild cognitive impairment.

Anticholinergics still are used in certain neurodegenerative disease emergencies (e.g., to reduce severe tremors) and for other non-dementia related (e.g., gastric problems, ulcerative colon, nausea/vomiting, sedation, cystitis, prostatitis, asthma, bronchitis, and insomnia) therapeutic reasons (Janacak et. al., 2011). Among anticholinergic agents still found useful are atropine, diphenhydramine (Benadryl), trihexaphenidyl (Artane), biperiden (Akineton), and benztropine (Cogentin).

Psychotic symptoms, including hallucinations and delusions, may be present in some types of dementia, in particular during the advanced stages of the disease process. Among individuals without dementia, the second generation of atypical antipsychotics would be the first-line class of medications to address these symptoms. The FDA twice has issued black box warnings, however, for the use of the second generation of atypical antipsychotics in elderly populations with dementia, cautioning that both conventional and atypical antipsychotics are associated with an increased risk of mortality in elderly patients being treated for dementia-related psychosis. In April of 2005, the FDA notified healthcare professionals that patients with dementia-related psychosis who are treated with atypical antipsychotic drugs are at an increased risk of death from both cardiovascular events and respiratory illness events, such as pneumonia. Since issuing that notification, the FDA has reviewed additional information that indicates mortality from all causes not only is associated with atypical antipsychotics but also is associated with conventional typical antipsychotics and issued a warning in 2008 to healthcare providers that antipsychotics are not indicated for the treatment of dementia-related psychosis. These advisories have been controversial, since other studies have failed to verify increased antipsychotic-related risk of death in this population (Elie et al., 2009; Simoni-Wastila et al., 2009). The fact that these medications are viewed as overprescribed, as are many other agents in this generally polypharmacy-overmedicated elderly population, is without question (Chen et al., 2010). In those individuals who truly require treatment due to severe symptoms, however, there is no good alternative. Antipsychotics have been reported to help relieving agitation, aggression, treatment noncompliance, psychosis, depression (especially as augmentation to antidepressants, such as Abilify or Seroquel plus an antidepressant), sleep phase delay problems, and inappropriate sexual behaviors (Julien et al., 2011).

Anxiolytics, such as benzodiazepines, also have to be used in addressing behavioral symptoms among patients with dementia, but extreme caution is warranted with their use due to problems associated with possible over-sedation (e.g., falls, confusion, blurred vision, memory problems, and increased agitation) on shorter acting, shorter half-life agents, such as alprazolam (Xanax). Paradoxically, however, Xanax, in small doses, is sometimes better than larger doses, which will accumulate in fatty tissue and have higher serum concentrations over time because of the much slower metabolism of elders (Stahl, 2013). It also is not as sedative and does not suppress respiration to the degree of clonazepam (Klonopin), which also has a long half-life. Xanax possibly may increase aggression and inhibition but usually only at higher doses (Janacak et al., 2011).

Promising and Future Pharmacology for Dementia

Huperzine A

Huperzine A, a naturally occurring sesquiterpene alkaloid compound derived from a plant used for its purported medicinal qualities, huperzia serrata, may be useful as an alternative to synthetic ChEIs. In the United States, Huperzine A is sold as a dietary supplement for improving memory. Early trials have shown modest efficacy but have suffered from design flaws and small samples; thus, it cannot yet be recommended for the treatment of mild cognitive impairment or AD. (Desilets, Gickas, & Dunican, 2009).

Insulin

Research suggests that the hormone insulin plays an important role in AD and that restoration of insulin to normal levels in the brain may preserve cognition in people with mild cognitive impairment and AD. People with Alzheimer's disease have fewer insulin receptors than healthy individuals, and insulin appears to affect the brain's ability to clear away amyloid beta, which may explain why individuals with diabetes mellitus have a greater risk of dementia as compared with individuals without diabetes mellitus (Gasparini et al., 2001).

Getting insulin to the brain without impacting serum levels can be accomplished by intranasal administration (nasal spray). Intranasal administration allows insulin to reach the brain within minutes; minimal amounts are absorbed into general circulation. In a study in 104 older participants in which 64 had mild cognitive impairment and 40 had mild to moderate AD, participants were randomly assigned to one of three groups consisting of nasal spray containing 10 international units (IUs) of insulin, nasal spray containing 20 IUs of insulin, or nasal spray containing saline. Some participants had positron emission tomography (PET) scans for assessment of effective brain utilization of glucose. After four months of nasal spray use twice per day, both doses of insulin preserved ability to perform daily living activities and, in younger patients, general cognitive function; 20 IUs of intranasal insulin improved memory. No memory improvement was evident in the saline-spray group. The benefits in both insulin-treated groups continued at two months follow-up post treatment. The cognitive and functional abilities of saline-treated participants declined. PET scanning, performed in a subgroup, showed that brain metabolism in regions affected in early AD was preserved in the insulin-treated groups but not in the saline-treated group. No deleterious side effects were observed in either insulin spray treatment group (Craft et al., 2012).

Another study, however, found that intranasal insulin increased blood levels of amyloid beta (Kulstad et al., 2006). This may indicate that insulin removed amyloid beta from the brain and transferred it to serum for elimination through the liver, kidneys or bowels; other explanations also are possible.

Nonsteroidal Anti-Inflammatory Drugs

That theory that nonsteroidal anti-inflammatory drugs (NSAIDs) may act to prevent Alzheimer's disease comes from the observation that individuals with rheumatoid arthritis are much less likely to have AD (Ballard et al., 2011). Because most patients with rheumatoid arthritis take NSAIDs, such as ibuprofen (Advil) or naproxen (Aleve) for pain control, it was hypothesized that these agents might provide neuroprotection against Alzheimer's disease by reducing inflammation in arteries and possibly other locations in the brain. Inflammatory proteins, including cytokines, C-reactive protein, and thrombin and are found in the brains and blood samples of people with AD, and levels of these inflammatory proteins are elevated even before the onset of Alzheimer's disease and vascular dementia (Tarkowski, Andreasen, Tarkowski, & Blennow, 2003). Studies have shown the risk of developing AD is reduced in NSAIDs users by as much as 58% in persons who have used ibuprofen and aspirin for greater than three years as compared with those who have not used these drugs. Increased duration of use was associated with greater risk reduction. Regular use of acetaminophen (Tylenol), not an NSAID, did not decrease the risk of AD (Zandi et al., 2002). Another study found that elders who took NSAIDs, however, were more likely to develop dementia and Alzheimer's disease (Breitner et al., 2009).

When NSAIDs have been given to people who already have been diagnosed with mild cognitive impairment or AD as a means of slowing cognitive decline, the medications have had no effect. In a large study of healthy people age 70 years or older who had a family history of Alzheimer's disease, the NSAIDs celecoxib (Celebrex) and naproxen showed no ability to prevent the disease (ADAPT Research Group et al., 2007). Another study found that the one-year mean change in scores on a measure of cognitive functioning in participants treated with naproxen or rofecoxib was not significantly different from the change in participants treated with placebo (Aisen et al., 2003). Results of secondary analyses showed no consistent benefit of either treatment. Fatigue, dizziness, and hypertension were more common in the NSAID groups, and more serious adverse events were found in the NSAID groups than in the placebo group. The results of this study indicate that neither low-dose naproxen nor rofecoxib slow cognitive decline in patients with mild-to-moderate AD. Until more definitive research is completed, physicians advise against taking NSAIDs in an attempt to prevent Alzheimer's disease, because the drugs can have potentially serious side effects in high doses or when used long term (ADAPT Research Group et. al., 2007).

Hormone Replacement Therapy

Initial evidence suggested that hormone replacement therapy (HRT) with estrogen and progestin protected postmenopausal women against Alzheimer's disease (Simpkins, Yang, Wen, & Singh, 2005). Two later studies, however, found the opposite effect. The first (Shumaker et al., 2004) reported that women assigned to take HRT actually were slightly more likely to experience significant cognitive decline (7%) than those taking a placebo (5%). The second found that women taking HRT were twice as likely to develop dementia as those taking a placebo (Espeland et al., 2004). Currently, experts recommend against taking HRT to prevent dementia. Moreover, a recent study suggested that estrogen therapy alone confers the same risks (Loucks & Berga, 2009).

Lithium

Lithium is a glycogen synthase kinase-3 (GSK-3) inhibitor, and inhibition of GSK-3 beta by lithium reduces tau protein phosphorylation.

This effect is produced at clinical lithium concentrations. Tau hyperphosphorylation occurs in early AD and appears to precede disruption of the microtubules, which are major elements in the neural or nerve cell cytoskeleton. Cyclic AMP response element binding protein 1 (CREB-1) has major roles in mediating adaptive responses at glutamatergic synapses and in the neuroprotective effects of neurotrophins. CREB-1 appears to be a mediator of antidepressant pharmacodynamics. In vitro, chronic lithium treatment has been shown to promote neuronal cell survival (i.e., decreased apoptosis). Lithium as a neuroprotective agent would have an effect on P53 gene production and result in earlier repair of damaged cells (Jope, 1999; Stahl, 2013).

Nicotine

Nicotine stimulates acetylcholine nicotinic subtype receptors, especially the $\alpha4\beta2$ receptor, which is implicated in learning, memory, and addiction (Julien et al., 2011; Stahl, 2011). Targacept (ispronicline), with partial action at the $\alpha4\beta2$ receptor, currently is in trials for treating dementia with promising results on standard measures of memory/attention and faster reaction times (Dunbar et. al., 2013; Dunbar & Kuchibhatla, 2006). Nicotine patches reduce symptoms of mild cognitive impairment and improve delayed-word-recall accuracy and memory processing speed in this population (Newhouse et al., 2012).

These are just a few of the promising mechanisms for the pharmacological treatment of dementia. Though numerous leads exist, there is little solid evidence that pharmacological research will be developing the miracle drug that will cure AD and other dementing illnesses in the near future. For the time being, medical professionals are left with less than a handful of drugs to prescribe in attempting to address the cognitive and functional deficits associated with dementia. According to Mancuso et al. (2011), however, the ChEIs do not produce long-lasting improvement in memory and cognitive function, as they have a narrow therapeutic window restricted to the first 12 months of therapy, and the clinical benefit of memantine, either as monotherapy or administered together with donepezil, is still questionable. In this light, non-pharmacological approaches may offer the best hope for promoting brain health, offering neuroprotection, and slowing the cognitive and functional deterioration associated with Alzheimer's disease and other forms of dementia.

References

Aarsland, D., Ballard, C., Walker, Z, Bostrom, F., Alves, G., Kossakowski, K., Leroi, I., Pozo- Rodriguez, F., Minthon, L., & Londos, E. (2009). Memantine in patients with Parkinson's disease dementia or dementia with Lewy bodies: A double-blind, placebo-controlled, multicentre trial. *Lancet Neurology, 8,* 613–618.

ADAPT Research Group, Lyketsos, C. G., Breitner, J. C., Green, R. C., Martin, B. K., Meinert, C., Piantadosi, S., & Sabbagh, M. (2007). Naproxen and celecoxib do not prevent AD in early results from a randomized controlled trial. *Neurology, 68,* 1800-1808.

Aisen, P. S., Schafer, K. A., Grundman, M., Pfeiffer, E., Sano, M., Davis, K. L., Farlow, M. R., Jin, S., Thomas, R. G., Thal, L. J., & Alzheimer's Disease Cooperative Study. (2003). Effects of rofecoxib or naproxen vs placebo on Alzheimer disease progression: A randomized controlled trial. *JAMA, 289,* 2819-2826.

Ballard, C., Gauthier, S., Corbett, A., Brayne, C., Aarsland, D., & Jones, E. (2011). Alzheimer's disease. *Lancet, 377,* 1019-1031.

Beatty, W. W. (2008). Assessment for rehabilitation of patients with multiple sclerosis. In S. T. Gontkovsky & C. J. Golden (Eds.), *Neuropsychology within the inpatient rehabilitation environment* (pp. 99-131). Hauppauge, NY: Nova Science.

Breitner, J. C., Haneuse, S. J., Walker, R., Dublin, S., Crane, P. K., Gray, S. L., & Larson, E. B. (2009). Risk of dementia and AD with prior exposure to NSAIDs in an elderly community-based cohort. *Neurology, 72,* 1899-1905.

Brodaty, H., Corey-Bloom, J., Potocnik, F. C., Truyen, L., Gold, M., & Damaraju, C. R. (2005). Galantamine prolonged-release formulation in the treatment of mild to moderate Alzheimer's disease. *Dementia and Geriatric Cognitive Disorders, 20,* 120-132.

Burns , A., Bernabei , R., Bullock, R., Cruz Jentoft , A. J., Frölich, L., Hock ,C., Raivio, M., Triau, E., Vandewoude , M., Wimo, A., Came, E.,

Van Baelen, B., Hammond, G. L., van Oene, J. C., & Schwalen, S. (2009). Safety and efficacy of galantamine (Reminyl) in severe Alzheimer's disease (the SERAD study): A randomised, placebo-controlled, double-blind trial. *Lancet Neurology, 8*, 39-47.

Burns, A, Rossor, M., Hecker, J., Gauthier, S., Petit, H., Möller, H. J., Rogers, S. L., & Friedhoff, L. T. (1999). The effects of donepezil in Alzheimer's disease - Results from a multinational trial. *Dementia and Geriatric Cognitive Disorders, 10*, 237-244.

Cai, X., Campbell, N., Khan, B., Callahan, C., & Boustani, M. (2013). Long-term anticholinergic use and the aging brain. *Alzheimer's and Dementia, 9*, 377-385.

Chen, Y., Briesacher, B. A., Field, T. S., Tjia, J., Lau, D. T., & Gurwitz, J. H. (2010). Unexplained variation across US nursing homes in antipsychotic prescribing rates. *Archives of Internal Medicine, 170*, 89-95.

Craft, S., Baker, L. D., Montine, T. J., Minoshima, S., Watson, G. S., Claxton, A., Callaghan, M., Tsai, E., Plymate, S. R., Green, P. S., Leverenz, J., Cross, D., & Gerton, B. (2012). Intranasal insulin therapy for Alzheimer disease and amnestic mild cognitive impairment: A pilot clinical trial. *Archives of Neurology, 69*, 29-38.

Desilets, A. R., Gickas, J. J., & Dunican, K. C. (2009). Role of huperzine A in the treatment of Alzheimer's disease. *Annals of Pharmacotherapy, 43*, 514-518.s

Diamond, R. J. (2009). *Instant psychopharmacology* (3rd ed.). New York: W. W. Norton & Sons.

Dunbar, G., Demazières, A., Monreal, A., Cisterni, C., Metzger, D., Kuchibhatla, R., & Luthringer, R. (2013). Pharmacokinetics and safety profile of ispronicline (TC-1734), a new brain nicotinic receptor partial agonist, in young healthy male volunteers. *Journal of Clinical Pharmacology, 46*, 715-736.

Dunbar, G. C., & Kuchibhatla, R. (2006). Cognitive enhancement in man with ispronicline, a nicotinic partial agonist. *Journal of Molecular Neuroscience, 30*, 169-172.

Elie, M., Boss, K., Cole, M. G., McCusker, J., Belzile, E., & Ciampi, A. (2009). A retrospective, exploratory, secondary analysis of the association between antipsychotic use and mortality in elderly patients with delirium. *International Psychogeriatrics, 21*, 588-592.

Espeland, M. A., Rapp, S. R., Shumaker, S. A., Brunner, R., Manson, J. E., Sherwin, B. B., Hsia, J., Margolis, K. L., Hogan, P. E., Wallace, R., Dailey, M., Freeman, R., Hays, J., & Women's Health Initiative Memory Study. (2004). Conjugated equine estrogens and global cognitive function in postmenopausal women: Women's health initiative memory study. *JAMA, 291*, 2959-2968.

Etemad, B., Anand, R., & Hartman, R. (2001, September). *Behavioural and cognitive benefits of rivastigmine in nursing home patients with Alzheimer's disease and related dementias: A 26-week follow-up.* Poster session presented at the annual meeting of the International Congress of the International Psychogeriatric Association, Nice, France.

Farlow, M., Gracon, S. I., Hershey, L. A., Lewis, K. W., Sadowsky, C. H., & Dolan-Ureno, J. (1992). A controlled trial of tacrine in Alzheimer's disease. The tacrine study group. *JAMA, 268*, 2523-2529.

Farlow, M. R., Salloway, S., Tariot, P. N., Yardley, J., Moline, M. L., Wang, Q., Brand Schieber, E., Zou, H., Hsu, T., & Satlin, A. (2010). Effectiveness and tolerability of high-dose (23 mg/day) versus standard-dose (10 mg/day) donepezil in moderate to severe Alzheimer's disease: A 24-week, randomized, double-blind study. *Clinical Therapeutics, 32*, 1234-1251.

Folstein, M. F., Folstein, S. E., & McHugh, P. R. (1975). "Mini-Mental State": A practical method for grading the cognitive state of outpatients for the clinician. *Journal of Psychiatric Research, 12*, 189-198.

Food and Drug Administration. (2010, February 3). [Letter to Gary Wieczorek, Eisai Medical Research Inc]. Retrieved October 25, 2013, from http://www.fda.gov/downloads/Drugs/GuidanceComplianceRegulatoryInformation/EnforcementActivitiesbyFDA/WarningLettersandNoticeofViolationLetterstoPharmaceuticalCompanies/UCM201238.pdf.

Funk, K. E., Mrak, R. E., & Kuret, J. (2011). Granulovacuolar degeneration (GVD) bodies of Alzheimer's disease (AD) resemble late-stage autophagic organelles. *Neuropathology and Applied Neurobiology, 37*, 295-306.

Gasparini, L., Gouras, G. K., Wang, R., Gross, R. S., Beal, M. F., Greengard, P., & Xu, H. (2001). Stimulation of beta-amyloid precursor protein trafficking by insulin reduces intraneuronal beta-amyloid and requires mitogen-activated protein kinase signaling. *Journal of Neuroscience, 21*, 2561-2570.

Green, R. C., Schneider, L. S., Amato, D. A., Beelen, A. P., Wilcock, G., Swabb, E. A., Zavitz, K. H., & Tarenflurbil Phase 3 Study Group. (2009). Effect of tarenflurbil on cognitive decline and activities of daily living in patients with mild Alzheimer disease: A randomized controlled trial. *JAMA, 302*, 2557-2564.

Hogan, D. B. (2007). Improving drug trials for mild to moderate Alzheimer's disease. *Canadian Journal of Neurological Sciences, 34*(Suppl. 1), S97-S102.

Janicak, P. G., Marder, S. R., & Pavuluri, M. N. (2011). *Principles and practice of psychopharmacotherapy* (5th ed.). Philadelphia: Wolters Kluwer/Lippincott Williams and Wilkins.

Jope, R. S. (1999). A bimodal model of the mechanism of action of lithium. *Molecular Psychiatry, 4*, 21-25.

Julien, R. M., Advokat, C. D., & Comaty, J. E. (2011). *A primer of drug action* (12th ed.) New York: Worth.

Katzung, B. G. (2004). *Basic and clinical pharmacology* (9th ed.). New York: McGraw Hill.

Knopman, D., Schnieder, L., Davis, K., Talwalker, S., Smith, F., Hoover, T., & Gracon, S. (1996). Long-term tacrine (cognex) treatment: Effects on nursing home placement and maortality, tacrine study group. *Neurology, 47*, 166-177.

Kulstad, J. J., Green, P. S., Cook, D. G., Watson, G. S., Reger, M. A., Baker, L. D., Plymate, S. R., Asthana, S., Rhoads, K., Mehta, P. D., & Craft, S. (2006). Differential modulation of plasma beta-amyloid by insulin in patients with Alzheimer disease. *Neurology, 66*, 1506-1510.

Lanctôt, K. L., Rajaram, R. D., & Herrmann, N. (2009). Therapy for Alzheimer's disease: How effective are current treatments? *Therapeutic Advances in Neurological Disorders, 2*, 163-180.

Loucks, T. L., & Berga, S. L. (2009). Does postmenopausal estrogen use confer neuroprotection? *Seminars in Reproductive Medicine, 27*, 260-274.

Mancuso, C., Siciliano, R., Barone, E., Butterfield, D. A., & Preziosi, P. (2011). Pharmacologists and Alzheimer disease therapy: To boldly go where no scientist has gone before. *Expert Opinion on Investigational Drugs, 20*, 1243-1261.

McKeith, I., Del Ser, T., Spano, P., Emre, M., Wesnes, K., Anand, R., Cicin-Sain, A., Ferrara, R., & Spiegel, R. (2000). Efficacy of rivastigmine in dementia with Lewy bodies: A randomised, double-blind, placebo-controlled international study. *Lancet, 356*, 2031-2036.

Newhouse, P., Kellar, K., Aisen, P., White, H., Wesnes, K., Coderre, E., Pfaff, A., Wilkins, H., Howard, D., & Levin, E. D. (2012). Nicotine treatment of mild cognitive impairment: A 6-month double-blind pilot clinical trial. *Neurology, 78*, 91-101.

Novartis Pharmaceuticals. (2013). Effects of Rivastigmine Patch on Activities of Daily Living and Cognition in Patients With Severe Dementia of the Alzheimer's Type (ACTION) (Study Protocol CENA713DUS44, NCT00948766) and a 24 Week Open-label Extension to Study CENA713DUS44. Retrieved October 22, 2013, from http://clinicaltrials.gov/show/NCT01054755.

Overshott, R., & Burns, A. (2005). Treatment of dementia. *Journal of Neurology, Neurosurgery and Psychiatry, 76*(Suppl. V), v53-v59.

Preston, J., O'Neal, J. H., & Talaga, M. C. (2013). *Handbook of clinical psychopharmacology for therapists* (7th ed.). Oakland, CA: New Harbinger.

Qizilbash, N., Whitehead, A., Higgins, J., Wilcock, G., Schneider, L., & Farlow, M. (1998). Cholinesterase inhibition for Alzheimer's Disease: A meta-analysis of the Tacrine trials. Dementia trialists' collaboration. *JAMA, 280,* 1777-1782.

Raskind, M. A., Peskind, E. R., Wessel, T., & Yuan, W. (2000). Galantamine in AD: A 6-month randomized, placebo-controlled trial with a 6-month extension. *The galantamine USA-1 study group Neurology, 54,* 2261-2268.

Reisberg, B., Doody, R., Stöffler, A., Schmitt, F., Ferris, S., Möbius, H. J., & Memantine Study Group. (2003). Memantine in moderate-to-severe Alzheimer's disease. *New England Journal of Medicine, 348,* 1333-1341.

Reynolds, C. F. III, Dew, M. A., Pollock, B. G., Mulsant, B. H., Frank, E., Miller, M. D., Houck, P. R., Mazumdar, S., Butters, M. A., Stack, J. A., Schlernitzauer, M. A., Whyte, E. M., Gildengers, A., Karp, J., Lenze, E., Szanto, K., Bensasi, S., & Kupfer D. J. (2006). Maintenance treatment of major depression in old age. *New England Journal of Medicine, 354,* 1130-1138.

Rockwood, K., Mintzer, J., Truyen, L., Wessel, T., & Wilkinson, D. (2001). Effects of a flexible   galantamine dose in Alzheimer's disease: A randomised, controlled trial. *Journal of Neurology, Neurosurgery and Psychiatry, 71,* 589-595.

Rogers S. L., Farlow, M. R., Doody, R. S., Mohs, R., & Friedhoff, L. T. (1998). A 24-week, double-blind, placebo-controlled trial of donepezil in patients with Alzheimer's disease. *Donepezil study group. Neurology, 50,* 136-145.

Shumaker, S. A., Legault, C., Kuller, L., Rapp, S. R., Thal, L., Lane, D. S., Fillit, H., Stefanick, M. L., Hendrix, S. L., Lewis, C. E., Masaki, K., Coker, L. H., & Women's Health Initiative Memory Study. (2004). Conjugated equine estrogens and incidence of probable dementia and mild cognitive impairment in postmenopausal women: Women's health initiative memory study. *JAMA, 291,* 2947-2958.

Simoni-Wastila, L., Ryder, P. T., Qian, J., Zuckerman, I. H., Shaffer, T., & Zhao, L. (2009). Association of antipsychotic use with hospital events and mortality among medicare beneficiaries residing in long-term care facilities. *American Journal of Geriatric Psychiatry, 17,* 417-427.

Simpkins, J. W., Yang, S. H., Wen, Y., & Singh, M. (2005). Estrogens, progestins, menopause and neurodegeneration: Basic and clinical studies. *Cellular and Molecular Life Sciences, 62,* 271-280.

Stahl, S. M. (2011). *Stahl's essential psychopharmacology: The prescriber's guide* (4th ed.). New York: Cambridge University Press.

Stahl, S. M. (2013). *Stahl's essential psychopharmacology: Neuroscientific basis and practical applications* (4th ed.). New York: Cambridge University Press.

Tariot, P. N., Farlow, M. R., Grossberg, G. T., Graham, S. M., McDonald, S., Gergel, I., & Memantine Study Group (2004). Memantine treatment in patients with moderate to severe Alzheimer disease already receiving donepezil: A randomized controlled trial. *JAMA, 291,* 317-324.

Tarkowski, E., Andreasen, N., Tarkowski, A., & Blennow, K. (2003). Intrathecal inflammation precedes development of Alzheimer's disease. *Journal of Neurology, Neurosurgery and Psychiatry, 74,* 1200-1205.

The Elder Care Team. (2013). FDA slaps Aricept ads. Retrieved October 25, 2013, from http://www.eldercareteam.com/public/735.cfm?sd=34. van Dyck, C. H., Schmitt, F. A., Olin, J. T., & Memantine MEM-MD-02 Study Group. (2006). A responder analysis of memantine treatment in patients with Alzheimer disease maintained on donepezil. *American Journal of Geriatric Psychiatry, 14,* 428-437.

Wilcock, G. K., Ballard, C. G., Cooper, J. A., & Loft, H. (2008). Memantine for agitation/aggression and psychosis in moderately severe to severe Alzheimer's disease: A pooled analysis of 3 studies. *Journal of Clinical Psychiatry, 69,* 341–348.

Wilcock, G. K., Lilienfeld, S., & Gaens, E. (2000). Efficacy and safety of galantamine in patients with mild to moderate Alzheimer's disease: Multicentre randomised controlled trial. Galantamine international-1 study group. *BMJ, 321,* 1445-1449.

Winblad B., & Poritis, N. (1999). Memantine in severe dementia: Results of the 9M-best study (Benefit and efficacy in severely demented patients during treatment with memantine). *International Journal of Geriatric Psychiatry, 14,* 135-146.

Zandi, P. P., Anthony, J. C., Hayden, K. M., Mehta, K., Mayer, L., Breitner, J. C., & Cache county study investigators. (2002). Reduced incidence of AD with NSAID but not H2 receptor antagonists: The Cache County Study. *Neurology, 59,* 880-886.

CHAPTER 3

Neuroplasticity: The Foundation for Non-Pharmacological Interventions in Dementia

Scott W. Sumerall, Joseph J. Ryan, and Samuel T. Gontkovsky

Plasticity refers to the quality of being able to be altered, shaped, or modified. Neuroplasticity refers to the fact that experiential and environmental influences often produce changes in the central nervous system (Davidson & Lutz, 2008), both structurally and functionally. The term describes the nervous system's potential for alterations through reorganization that enhance not only its adaptability to environmental change, but also its capability to compensate for injury or disease (Kolb & Whishaw, 2006). A major misconception regarding the human adult brain has been that it is unable to change, or exhibit such plasticity (Erickson, Miller, Weinstein, Akl, & Banducci, 2012). Contemporary research has debunked this line of thinking, and opened the door to exciting research avenues exploring the role of neuroplasticity across the lifespan. It is now known that components of the central nervous system do indeed have the capacity to respond to stimulation, both intrinsic and extrinsic, by reorganizing their structures and functions. Neuroplasticity often is used to refer to changes that can occur in the context of rehabilitation (e.g., after stroke or traumatic brain injury), where the objective is for undamaged brain regions to take over some or all of the functioning of the damaged brain regions. The term is also used to refer to the changes that can take place through lifestyle, such as those produced by the consumption of certain foods (e.g., cold water fish that provide omega-3 fatty acids), commitment to an aerobic exercise program (e.g., regular brisk walking), or the pursuit of novel cognitive experiences (e.g., learning to play the violin or enrolling in college courses). Many of the behaviors in which we engage therefore have the potential to change our brains, which consequently may then translate into further behavioral and functional changes.

Brain Development and Neurogenesis

During development, the brain does not form in a completely fixed state. The morphogenesis of the human brain occurs in the three stages of cell production, cell migration, and cell differentiation and growth (Sidman & Rakic, 1982). Neurogenesis is the term used to describe the birth of new brain cells, or neurons. It is the process by which neurons are generated from neural stem and progenitor cells, primarily during prenatal development in order to populate the growing brain. In the mid to late first trimester, neuronal cell production begins and continues through the fifth month (Caviness, Takahaski, & Nowakowski, 2003). The neurons must then be properly placed within the developing brain. Migration begins along with neuronal development and continues to approximately the end of the second trimester. As Lois and Alvarez-Buylla (1994) state, the cells migrate to their ultimate destinations. There likely are many means and routes of migration, but one well-studied path involves neurons following the guidance of the ascending fibers of the radial glial cells (Gadisseux, Evrard, Misson, & Caviness, 1989; Gadisseux, Kadhim, van den Bosch, Caviness, & Evrard, 1990; Rakic, 1995, 2003). This process allows the neurons to follow the scaffolding until they reach their proper locations.

If the neurons do not migrate effectively, various disorders can result. In mice, this has been noted to occur secondary to genetic mutations (Gleeson & Walsh, 2000) and also external agents (Gierdalski & Juliano, 2003). Unfortunately, migratory failure is relatively frequent in humans (Rakic, 1988; Volpe, 2001), and may lead to a multitude of disorders. One such disorder is lissencephaly, in which the surface of the cerebral cortex is smooth, lacking the normal convolutions, and has only four layers as opposed to the normal six layers (Kato & Dobyns, 2003; Noggle, Dean, & Horton, 2012). Another disorder that may emerge is agyria-pachygyria with polymicrogyria (Ferrie, Jackson, Giannakodomis, & Panayiotopoulos, 1995), which involves some of the same features of lissencephaly along with numerous convolutions across the cortex. The typical outcome of such an alteration of neuronal development is significant cognitive limitations. It also is possible that improper neuronal migration is associated with some of the more commonly known disorders, such as schizophrenia (Deutsch, Burkett, & Katz, 2010).

The differentiation and growth of the neocortex start at the completion of migration and continue through childhood and until at least the age of 15 years (Caviness et al., 2003). There are many other changes, however, that occur within the brain throughout life. It was long believed that the brain did not produce additional neurons in adulthood. Evidence began to be accumulated, however, that indicated this was not the case, though it remained unclear for some time as to whether these new neurons produced any functional effect. Recently, Spalding, et al. (2013) demonstrated an annual turnover rate of 1.75% of neurons in the adult hippocampus. It was suggested that this degree of neurogenesis may impact brain functioning. Other research also corroborates these findings. For example, Lacefield, Itskov, Reardon, Hen, and Gordon (2012) reported that the cessation of adult neurogenesis in rodents led to cognitive deficits, implying that these cells do indeed have an effect on cognitive functioning and behavior. It appears that these adult-generated cells are successfully integrated into existing neuronal circuits (Mongiat & Schinder, 2011) and that this plasticity may function to assist neuronal circuits in meeting constantly changing external demands (Kelsch, Sim, & Lois, 2010).

At the other end of cell life is apoptosis, which essentially is programmed cell death. When a cell is no longer necessary or is somehow a threat to the organism, the cell self-destructs (Alberts et al., 2002). This is accomplished through proteolytic enzymes known as caspases. These enzymes cause cell death by destroying certain proteins in the nucleus and cytoplasm of the cell. Shimohama (2000) presented evidence that apoptosis is heavily involved in the course of Alzheimer's disease (AD). Thus, as neurons become affected by the disease process, they destroy themselves. The course of disease and apoptotic cell death in AD greatly impacts neuronal communication and the capacity of the brain to function as a well-coordinated whole. The result is the devastating cognitive changes experienced by individuals as they progress through the course of the disease process. There are, of course, a variety of other mechanisms by which neurons may die (e.g., trauma and anoxia).

Synaptic Plasticity and Synaptogenesis

A synapse is the location where one neuron connects with another. A very small space, approximately 20 nanometers, separates the two. The inside of an axon is negatively charged as compared to the outside. This is referred to as the resting potential. A neuron averages all of the electrical inputs onto it and if it reaches the threshold potential causing a depolarization, it will fire. This is referred to as the action potential, which travels the length of the axon ending in the terminal button. At that point, a neurotransmitter, a chemical produced by the presynaptic neuron, is released into the synapse to have an effect on the postsynaptic neuron. That chemical crosses the synaptic cleft and attaches itself in a binding site, a space into which the neurotransmitter fits perfectly. Ion channels are ultimately opened as a result of the connection, and this may cause the postsynaptic neuron to be more likely or less likely to fire. Multiple neurons connect with one another, and each has its own effect on the postsynaptic neuron. Whether or not a neuron fires is determined by the overall inputs from other neurons. This is referred to as neural integration.

Most learning is dependent upon synaptic plasticity, or the strengthening or weakening of a synapse. There two main forms of synaptic plasticity are referred to as intrinsic and extrinsic (Byrne, 2013). Within an intrinsic mechanism of plasticity, change in the strength of a synapse occurs due to the synapse's own actions. A neuron may have a weakened secondary response as the result of synaptic depression. This may occur from a variety causes, including low frequency stimulation or internal/local changes (e.g., reduced calcium ions in the extracellular fluid or inactivation of release sites; von Gersdorff & Borst, 2002). It is possible that synaptic depression occurs secondary to the neurotransmitter being largely depleted after an initial release. This may be due to a reduced supply of the neurotransmitter having been produced and stored in the vesicles. Inhibitory autoreceptors on a neuron also may limit availability of a neurotransmitter. Synaptic facilitation also may result. In this event, a second action potential that occurs quickly after the first action potential may result in calcium levels not having had enough time to return to baseline. As a result, when the calcium channels are again opened, the amount of calcium inside increases and more neurotransmitter is released (Byrne, 2013).

Extrinsic synaptic plasticity involves both presynaptic facilitation and presynaptic inhibition. A modulatory neuron affects the degree of excitability of a neuron. It may have a synapse somewhere on the postsynaptic neuron. If the modulatory neuron fires, it may either facilitate or inhibit the firing of the postsynaptic neuron. As a result, when a presynaptic neuron fires, the modulatory neuron's effect will alter what would have occurred, either making it stronger (presynaptic facilitation) or weaker (presynaptic inhibition). Long-term potentiation (LTP) is a powerful and long-lasting heightening in signal communication between neurons that may involve repetitive, synchronous stimulation. LTP is a form of facilitation and may comprise both intrinsic and extrinsic synaptic plasticity (Byrne, 2013). Long-term depression may occur due to repetitive desynchronous stimulation. This is a durable form of inhibition and impedes the communication between neurons. Long-term potentiation and depression account for most of the models of memory (Abbott & Nelson, 2000). Thus, it may be that as we learn something new, LTP develops that allows us to easily retrieve that information at a later point. Synaptic plasticity through the increasing of synaptic strength is the key element in turning an experience it into a memory (Citri & Malenka, 2008). These electrophysiological alterations allow one to easily remember new information and to use that information to perform complex tasks more effectively and efficiently.

Synaptogenesis is the concept of increasing connections among neurons. During early development, axons grow and connect with other neurons, ultimately leading to a synapse. It may be that when learning a new skill as an adult, new synapses develop among neurons involved with that task. This may occur through dendrites taking on new connections with nearby axons of other neurons. The number of synapses may be measured through staining and follow-up analysis with fluorescence microscopy. Some studies have suggested that new connections are formed when engaging in various learning activities. For example, Kleim et al. (2004) found an increase in synapse formation (more synapses per neuron) in the rat motor cortex after the rats had engaged in a task requiring a skilled motor movement. In contrast, Geinisman et al. (2000) did not find evidence of increased synapses after animal conditioning involving a tone and corneal air-puff. In fact, many studies have failed to find an increase in synaptic connections after learning new behavior. Though a definitive answer to this question remains elusive, one suggestion is that learning new information or behavior simply may rearrange the existing synapses and not result in a net overall increase in the number synaptic connections (Geinisman, Berry, & Ganeshina, 2004).

Studies of Cortical Reorganization and Neuroplasticity

Non-Clinical Examples

Numerous research studies have been conducted exploring differing aspects of neuroplasticity as well as the various factors that may lead to neuroplasticity in both animals and humans. There exist several lines of research in both clinical and non-clinical samples demonstrating that experiences and behaviors can modify the various structures and functions of the brain. For example, Klein, Barbay, and Nudo (1998) had rats learn a skilled or unskilled reaching task. Afterward, microelectrode stimulation was conducted to learn the limb representations of the motor cortex. They found that the portions of the motor cortex that were associated with more skilled movement (wrist and digit) were larger in those rats who learned the skilled task. Also, the motor area associated with elbow and shoulder regions had decreased in comparison to the rats that had learned a general unskilled motor task. They concluded that motor skill learning was associated with a reorganization of the motion representation of the rat motor cortex.

An interesting area of non-clinical, human research has focused on the studying of the brains of musicians, examining the manner in which practice reorganizes the cortex to maximize performance of a particular musical skill. For example, Elbert, Pantev, Wienbruch, Rockstroh, and Taub (1995) reported that a larger than expected section of the postcentral gyrus of individuals who played stringed instruments was devoted to representing the fingers of the left hand, which are used to control the strings of the instruments. Further, they noted that this region devoted to the left fingers was largest among those participants who began the practice of music earlier and continued for a longer period of time.

An investigation by Schneider et al. (2002) using magnetoencephalography to examine the processing of sinusoidal tones in the auditory cortex of non-musicians, professional musicians, and amateur musicians revealed both neurophysiological and anatomical differences between the groups. In professional musicians as compared to non-musicians, for example, the activity evoked in primary auditory cortex was 102% larger, and the gray matter volume of the anteromedial portion of

Heschl's gyrus was 130% larger. Further, both quantities were highly correlated with musical aptitude. Findings were thought to indicate that both the morphology and neurophysiology of Heschl's gyrus have an essential impact on musical aptitude. It was not known, however, whether the brains of participants were equal prior to initiating participation in music. In other words, are individuals with certain predispositions more likely than others to become musicians?

The following year, Gaser and Schlaug (2003) published a report in which they described gray matter volume differences detected using a voxel-by-voxel morphometric technique in the motor, auditory, and visual-spatial brain regions when comparing professional keyboard musicians with matched groups of amateur musicians and non-musicians. The authors believed, even though some of these multi-regional differences could be attributable to innate predisposition, that differences represent structural adaptations in response to long-term skill acquisition and the repetitive rehearsal of those skills. The hypothesis was supported by the strong association found between structural differences, musician status, and practice intensity, as well as the wealth of supporting animal data showing structural changes in response to long-term motor training.

Along a differing line of research, Tang, Lu, Fan, Yang, and Posner (2012) found evidence that a form of mindfulness meditation (integrated body-mind training) resulted in either an increased number of brain fibers or greater diameter of the existing fibers. This occurred in areas surrounding the anterior cingulate cortex after only four weeks of practice with the meditation techniques. Research has suggested that the anterior cingulate cortex is related to a variety of cognitive and emotional activities (Brody et al., 2001; Posner & DiGirolamo, 1998). Thus, after a relatively brief intervention, an alteration in brain morphology appears to have occurred in a region that is heavily involved with many aspects of human experience.

Although various brain regions may become active during different types of meditation, the frontal and prefrontal areas are often among the most often mentioned as being active during this acitivty (Cahn & Polich, 2006). Qigong meditation is an ancient form of meditation that involves attention to the mind, body, and breathing. In a study in which deoxyhemoglobin (hemoglobin that has released its oxygen to be used by tissue) changes were evaluated, Qigong meditation was shown to increase prefrontal activity (Cheng, Borrett, Cheng, Kwan, & Cheng, 2010). Furthermore, Fell, Axmacher, and Haupt (2010) suggested that the active brain states associated with meditation also are involved with cognitive restructuring. EEG research demonstrated that the brain is not passive during meditation. The authors reported that experienced meditators were found to be more likely to have synchronized gamma waves than those with minimal experience in meditation.

Lazar et al. (2005) conducted a study comparing long-term users of insight meditation with those who had no experience in meditation. The former averaged approximately nine years of experience in meditation, while the latter had no meditation background, whatsoever. Using a well-established method (Fischl & Dale, 2000) of determining cortical thickness through the use of magnetic resonance imaging (MRI) scans, Lazar et al. were able to determine that those who had practiced meditation for years had thicker prefrontal and insular cortex regions. In addition, another study (Pagnoni & Cekic, 2007) stated that as people age, they are expected to show a decline in gray matter volume and also in attention performance. Using a morphometric procedure with MRI scans along with a sustained attention task, it was found that individuals with a lengthy history of meditation appeared to have less decline in gray matter with age and that performance on the attention task did not decline to the same degree as those who did not practice meditation. It also was found that the largest difference in volume between those who did not engage in meditation and those who did was in the putamen, a region that has been highly associated with attention (Pagnoni & Cekic, 2007). Thus, mindfulness/meditation may have a neuroprotective effect that is morphologically visible.

Woollett and Maguire (2011) carried out an innovative study involving taxi drivers in London, England. In order to be licensed as a taxi driver in London, one has to acquire a massive amount of visuospatial information. The city's complex geographical system, which involves approximately 25,000 streets within a six-mile radius of Charing Cross Station, must be learned. Each applicant must learn the various streets and their locations and pass examinations on this material. Successful completion of this process and the adequate learning of the street system generally takes three to four years. Learning such data was theorized to alter the hippocampus, and the authors developed a study in which they conducted MRI examinations and memory tests with persons desiring to become taxi drivers and with control participants. They found that the posterior hippocampi of those who became drivers enlarged significantly between time 1 (prior to initiating the learning process) and time 2 (upon completion of the training). This appears to indicate neuroplasticity in adults and may be due to neurogenesis and/or synaptogenesis (Wollett & Maguire, 2011).

Clinical Examples

The reorganization of the brain's cortical motor map has frequently been seen with recovery after injury, including stroke, traumatic brain injury, and peripheral nerve damage (Conner, Chiba, & Tuszynski, 2005). This has led to the view that neuroplasticity of the cortical map is a vital component of recovery. In rats, damage to the nucleus basalis, which is heavily involved with memory, has been shown to negatively impact plasticity and recovery of function after injury (Conner et al., 2005). Thus, some of the same regions/skills involved in normal learning seem to be required for recovery following neuronal damage. The finding that specific regions are important for relearning skill sets suggests that additional activation of certain brain systems may aid rehabilitation.

In a classic study examining changes in the motor cortex maps of adult squirrel monkeys following brain damage secondary to focal ischemic infarct, Nudo, Wise, SiFuentes, and Milliken (1996) demonstrated the occurrence of substantial functional reorganization. Knowing that a subtotal lesion confined to a small portion of the cortical representation of one hand would result in a further loss of hand territory in the adjacent, undamaged cortex of these monkeys, the researchers provided retraining of skilled hand use after similar infarcts, which resulted in prevention of the loss of hand territory adjacent to the infarct. In some instances, the hand representations expanded into regions that were formerly occupied by cortical representations of the elbow and shoulder. This functional reorganization in the undamaged motor cortex was accompanied by behavioral recovery of skilled hand function, suggesting that subsequent to local damage in the motor cortex rehabilitative training can shape subsequent reorganization in the adjacent intact cortex and that the undamaged motor cortex may play an important role in motor recovery.

Weiller, Chollet, Friston, Wise, and Frackowiak (1992) used positron emission tomography in humans to explore brain area usage for movement after striatocapsular motor strokes, which are large strokes involving the internal capsule and nearby putamen and caudate nucleus. After recovery from the stroke, using the hand that had been affected resulted in greater activation as observed by regional cerebral blood flow in certain brain regions (i.e., insulae, inferior parietal, prefrontal and anterior cingulate cortices, ipsilateral premotor cortex and basal ganglia, and contralateral cerebellum) than it did in people who had never had such strokes. The authors concluded that recovery from striatocapsular motor strokes involved utilizing various sensorimotor and cortical areas as well as bilateral motor paths. Thus, the brain appeared to demonstrate its plasticity by changing what was activated during certain motor movements. Overall, research, including those using functional MRI protocols, which assess changes in blood flow (as when a brain region is strongly utilized, blood flow to that area increases), has found that adaptation occurs in cerebral networks after a stroke has occurred (Ward, 2005).

Based on the concepts of cortical reorganization and neuroplasticity, Edward Taub developed a revolutionary form of rehabilitation, known as constraint-induced movement therapy, for upper extremity deficits following central nervous system damage through increased use of the affected upper limb. Application of his approaches to humans was derived from research with monkeys given somatosensory deafferentation. The common element of Taub's approaches is that they induce individuals with central nervous system injury and associated upper extremity impairments to greatly increase the use of a more-affected upper extremity for many hours per day over a period several weeks. These therapies have been shown to significantly improve quality of movement and to substantially increase the amount of use of a more-affected upper extremity in activities of daily living. A number of neuroimaging and transcranial magnetic stimulation studies also have demonstrated that the massed practice of constraint-induced movement therapy yields use-dependent cortical reorganization, which increases the area of cortex involved in the innervation of movement of the more-affected upper extremity (Taub & Morris, 2001; Winstein et al., 2003). Constraint-induced movement therapy also has been reported to produce significantly greater gains relative to more conventional rehabilitation in children with hemiparesis secondary to cerebral palsy

(Deluca, Echols, Law, Ramey, 2006). More recently, novel treatment protocols for facilitating or enhancing neuroplasticity following traumatic brain injury also have been discussed in the literature (DeFIna et al., 2009).

Medications that affect the cholinergic system as well as the dopaminergic, noradrenergic, and serotonergic systems can be useful in facilitating treatment following brain damage (Phillips, Devier, & Feeney, 2003). For example, an investigation by Zhu, Hamm, Reeves, Povishock, & Phillips (2000) suggested that dopaminergic/noradrenergic enhancement facilitates cognitive recovery after brain injury in rats and that noradrenergic fiber integrity is correlated with enhanced synaptic plasticity in the injured hippocampus. The use of amphetamines has been shown to accelerate improvement of speech following a stroke that led to aphasia (Walker-Batson, Smith, Curtis, & Unwin, 2004). Further, methylphenidate specifically has been reported to promote improved neurocognitive functioning in individuals with various central nervous system injuries and disorders, including traumatic brain injury (Whyte et al., 1997; Willmott & Ponsford, 2009) and brain tumors (Gontkovsky, & Winkelmann, 2006; Meyers, Weitzner, Valentine, & Levin, 1998).

Moucha and Kilgard (2006) also describe various factors that aid neuroplasticity and, consequently, promote the process of rehabilitation. These include attentional skills, proper use of medications, specific patterns of stimuli, temporal presentation (spaced versus massed), and duration of training, each of which contribute to the rehabilitation outcome. The appropriate duration of training can maximize the maintenance of learned skills. Elevating the difficulty level of an activity may function to maintain attention and motivation, and adding to the complexity of a task that is being learned over time may enhance a specific subset of skills. The use of background stimuli (Moucha & Kilgard, 2006) also may impact difficulty and foster improvement. Smith (2013) notes that although there exists a considerable focus on lifestyle and environmental factors associated with enhancing neuroplasticity, there also are modifiable factors that inhibit neuroplasticity, particularly stress, which should be a focus of investigation and treatment development. In this light, management of emotional issues clearly is important both prior to and following the onset of cognitive problems (see Chapter 8).

Moucha and Kilgard (2006) also describe various factors that aid neuroplasticity and, consequently, promote the process of rehabilitation. These include attentional skills, proper use of medications, specific patterns of stimuli, temporal presentation (spaced versus massed), and duration of training, each of which contribute to the rehabilitation outcome. The appropriate duration of training can maximize the maintenance of learned skills. Elevating the difficulty level of an activity may function to maintain attention and motivation, and adding to the complexity of a task that is being learned over time may enhance a specific subset of skills. The use of background stimuli (Moucha & Kilgard, 2006) also may impact difficulty and foster improvement. Smith (2013) notes that although there exists a considerable focus on lifestyle and environmental factors associated with enhancing neuroplasticity, there also are modifiable factors that inhibit neuroplasticity, particularly stress, which should be a focus of investigation and treatment development. In this light, management of emotional issues clearly is important both prior to and following the onset of cognitive problems (see Chapter 8).

Negative Neuroplasticity

Generally, the expanded cortical representation associated with experience and behavior is considered beneficial. In extreme cases, however, this reorganization can be problematic (Kalat, 2007). Recall the non-clinical example of neuroplasticity discussed above concerning musicians in which Elbert et al. (1995) reported that a larger than expected section of the postcentral gyrus of individuals who played stringed instruments was devoted to representing the fingers of the left hand, which are used to control the strings of the instruments. In some cases, one finger can come to excite mostly or entirely the same cortical areas as another finger, thereby resulting in the individual having difficulty distinguishing one finger from another by touch and, consequently, resulting in problems controlling them separately. This condition is known as focal hand dystonia, sometimes referred to as musician's cramp, and causes the fingers to become clumsy, fatigue easily, and make involuntary movements that interfere with tasks, which can be career ending for serious musicians (Kalat, 2007).

Turner and Green (2008) also have discussed the possibility of negative neuroplasticity within a clinical context, which involves a deleterious effect on brain morphology due to environmental variables. For example, after a TBI, withdrawal from friends, minimizing contact with the larger social community, and leaving the stimulation of employment were theorized to possibly result in brain changes beyond those expected from the actual effects of the TBI. Environmental enrichment may help to mitigate the changes due to ceasing or minimizing such stimulation (Frasca, Tomaszczyk, McFadyen, & Green, 2013). These are further indications of the impact the environment and behavior may have on the brain.

Potential Applications of Neuroplasticity and Brain Reorganization to Dementia

As discussed in this chapter, the majority of the basic and clinical research on neruoplasticity and brain reorganization traditionally has emphasized early development as well as neurological injuries and conditions other than dementia. More recently, however, increasing attention has been focused on opportunities to induce neuroplasticity in adulthood, in particular during the aging process when individuals are at an increased risk for development of Alzheimer's disease and other forms of dementia. Although there is some degree of neural deterioration that is expected to occur with aging, the brain also has the capacity to increase neural activity and develop neural scaffolding to regulate cognitive function (Park & Bischof, 2013). Thus, there may be methods that can be used to minimize the cognitive effects of aging. Greenwood and Parasuraman (2010) put forth a proposal that healthy cognitive functioning in older age may be achieved through a combination of neuronal and cognitive plasticity. Neuronal plasticity is related to synaptogenesis, neurogenesis, and similar changes that can be brought about by experience. Cognitive plasticity refers to changes in cognitive patterns, such as increasing use the executive system, which can be altered to have greater control over a task. There are clear indications that experience and training (behavior) are able to alter brain neuroplasticity (Goh & Park, 2009).

Novel stimulation (detection) is imperative for memory formation (Straube, Korz, & Frey, 2003). Furthermore, regularly changing the stimulation is important. Kempermann and Gage (1999) found that the effects of novel stimulation on brain and cognitive effects were not visible after six months. There also is evidence that new learning is necessary for recently developed neurons to persist (Mouret et al., 2008; Waddell & Shors, 2008). Therefore, aging well may require regular exposure not only to new and but also to changing cognitive challenges. This may involve learning new material, likely information unrelated to our current areas of knowledge. It also may require gaining new skills in various areas, not just learning new facts. These skills may be cognitive (e.g., problem solving, learning a language) in nature but also may be related to motor functioning (e.g., yoga, tai chi, sports). Erickson et al. (2012) stated that aerobic exercise seemed to have greatest improvements in prefrontal and hippocampal regions. Executive system functioning and memory may, therefore, be helped through exercise. In their review, Erickson, Gildengers, and Butters (2013) stated that exercise has been linked to both less cortical atrophy and improved cognitive functioning (see Chapter 7 for additional information concerning exercise and cognition).

The understanding of neuroplasticity and the various factors that contribute to it during the aging process will continue to improve as additional research is conducted. It is a complex process but one that likely can be manipulated and used to alter the outcome of aging and rehabilitation. Indeed, neuroplasticity can be conceptualized as a final common pathway of neurobiological processes, including structural, functional, or molecular mechanisms, which result in stability or compensation for age-related or disease-related changes (Smith, 2013). In this light, the following seven chapters review the scientific literature concerning non-pharmacological approaches for promoting brain health, delaying onset of dementia, and slowing the cognitive and functional decline following the development of dementia.

References

Abbott, L. F., & Nelson, S. B. (2000). Synaptic plasticity: Taming the beast. *Nature Neuroscience, 3*, 1178-1183.

Alberts, B., Johnson, A., Lewis, J., Raff, M., Roberts, K., & Walter, P. (2002). *Molecular biology of the cell* (4th ed.). New York: Garland Science.

Brody, A. L., Saxena, S., Mandelkern, M. A., Fairbanks, L. A., Ho, M. L., & Baxter, L. R. (2001). Brain metabolic changes associated with symptom factor improvement in major depressive disorder. *Biological Psychiatry, 50*, 171-178.

Byrne, J. H. (2013). Synaptic plasticity. *Neuroscience online: An electronic textbook for the neurosciences.* Houston, TX: Department of Neurobiology and Anatomy, University of Texas Medical School. Retrieved August 8, 2013, from http://neuroscience.uth.tmc.edu/s1/chapter07.html

Cahn, B. R., & Polich, J. (2006). Meditation states and traits: EEG, ERP, and neuroimaging studies. *Psychological Bulletin, 132*, 180-211.

Caviness, V. S., Takahashi, T., & Nowakowski, R. S. (2003). Morphogenesis of the human cerebral cortex. In P. G. Barth (Ed.), *Disorders of neuronal migration* (pp. 1-23). London, England: MacKieth Press.

Cheng, R. W., Borrett, D. S, Cheng, W., Kwan, H. C., & Cheng, R. S. (2010). Human prefrontal cortical response to the meditative state: A spectroscopy study. *International Journal of Neuroscience, 120*, 483-488.

Citri, A., & Malenka, R. C. (2008). Synaptic plasticity: Multiple forms, functions, and mechanisms. *Neuropsychopharmacology, 33*, 18-41.

Conner, J. M., Chiba, A. A., & Tuszynski, M. H. (2005). The basal forebrain cholinergic system is essential for cortical plasticity and functional recovery following brain injury. *Neuron, 46*, 173-179.

Davidson, R. J., & Lutz, A. (2008). Buddha's brain: Neuroplasticity and meditation. *Signal Processing, 25*, 176-174.

DeFIna, P., Fellus, J., Polito, M. Z., Thompson, J. W., Moser, R. S., & DeLuca, J. (2009). The new neuroscience frontier: Promoting neuroplasticity and brain repair in traumatic brain injury. *The Clinical Neuropsychologist, 23,* 1391-1399.

Deluca, S. C., Echols, K., Law, C. R., & Ramey, S. L. (2006). Intensive pediatric constraint induced therapy for children with cerebral palsy: Randomized, controlled, crossover trial. *Journal of Child Neurology, 21,* 931-938.

Deutsch, S. I., Burkett, J. A., & Katz, E. (2010). Does subtle disturbance of neuronal migration contribute to schizophrenia and other neurodevelopmental disorders? Potential genetic mechanisms with possible treatment implications. *European Neuropsychopharmacology, 20,* 281-287.

Elbert, T., Pantev, C., Wienbruch, C., Rockstroh, B., & Taub. E. (1995). Increased cortical representation of the fingers of the left hand in string players. *Science, 270,* 305-307.

Erickson, K. I., Gildengers, A. G., & Butters, M.A. (2013). Physical activity and brain plasticity in late adulthood. *Dialogues in Clinical Neuroscience, 15,* 99-108.

Erickson, K. I., Miller, D. L., Weinstein, A. M., Akl, S. L., & Banducci, S. E. (2012). Physical activity and brain plasticity in late adulthood: A conceptual review. *Ageing Research, 4,* 34-47.

Fell, J., Axmacher, N., & Haupt, S. (2010). From alpha to gamma: Electrophysiological correlates of meditation-related states of consciousness. *Medical Hypotheses, 75,* 218-224.

Ferrie, C. D., Jackson, G. D., GIannakodimos, S., & Panayiotopoulos, C. P. (1995). Posterior agyria-pachygyria with polymicrogyria: Evidence for an inherited neuronal migration disorder. *Neurology, 45,* 150-153.

Fischl, B., & Dale, A.M. (2000). Measuring the thickness of the human cerebral cortex from magnetic resonance images. *Proceedings of the National Academy of Sciences, 97,* 11050-11055.

Frasca, D., Tomaszczyk, J., McFadyen, B. J., & Green, R. E. (2013). Traumatic brain injury and   post-acute decline: What role does environmental enrichment play? A scoping review. *Frontiers in Human Neuroscience, 7*: 31. doi: 10.3389/fnhum.2013.00031

Gadisseux, J., Evrard, P., Misson, J-P., & Caviness, V. S. (1989). Dynamic changes in the density of radial glial fibers of the developing murine cerebral wall: A quantitative immunohistological analysis. *Journal of Comparative Neurology, 322*, 246-254.

Gadisseux, J., Kadhim, H., van den Bosch, P., Caviness, V. S., & Evrard, P. (1990). Neuron migration within the radial glial fiber system of the developing murine cerebrum: An electron microscopic autoradiographic analysis. *Developmental Brain Research, 52*, 39-56.

Gaser, C., & Schlaug, G. (2003). Brain structures differ between musicians and non-musicians. *Journal of Neuroscience, 23*, 9240-9245.

Geinisman, Y., Berry, R. W., & Ganeshina, O. T. (2004). Learning-induced synaptogenesis and structural synaptic remodeling. In G. Riedel & B. Platt (Eds.), *From messengers to molecules: Memories are made of these.* (pp. 543-563). New York: Plenum.

Geinisman, Y., Disterhoft, J. F., Gundersen, H. J., McEchron, M. D., Persina, I. S., Power, J. M., van der Zee, E. A., & West, M. J. (2000). Remodeling of hippocampal synapses after hippocampus-dependent associative learning. *Journal of Comparative Neurology, 417*, 49-59.

Gierdalski, M., & Juliano, S. L. (2003). Factors affecting the morphology of radial glia. *Cerebral Cortex, 13*, 572-579.

Gleeson, J. G., & Walsh, C. A. (2000). Neuronal migration disorders: From genetic diseases to developmental mechanisms. *Trends in Neuroscience, 23*, 352-359.

Goh, J. O., & Park, D. C. (2009). Neuroplasticity and cognitive aging: The scaffolding theory of aging and cognition. *Restorative Neurology and Neuroscience, 27*, 391-403.

Gontkovsky, S. T., & Winkelmann, M. H. (2006). Improved cognition with methylphenidate status post cerebellar tumor resection: A case report. *Journal of Cognitive Rehabilitation, 24*, 5-8.

Greenwood, P. M., & Parasuraman, R. (2010). Neuronal and cognitive plasticity: A neurocognitive framework for ameliorating cognitive aging. *Frontiers in Aging Neuroscience, 2*, doi: 10.3389/fnagi.2010.00150

Kalat, J. W. (2007). *Biological psychology* (9th ed.). Belmont, CA: Thompson Wadsworth.

Kato, M., & Dobyns, W. B. (2003). Lissencephaly and the molecular basis of neuronal migration. *Human Molecular Genetics, 12*, 89-96.

Kelsch, W., Sim, S., & Lois, C. (2010). Watching synaptogenesis in the adult brain. *Annual Review of Neuroscience, 33*, 131-149.

Kempermann, G., & Gage, F. H. (1999). Experience-dependent regulation of adult hippocampal neurogenesis: Effects of long-term stimulation and stimulus withdrawal. *Hippocampus, 9*, 321-332.

Kleim, J. A., Hogg, T. M., VandenBerg, P. M., Cooper, N. R., Bruneau, R., & Remple, M. (2004). Cortical synaptogenesis and motor map reorganization occur during late, but not early, phase of motor skill learning. *Journal of Neuroscience, 24*, 628-633.

Klein, J. A., Barbay, S., & Nudo, R. J. (1998). Functional reorganization of the rat motor cortex following motor skill learning. *Journal of Neurophysiology, 80*, 3321-3325.

Kolb, B., & Whishaw, I. Q. (2006). *An introduction to brain and behavior* (2nd ed.). New York: Worth.

Lacefield, C. O., Itskov, V., Reardon, T., Hen, R., & Gordon, J. A. (2012). Effects of adult-generated granule cells on coordinated network activity in the dentate gyrus. *Hippocampus, 22*, 106-116.

Lazar, S. W., Kerr, C. E., Wasserman, R. H., Gray, J. R., Greve, D. N., Treadway , M. T., McGarvey, M., Quinn, B. T., Dusek, J. A., Benson, H., Rauch, S. L., Moore, C. I., & Fischle, B. (2005). Meditation experience is associated with increased cortical thickness. *Neuroreport, 16*, 1893-1897.

Lois, C., & Alvarez-Buylla, A. (1994). Long-distance neuronal migration in the adult mammalian brain. *Science, 264*, 1145-1148.

Meyers, C. A., Weitzner, M. A., Valentine, A. D., & Levin, V. A. (1998). Methylphenidate therapy improves cognition, mood, and function of brain tumor patients. *Journal of Clinical Oncology, 16*, 2522-2527.

Mongiat, L. A., & Schinder, A. F. (2011). Adult neurogenesis and the plasticity of the dentate gyrus network. *European Journal of Neuroscience, 33*, 1055-1061.

Moucha, R., & Kilgard, M. P. (2006). Cortical plasticity and rehabilitation. *Progress in Brain Research, 157*, 111-122.

Mouret A., Gheusi G., Gabellec M. M., de Chaumont F., Olivo-Marin J. C., & Lledo P. M. (2008). Learning and survival of newly generated neurons: When time matters. *Journal of Neuroscience, 28*, 11511-11516.

Noggle, C. A., Dean, R. S., & Horton, A. M. (Eds.). (2012). *The encyclopedia of neuropsychological disorders*. New York: Springer.

Nudo, R. J., Wise, B. M., SiFuentes, F., & Milliken, G. W. (1996). Neural substrates for the effects of rehabilitative training on motor recovery after ischemic infarct. *Science, 272*, 1791-1794.

Pagnoni, G., & Cekic, M. (2007). Age effects on gray matter volume and attentional performance in Zen meditation. *Neurobiology of Aging, 28*, 1623-1627.

Park, D., & Bischof, G. (2013). The aging mind: Neuroplasticity in response to cognitive training. *Dialogues in Clinical Neurosciences, 15*, 109-119.

Phillips, J. P., Devier, D. J., & Feeney, D. M. (2003). Rehabilitation pharmacology: Bridging laboratory work to clinical application. *Journal of Head Trauma Rehabilitation, 18*, 342-356.

Posner, M. I., & DiGirolamo, G. (1998). Executive attention: Conflict, target detection and cognitive control. In R. Parasuraman (Ed.), *The attentive brain* (pp. 401-423). Cambridge, MA: MIT Press.

Rakic, P. (1988). Defects of neuronal migration and pathogenesis of cortical malformations. *Progress in Brain Research, 73*, 15-37.

Rakic, P. (1995). Radial glial cells: Scaffolding for brain construction. In H. Ketterman & B. R. Ransom (Eds.), *Neuroglial cells* (pp. 746-762). New York: Oxford University Press.

Rakic, P. (2003). Developmental and evolutionary adaptations of cortical radial glia. *Cerebral Cortex, 13*, 541-549.

Schneider, P., Scherg, M., Dosch, H. G., Specht, H. J., Gutschalk, A., & Rupp A. (2002). Morphology of Heschl's gyrus reflects enhanced activation in the auditory cortex of musicians. *Nature Neuroscience, 5*, 688-694.

Shimohama, S. (2000). Apoptosis in Alzheimer's disease-An update. *Apoptosis, 5*, 9-16.

Sidman, R. L., & Rakic, P. (1982). Development of the human central nervous system. In W. Haymaker & R. D. Adams (Eds.), Histology and histopathology of the nervous system (pp. 3-145). Springfield, IL: Charles C. Thomas. Smith, G. S. (2013). Aging and neuroplasticity. *Dialogues in Clinical Neuroscience, 15*, 3-5.

Spalding, K. L., Bergmann, O., Alkass, K., Bernard, S., Salehpour, M., Huttner, H. B., Bostrom, E., Westerlund, I., Vial, C., Buchholz, B. A., Possnert, G., Mash, D. C., Druid, H., & Frisen, J. (2013). Dynamics of neurogenesis in adult humans. *Cell, 153*, 1219-1227.

Straube T., Korz V., & Frey J. U. (2003). Bidirectional modulation of long-term potentiation by novelty-exploration in rat dentate gyrus. *Neuroscience Letters, 344*, 5-8.

Tang, Y., Lu, Q., Fan, M., Yang, Y., & Posner, M. (2012). Mechanisms of white matter changes induced by meditation. *Proceedings of the National Academy of Sciences, 109*, 10570-10574.

Taub, E., & Morris, D. M. (2001). Constraint-induced movement therapy to enhance recovery after stroke. *Current Atherosclerosis Reports, 3*, 279-286.

Turner G. R., & Green E. (2008). Cognitive remediation in aging and ABI: A question of negative plasticity? *Neuropsychological Rehabilitation, 18*, 372-384.

Volpe, J. J. (2001). Neurology of the newborn (4th ed.). Philadelphia: W.B. Saunders. von Gersdorff, H., & Borst, J. G. G. (2002). Short-term plasticity at the calyx of held. Nature Reviews. *Neuroscience, 3*, 53-64.

Waddell, J., & Shors, T. J. (2008). Neurogenesis, learning and associative strength. *European Journal of Neuroscience, 27*, 3020-3028.

Walker-Batson, D., Smith, P., Curtis, S., & Unwin, D. H. (2004). Neuromodulation paired with learning dependent practice to enhance stroke recovery? *Restorative Neurology and Neuroscience, 22*, 387-392.

Ward, N.S. (2005). Plasticity and the functional reorganization of the human brain. *International Journal of Psychophysiology, 58*, 158-161.

Weiller, C., Chollete, F., Friston, K. J., Wise, R. J. S., & Frackowiak, R. S. J. (1992). Functional reorganization of the brain in recovery from striatocapsular infarction in man. *Annals of Neurology, 31*, 463-472.

Whyte, J., Hart, T., Schuster, K., Fleming, M., Polansky, M., & Coslett, H. B. (1997). Effects of methylphenidate on attentional function after traumatic brain injury. A randomized, placebo-controlled trial. *American Journal of Physical Medicine and Rehabilitation, 76*, 440-450.

Willmott, C., & Ponsford, J. (2009). Efficacy of methylphenidate in the rehabilitation of attention following traumatic brain injury: A randomised, crossover, double blind, placebo controlled inpatient trial. *Journal of Neurology, Neurosurgery and Psychiatry, 80*, 552-557.

Winstein, C. J., Miller, J. P., Blanton, S., Taub, E., Uswatte, G., Morris, D., Nichols, D., & Wolf, S. (2003). Methods for a multisite randomized trial to investigate the effect of constraint-induced movement therapy in improving upper extremity function among adults recovering from a cerebrovascular stroke. *Neurorehabilitation and Neural Repair, 17,* 137-152.

Woollett, K., & Maguire, E. A. (2011). Acquiring "the Knowledge" of London's layout drives structural brain changes. *Current Biology, 21,* 2109-2114.

Zhu, J., Hamm, R. J., Reeves, T. M., Povishock, J. T., & Phillips, L. L. (2000). Postinjury administration of L-deprenyl improves cognitive function and enhances neuroplasticity after traumatic brain injury. *Experimental Neurology, 166,* 136-152.

CHAPTER 4

Socialization and Social Stimulation in Dementia
Sara L. Schara McAnulty and Katherine Hickok

Dementia can cause many difficulties in one's social life. As the ability to create new memories dissolves, making new social contacts becomes more difficult. As the old memories fade, it may also be challenging to hold onto one's current relationships. Social interaction is an essential factor in maintaining as high a level of cognition and functioning as possible. As the human lifespan is continuing to increase, many researchers have sought to further understand key factors in promoting cognitive and functional health into older age. Thus far, the protective and beneficial role of social stimulation on mood, cognition, and physical status has been the focus of much of the existing literature in this area.

Social stimulation and socialization are broad constructs that cover a range of activities and behaviors, often categorized as creative, educational, or interactive. A diverse spectrum of activities can fall under the realm of providing social stimulation and socialization, for example attending the theater, traveling, playing cards and games, participating in social groups or organizations, and engaging in volunteerism (Wang, Karp, Winblad, & Fratiglioni, 2002). Some researchers have sought to further explore the nature of social stimulation by focusing on specific elements that differentiate components of socialization, such as social networks, social activities, social engagement, and companionship, which may differentially contribute to positive benefits for aging individuals. Social networks represent the web-like connections among individuals, with the literature support associations between having active social networks and health benefits. Social activities include engaging in activities either directly with others or in social environments. Social engagement is a related term that includes participation in social and productive activities; in contrast, companionship typically refers to doing enjoyable activities with others in a non-productive manner. While social stimulation involves many different skills and components, various studies have supported a relationship between social stimulation and cognitive health (Flatt & Hughes, 2013). Karp et al., (2006) noted that there can be accumulated mental, physical, and social components across several activities and still make a beneficial impact. Activities often fall within multiple realms, for example dancing being both a form of exercise and social interaction, that serves as both a social activity and opportunity for developing and using fine motors. Activities provide for an easy ice-breaker for meeting new people and initiating conversation (Morgan & Stewart, 1997).

For persons experiencing advanced disease progression, activities can be scaled down to be more achievable while still providing associated benefits. For someone with mild dementia, in the first stages of development, playing checkers or crafting can be an option, while individuals experiencing moderate disease progression find a chaperoned walk in a park a more suitable activity. Persons with severe dementia may still experience social stimulation even in the context of seemingly simple activities such as by looking in a mirror with a caregiver (Richards, Beck, O'Sullivan, & Shue, 2005). Many of these activities can be adjusted for small groups of people to do together, further increasing the socialization in the interaction.

Socialization as Prevention

While many health initiatives focus on the treatment of disease, prevention is also an important area of study. Recent years have seen a shift in resources and energy from purely treatment-focused to preventive, consistent with a societal recognition of the value of preventing or slowing the progression of disease rather than simply taking action once the disease has already progressed. Prevention paradigms offer many opportunities and formats to intervene, and this is particularly true with regards to social stimulation. Especially given that the deterioration of social ties can be particularly challenging for individuals with dementia and their caregivers, a focus on strengthening and bolstering social stimulation before disease progression makes this less possible is a worthy endeavor. Some researchers have found that persons who were more socially disengaged or experienced unsatisfying contact with their children were at greater risk for developing dementia or cognitive decline (Glei et al., 2005). Animal studies on dementia have shown that environmentally enriched conditions have the potential to prevent or reduce cognitive deficits in young- and adult-age rats. Moreover, the deleterious effects of an impoverished environment on memory and learning are partially reversible, underscoring the role of social stimulation on plasticity (Fratiglioni, Paillard-Borg, & Winblad 2004).

Thus, social enrichment for a person who may be at risk for dementia may hold preventive benefits.

Social stimulation has also been associated with prevention in dementia in studies exploring the role of older adults in various social activities (Wang et al., 2002). Wang and colleagues (2002) reported that seniors who participated in social activities had a lower incidence of dementia development; Karp et al. (2006) also found that a rich social network with recreational activities was associated with protective effects in dementia. Glei et al. (2005) noted a dose effect, such that the higher the level of social-recreation participation, the greater the benefit. Both the type and the frequency of social contact also seem to play a part in how beneficial the social stimulation can be for the prevention of dementia. Through validated measures of social networks and cognitive status, Crooks, Lubben, Petitti, Little, and Chiu (2008) also found evidence that a large social network and daily contact was associated with a decreased dementia risk. Glei et al. found that participating in social activities provided a greater protection against cognitive decline than simply maintaining contact with friends and relatives. Simply stated, when considering the potential preventive benefits of social activities, above and beyond the simple presence of a social network, it is the level and nature of interaction that are meaningful. Crooks et al. (2008) noted a gender effect such that the mere presence of social interactions, such as conversing with friends, as opposed to more active social engagement was associated with lower cognitive decline for women, but not for men, thus underscoring the importance of includingg an activity while socializing.

In a 2004 study by Fratiglioni et al., the health-promoting effects of social relationships are discussed as having widespread benefits across the lifespan. Social networks benefit health through social support, social influence, social engagement, person-to-person contact, and access to resources and material goods. Karp et al. (2006) note that social leisure activities may be related to the immune system by impacting inflammatory processes in the brain linked to dementia. Socialization may be associated with general health improvements as well as a possible slowing of the progression of the disease. Given that socialization offers opportunities for greater physical exercise and activity, it is worth noting that increased exercise may be associated with higher levels of cerebral oxygenation and ultimately, better neurotransmitter metabolism (Karp et al., 2006). Kramer, Colcombe,

McAuley, Scalf, and Erickson (2005) also found that physical activity may selectively improve neurocognitive function. Social interactions have also been associated with decreased mortality and morbidity (Smith & Christakis, 2008). In a study by Sampson, Bulpitt, and Fletcher (2009), participants with the lowest social engagement composite score had a small, but significantly greater, mortality risk. A review by House, Landis, and Umberson (1988) found that people with a small quantity and low quality of social relationships were at increased risk of death, after controlling for baseline health status.

Participation in social activities has also been associated with preservation of cognitive abilities. Social networks and leisure activities provide social stimulation and protect cognitive functions. Various studies have found that more improved social networks and greater participation in social activities have been associated with lower incidence of cognitive decline. A large social network was found to be associated with greater cognitive health in old age in several observational studies (Flatt & Hughes, 2013). In fact, one such longitudinal study found that of the 469 elderly non-demented participants, those individuals who participated in cognitively stimulating leisure activities, such as board games, experienced a greater protective effect against the development of dementia. In contrast, individuals who were more socially disengaged and had unsatisfying contact with their children were at a greater risk of subsequent dementia or diminished cognition. Research from the Rush Memory and Aging Project found that participation in social activities was related to a reduced rate of cognitive decline over a five-year span (James, Wilson, Barnes, & Bennett, 2011). The absence of social connections was found to double one's risk of cognitive decline (Bassuk, Glass, & Berkman, 1999). Similarly, Fratiglioni et al. (2004) found that single persons were at a greater risk for dementia compared to their married peers, suggesting that marriage may offer increased socialization and a protective benefit with regards to cognition.

It is unclear whether the same benefits extend to familial relationships, however. Glei et al. (2005) conducted a longitudinal, population-based study of nearly 2,400 elderly Taiwanese, for whom family-centered culture and social structure typically dictate that elderly parents live with their children. Despite the social culture, the researchers did not find evidence of a relationship between familial social contact and cognitive ability. More important, however, they found that participation in voluntary social activities was a greater protective factor against cognitive decline than the mere maintaining of social contacts or networks with friends and family. Individuals who participated in one or two social activities experienced lower risk of cognitive decline as compared to those who did not participate in any social activities. Glei et al. emphasized this graded relationship; the higher the level of participation in social activities, the greater the benefit. The Whitehall II study echoed similar findings, with social activities offering higher levels of social interaction associated with better cognitive health (Singh-Manoux, Richards, & Marmot, 2003).

Social Stimulation Effects

Since prevention is not always possible, treatment may need to occur into the progression of the dementia. Ascribing to a 'use it or lose it' philosophy, continuing to participate in social activities and interactions is thought to keep one's social abilities more salient and ingrained in a daily routine. As work-related activities often contribute to a greater portion of one's socialization in adult life, when individuals reach retirement, access to those activities and associated networks typically diminishes. Leisure activities, that may have previously only filled weekends and some evenings, will now become the primary source of mental stimulation, social engagement, and physical activity (Karp et al., 2006). Individuals who did not achieve work-life balance before retirement may have a harder time integrating more leisure activities, particularly if it requires learning new skills. For those with dementia, staying active and rejecting a sedentary life are proving to be crucial steps in slowing the course of the disease.

Making efforts to enrich the social environment throughout dementia progression is important. Though it can be beneficial at any point, at the first awareness of a shrinking social life, individuals are encouraged to increase the amount and intensity of social involvement in daily interactions. Morgan and Stewart (1997) emphasized that no matter the efforts made in the physical environment to enrich one's life, such efforts cannot make up for deficiencies in the social environment. If involvement, such as volunteering once a day, is a bit too intense or exhausting, a few smaller social activities, such a weekly card game with friends, may be just as helpful.

The question of how socialization through social networks, social engagement, and social offers a protective benefit against cognitive decline and dementia is one of interest to many researchers. Various theories have been raised regarding possible mechanisms exacting cognitive health benefits. Four theories will be briefly considered here: the brain/cognitive reserve theory, the vascular hypothesis, the stress theory, and the impact of mood.

The brain/cognitive reserve hypothesis seeks to explain the brain's ability to compensate for disease pathology or age-related neural deficits that can prevent or delay cognitive decline. Neuroimaging studies also support the theory, as individuals with greater reserve may tolerate greater pathology. That is, level of pathology on imaging studies was not consistently predictive of cognitive performance in old age. Other studies suggest a dedifferentiation of cognitive operations, thought to be a compensatory function as regions of a brain recruited to complete a task are less specific on neuroimaging studies. The brain reserve component postulates that either a larger brain or increased neural count can protect against cognitive deficits (Flatt & Hughes, 2013). Furthermore, the level and strength of interconnections are indicative of brain health. Its counterpart, the cognitive reserve component represents the flexibility of the brain through neuroplasticity and neurogenesis as well as the brain's efficiency in accessing brain reserve. The cognitive reserve hypothesis has also found favor through a series of experimental studies. Animal studies found that environmentally enriched conditions have the potential to reduce or prevent cognitive deficits in both young and adult rats. Studies on plasticity found that plasticity is elicited with activity, as opposed to other stimuli. Some have suggested that complex social engagement may ignite neural adaptation (Flatt & Hughes, 2013). Similarly, cognitive engagement theories rest on the adage 'use it or lose it' and equate to a 'disuse' hypothesis. That is, individuals who don't use their cognitive abilities or engage in activities on a daily basis may be subject to atrophy or disuse. Viewing the brain as a muscle, individuals who engage in social activities may benefit through improved brain health by exercising areas of the brain responsible for carrying out cognitive tasks such as memory, problem solving, and comprehension (Flatt & Hughes, 2013). Processing of information related to social interactions about oneself, others, and the interaction is also engaging for the brain. This social cognition requires individuals to engage in higher level abilities, such as discerning people's personalities and motives, responding to social interchanges, reading and understanding facial expressions, and other social cues (Flatt & Hughes, 2013). Processing emotional reactions and experiences is also a part of social cognition. Flatt and Hughes (2013) further theorized that enjoyment was an essential element in boosting cognitive health by increasing engagement and mediating the effects of stress and mood on cognition. Collectively, engaging in such higher level abilities may promote cognitive health in old age.

The vascular hypothesis postulates that various vascular risk factors, vascular disorders, etc. are involved in the pathogenesis and progression of dementia. One such risk factor, severe atherosclerosis, has been linked in experimental, neuropathological, and epidemiological studies with direct and indirect effects on dementia and Alzheimer's disease (AD) in the elderly. Other theorists have suggested that cerebrovascular disorders may alter the clinical presentation or symptomatology of dementia or AD. Changes in cerebrovasculature secondary to mood disorders, which may impact brain structures and functioning, have also been highlighted in a National Institute of Health Cognitive and Emotional Health Project (Hendrie et al., 2006). That is, emotions were investigated for their etiological role in cognitive decline, with the recommendation for future research to study both cognitive and emotional health simultaneously. More research on the interactions of vascular risk factors and dementia pathology is needed.

The stress hypothesis suggests that individuals who are more connected and socially engaged with more frequent interactions experience a greater positive response via improved self-esteem, social competence, and better mood, which lowers stress. Those who do not adapt as successfully to stress may have a greater risk for the development of dementia. Wilson and colleagues (2003) found that persons experiencing a high susceptibility to distress were twice as susceptible to developing AD. That is, persons who were not as able to adapt to stress were more vulnerable to the effects of stress. This is particularly challenging in late life, as the older brain is more susceptible to stress (Lupien, McEwen, Gunnar, & Heim, 2009). Prolonged stress is harmful in that it contributes to overproduction of cortisol, a stress hormone. The glucocorticoid cascade hypothesis suggests that a permanent loss of hippocampal neurons occurs during a sustained stress response. Although not all research has supported a consistent finding, some have associated elevated cortisol levels with worsened visuo-spatial memory, executive functioning, and processing speed (Franz et al., 2011). The impact of chronic stress on one's body over time, or the 'wear and tear' of stress, has been referred to as allostatic load. Individuals with a high allostatic load are at risk for vascular disease, increased mortality, and physical and cognitive problems (Seeman, Singer, Ryff, Deinberg Love, & Levy-Storms, 2002). These authors also demonstrated that a lower allostatic load has been associated with positive social experiences. Specifically, those older adults with three or more social ties had a lower allostatic load than their peers with fewer ties. Having more social contacts and participating in more social activities may boost an individual's ability to cope with late-life stressors.

For an individual experiencing the presence of a mood disorder, he or she may have an associated greater risk of impaired cognition. Some have found the presence of a mood disorder to predict future cognitive decline (Simard, Hudon, & Van Reekum, 2009). A review of the literature on the effects of depression on cognitive decline and dementia is available in Butters et al. (2008) and discussed in Chapter 8. While mood disorders have been associated with cognitive decline, as individuals experience greater cognitive challenges, they also experience greater anxiety and mood disturbance, contributing to a reciprocal and ongoing interaction.

The convergence of these various theories certainly underscore that a more active and socially engaged lifestyle appears to offer protective benefits against the onset of dementia or Alzheimer's disease. The precise nature of the interactions and underlying mechanisms remain areas for future research.

Prevention or Foreshadowing?

While many epidemiological and population-based studies suggest a correlation or association between the beneficial effects of social and cognitive decline prevention, causative relationships have been more challenging to demonstrate, largely due to methodological constraints. In other words, it is possible that the behaviors thought to be preventative may actually simply occur at a higher frequency among those not at risk for dementia. That is, limited leisure activities or poor social networks may be consequences of early manifestations of dementia in individuals, rather than premorbid risk factors (Fratiglioni et al., 2004). Alternatively, Gallacher, Bayer, and Ben-Shlomo (2005) discuss reverse causality as worthy of consideration;

individuals experiencing incipient decline may be more or less likely to seek cognitive stimulation. Lack of social interaction may simply be the patient's disinterest in struggling to use the parts of their mind they sense themselves losing, somewhat foreshadowing the dementia to come. In much the same way, those who maintain a greater cognitive ability would not only be more likely to engage in social activities but also better able to compensate even if confronted with pathology. These same individuals may be able to sustain such activities and demonstrate higher performances on cognitive testing (Gallacher et al., 2005). Those with no risk for dementia may be more likely to engage in activities of a social nature. Individuals who choose social activities become socially stronger, which helps them battle any oncoming dementia they may have to face. With questions remaining, the challenge is set forth for researchers to explore more controlled methodological paradigm in studying the prevention of dementia.

Social Challenges for Persons with Dementia

For those individuals who experience the onset of cognitive decline or dementia, social stimulation can also be beneficial in limiting further cognitive decline as well as serving as a treatment or therapeutic intervention. Individuals experiencing the early stages of dementia and grappling with feelings of loneliness or depression and apathy, therapeutic interventions can be a viable and preferred treatment approach. As others struggle with the manifestation of sleep disturbances, agitation behavior, or concerns regarding quality of life, social stimulation can serve as a valuable asset for intervention.

Loneliness

A recent study found that individuals who reported feeling lonely were almost twice as likely to develop dementia as those who did not, and feelings of loneliness were not limited to people who lived alone (Holwerda et al., 2012). Fratiglioni and colleagues (2004) found that social isolation accelerates cognitive decline in aging, while a strong social network and active life improve health, in general, with less incidence of disease. Furthermore, decline in cognition can lead to even less socialization, causing a reciprocal effect that continues to lower quality of life, overall (Glei et al., 2005). Less socialization is not an uncommon manifestation of cognitive decline, given that individuals with dementia have a greater difficulty maintaining their social role and social pragmatics.

Beyond mitigating the effects of isolation and loneliness, participation in social activities has been associated with many potential benefits. For example, individuals who participate in cognitively stimulating environments may experience an improvement in psychological functioning. Fratiglioni et al. (2004) found that more opportunities to engage with others lead to positive emotional states, such as greater self-esteem, social competence, and improvement of mood; these positive emotional effects lead to lower stress. According to the stress hypothesis discussed above, persons who were not as able to adapt to stress were more vulnerable to the effects of stress. Individuals who have a social network and mechanisms in place are more likely to manage stress more effectively through greater emotional support, feelings of integration, and belonging as well as a sense of purpose and meaning in life.

Shared positive experiences are also an important byproduct of social interactions and eliciting positive emotions. More recent studies utilizing brain imaging have found a link between humor and activation of the positive reward system in the brain, leading to an increase in dopamine. Responsible for controlling the brain's pleasure center, neurotransmitters, such as dopamine, endorphins, and serotonin, help regulate emotional responses through anticipating the reward and experiencing the reward itself. As individuals observe their environment and see smiling faces and hear laughter, a positive emotional response and feelings of happiness are elicited. In fact, the act of smiling and stimulating musculature around the mouth begins the cascade of activating neurotransmitters and ultimately, positive emotions. Knowing that humor also has the effect of opening the doors of communication, some care facilities have turned to the use of therapeutic clowning. The funny clown costumes, props, and make-up cue the anticipation of humor, facilitating the boost in observer mood in the interactions with the therapeutic clowns.

Depression and Apathy

As patients are confronted with cognitive difficulties or decline, not uncommonly they may experience difficulty adjusting to their challenges and circumstances. Persons experiencing loss of any type may also have a low or depressed mood. Depression is a common response, particularly when faced with losing one's usual mental abilities and memories. As above, social interaction has a large, noticeable impact on emotional states of individuals with dementia.

Often mistaken for depression, patients experiencing the onset of dementia may also encounter apathy. Because depression and apathy share many common symptoms, and apathy can arise alongside depression, it may be overlooked and undiagnosed (Landes, Sperry, Strauss, & Geldmacher, 2001). Despite being undiagnosed, apathy is prevalent and found to occur in up to 92% of patients, cited as the most common behavioral symptom in AD (Landes et al., 2001). Apathy can cause one to be less likely to participate in therapy, in social activities, and even in activities of daily living, ultimately requiring the patient with dementia to need greater management and support. Unlike depression, interventions and techniques can be used to initiate activities for apathetic patients, allowing for a greater capacity to initiate a response when provided greater structure and cues. If untreated, apathy has been associated with myriad adverse outcomes, including physical deconditioning, lack of progress in rehabilitation, increased difficulties with activities of daily living, uncooperativeness, combativeness, social isolation, and caregiver distress (Politis et al., 2004). Furthermore, other researchers identified associated difficulties to include loss of motivation, decreased initiation, anhedonia, indifference, poor social engagement, blunted emotional responsiveness, and diminished insight (Landes et al., 2001). Since apathy can contribute to even further social isolation for a person with dementia, it is an important focus for concern. Apathy, however, can be combated with social interaction and assistance. Oftentimes, apathetic patients simply needs someone to increase their level of arousal and stimulation to perform a task or participate in an activity, though social interaction can have a lasting effect on their motivation later on, too. Apathetic individuals with dementia may be responsive to individualized attention. Caretakers investing 30 minutes a few times a week is beneficial (Politis et al., 2004).

Behavioral Challenges

Not uncommonly, many persons with dementia may experience a host of behavioral symptoms as a manifestation of their disease process. More challenging behavioral symptoms of dementia, such as physical aggression, delusions or hallucinations, wandering behavior, incontinence, and abnormal vocalizations can challenge caregiver resources and ultimately contribute to greater rates of institutionalization (McCabe, Baun, Speich, & Agrawal, 2002). As the disease progresses, these types of behaviors can increase the suffering of the patient and the burden on the caregivers, resulting in more restrictive care and sometimes the application of pharmacologic treatments (Cohen-Mansfield, 2001). The cumulative effect of the symptoms creates somewhat of a domino effect, with worsening behaviors contributing to higher levels of care needed and greater dependence. Unfortunately, these behavioral challenges may further limit one's ability to participate in social activities.

Agitation

A common problem for persons experiencing dementia, especially challenging caregivers and residential care situations, involves agitation and aggressive behaviors. While agitation may contribute to the need for higher levels of care, when patients are transitioned to a new care environment, they may, intentionally or not, act out from frustration with difficulty processing changes occurring in both their lives and their disease. Patients who have difficulty adapting to a novel environment may experience greater confusion, which can lead to agitation. These behaviors can be unintentionally reinforced by caregivers, especially in a care setting where there may be a low caregiver-to-patient ratio and caregivers are more likely to react or provide greater attention to the patient displaying challenging behaviors (Cohen-Mansfield, 2001).

Social interaction can both subdue and exacerbate agitated behaviors, prompting the need for balanced moderation. In crowded nursing homes, agitation may escalate, and further provoke similar responses from nearby residents. In a study by Morgan and Stewart (1997), a nursing home population was spread out to attempt to lessen agitation. While using strategic spacing lessened incidence of agitation, residents also experienced greater boredom. To achieve a balanced environment, more one-on-one quiet interaction was utilized for those who do not enjoy a busy atmosphere, while conversely providing more exciting situations for those who experienced greater boredom. Politis et al. (2004) found that when provided one-on-one interaction, patients engaged well and appeared to experience less irritability and combativeness. When individualized to the patient's needs, social stimulation can be a therapeutic and beneficial choice.

Sleep Patterns

Sleep patterns can influence cognition, emotional responses, and physical ability in a normal, or non-demented, population. Disruptions in sleep patterns can be even more challenging for patients with dementia and their loved ones. Richards et al. (2005) note that sleep disturbances were related to increased falls and weakened immune function. Furthermore, sleep challenges were associated with poor quality of life and poor life satisfaction as well as depression and anxiety. Cognitive changes with impaired concentration and memory were also acknowledged. For individuals already taxed by sleep challenges, dementia tends to exacerbate sleep-pattern disturbances, causing more nighttime awakenings, and thus greater cognitive and functional decline. Ultimately, these individuals have higher odds of nursing home placement. Though nursing home placement is often intended to help the patient by providing a safer setting, institutions can often magnify the problem. As Richards et al. note, the nighttime routine in an institution can include multiple wetness bed checks and up to 80 intercom noise events of 60 decibels or higher, which can cause further sleep disturbances and awakenings.

Lack of sleep and the related problems that come from poor sleep can further increase the behaviors that make socialization difficult and lower the motivation that is needed to initiate social interaction. In one study assessing the utility of individualized social activity interventions (ISAI) as a means of addressing sleep fragmentation and sleep/wake pattern disturbances, Richards and colleagues (2005) found that social stimulation activities were beneficial in regulating daytime sleepiness and providing for a more beneficial night's sleep. Social interaction was found to increase slow-wave sleep and improve performance for memory-related tasks. Patients receiving social stimulation interventions in this study were less likely to sleep in the daytime, and napping decreased from two hours per day to 1.25 hours per day, on average; they also fell asleep faster and slept about 40 minutes longer per night, with less time overall spent awake at night, and had higher sleep efficiency (Richards et al., 2005). This finding implies that socialization can have an overall beneficial effect on sleep and sleep/wake pattern regulation, gives the patients something to do that keeps them alert, and is more motivating and interesting than napping. The researchers also noted a trend in individuals who seemed happier and initiated more positive interactions with others after participating in the ISAI (Richards et al., 2005).

Quality of Life

The cumulative effect of multiple life changes and declining cognitive facility can adversely impact quality of life, a complex construct that is often loosely defined as one's overall well-being and satisfaction with life across various domains. An individual's assessment of quality of life can be a strong overall appraisal of the adequacy of the current level of care and resources. Quality of life can decline as coping skills are overextended; persons with dementia may lose grasp of their coping abilities and have a lower threshold for stress, contributing to greater mood disturbance and behavioral challenges (Cohen-Mansfield, 2001).

Oftentimes, in the hopes of avoiding undesirable or dangerous behaviors, persons with dementia are subjected to more secure and less interesting or stimulating environments. This kind of inactivity can result in feelings of isolation, diminished self-esteem, greater disability, and more unoccupied time, bringing the quality of life, despite its intended safety, to an unacceptably low level (Richards et al., 2005). Many might object that no measure of safety can justify a life spent cooped up within an environment marked by sensory deprivation, ongoing boredom, and social loneliness commonly suffered by nursing home residents who exhibit less desirable or inappropriate behaviors (Cohen-Mansfield, 2001).

The physical surroundings are not the only factor influencing quality of life. Many residential care settings attempt to create a sense of home so residents do not feel as bored and isolated, as they might in a more hospital-like setting. Priorities placed on pleasant, aesthetically-pleasing environments have been challenged on the basis that one's home is more often characterized by experiences and interpersonal relationships, as opposed to physical features, and cannot be created by simply hanging pictures and placing house plants (Slaughter, Calkins, Eliasziw, & Reimer, 2006). Creating a strong quality of life depends on having the social settings and support that one would desire in his or her own home, one in which boredom, loneliness, and isolation were not a commonly-faced problem.

Quality of life can be difficult to sum up in any numerically measureable criteria. One of the most valuable ways to find out how the quality of life is for someone, and what they would need to consider their needs met, is to ask them. For persons without dementia, this is a fairly simple task; however, for those with dementia, it will take longer, will require greater patience, and may require that the questions asked focus on current feelings and perceptions. In a 1997 qualitative study by Morgan and Stewart, patients with dementia were interviewed to learn more about their views were on recent placement in a residential care facility. One patient interviewed summed up her view of quality of life into a single, poignant sentence, "You can have the most beautiful castle in the world, but if you don't have other people and things going on, it can be a very lonely place" (Morgan & Stewart, p. 751). Morgan and Stewart also found that interactions with the staff, meeting social or other needs, can provide a sense of security to the residents. Social interaction, it seems, is a mainstay for a greater quality of life.

Social Stimulation Through Therapeutic Activities

Social stimulation can occur naturally through casual social interactions, while other sources of social stimulation can be developed through therapeutic interventions. Whether casually occurring or strategically initiated, social stimulation will be very dependent on the individual's tastes, preferences, motivations, and abilities. Morgan and Stewart (1997) made note that when choosing the optimal level of stimulation, there was much variance in individuals' responses. If the option exists to tailor the interventions to each individual, then as much effort as possible should be taken to structure the program to be tailored for each person. Aggarwal et al. (2003) found that interviewing patients, though often avoided because it is difficult and somewhat time consuming, was a very effective way to find the key points to follow for the individual. When interviewing people with dementia,

Aggarwal et al. found that the employment of an individualized approach, taking into account personal preferences and the severity of the dementia, through open-ended broad questions, was most informative and less distressing for the individual. The main goal for tailoring the social stimulation interventions to an individual is to reach the optimal levels of social interaction to provide as much benefit to the patient as possible, without going over the top into an overwhelming level (Morgan & Stewart, 1997). Two such therapeutic activities, social dancing and animal-assisted therapy, are presented to highlight the beneficial effects of using social stimulation as a therapeutic intervention.

Social Dancing

Social dancing is one social activity and source of social stimulation in particular that has been shown to improve overall level of functioning and support greater independence, as highlighted by Palo-Bengtsson, Winblad, and Ekman (1998). In their study, nursing home residents who participated in social dancing were observed to more readily experience positive emotions, such as joy and happiness. Social dancing also offered a means of enhancing people's ability to express themselves nonverbally. Social dancing facilitated the participant's ability to express positive feelings towards others by dancing together. The more structured activity fostered the chance to develop and maintain social contacts to those who would otherwise have to initiate interactions themselves. As a shared activity with others, even those individuals experiencing greater loss from dementia were able to fall back into previously acquired social roles and social competence. Participants demonstrated an increased awareness of the social norms, initiating positive interactions with dance partners, which also served to reaffirm the dancer's identity and encourage autonomy. It was natural for male patients to escort the dance partner back to their place, fostering their social role and independence through the remembrance of old social patterns. Social dancing was also thought to bolster social contacts and stimulate reminiscence of earlier memories. Inherent in social dancing activities, participants were able to pull on previously acquired skills, particularly the more robust motor memory, and thus, they were not confronted with the loss of a skill set. The exchange of positive interactions, such as enjoyment of dancing and music, offered a distraction from diminished capacities and negative feelings they might otherwise confront

(Palo-Bengtsson et al., 1998). Collectively, the dancing included aspects of recalling social practices and old dance steps and focused on using music the residents would remember in conjunction with incorporating movement, laughter, and talking, giving the activity a well-rounded involvement and benefit for those involved.

Animal-Assisted Social Therapy

Social support and interaction does not always have to be provided by another human being. Important facets of social support, including emotional support, esteem support, and nurturance can also be facilitated in human-animal relationships and bonds (Kaiser, Spence, McGavin, Struble, & Keilman, 2002). Animals kept as pets are often thought of as part of one's family, showing the strong connection and emotional ties a person can have with an animal.

Animals used for social stimulation have the benefit of also providing multiple kinds of sensory stimulation as well as a calming effect. Animals can be used passively or actively as diversions for patients to play, exercise, or experience sensory stimulation (Barba, 1995). Association with animals has been long proven to provide many benefits to humans, including lowered blood pressure, reduced heart rate, decreased muscle rigidity, greater self-esteem, feelings of security, reduced stress and anxiety, improved social interactions, better communications, and sensory stimulation (Barba, 1995). One of the major benefits of incorporating animals into therapy is the availability of the animal to provide long periods of attention at a much lower cost than a human caregiver. Animals do not exhibit feelings of disinterest from obligation when visiting patients, as may be seen in a human visitor. In contrast, they provide an easy form of attention for the patients when they may otherwise not have the opportunity (Sellers, 2006).

Although having an animal companion may be the best form of social stimulation for some, animals can also be used to enhance the therapeutic relationship, serving as a bonding agent and placing elders at ease, with a near immediate sense of intimacy. With animals present, the therapist often is viewed as less threatening and helps the patient feel at ease (Sellers, 2006). In animal-assisted therapy, wherein the animal can be used to help facilitate therapy, the major premise is the animal is considered a co-therapist, rather than a visitor or an object in the room (Macauley, 2006). This helps both the patient and therapist to avoid ignoring the animal and makes sure the animal is incorporated, as needed, to provide benefit to the patient. Sellers points out that incorporating an animal into therapy creates a welcoming environment for changes and helps assist behavior modification. Though a structured animal-assisted therapy program can provide much benefit to the therapy, Barba (1995) notes that desirable fringe benefits also include having animals visit for fun and laughter.

One common use for animal-assisted therapy is to help lessen irritable behaviors in older adults with dementia. Cohen-Mansfield (2001) found that having a pet present at home was associated with lower incidents of verbal aggression among demented persons. This benefit can come from having a pet living in the residence or with a few visits throughout the week. McCabe et al. (2002) found that the presence of a resident dog in the residential care facility decreased behavioral problems in the daylight hours. Cohen-Mansfield observed an improvement as quantified on the Irritable Behavior Scale, from only a one-hour intervention daily for five days.

In some cases, social stimulation with an animal may be the preferred option since oftentimes human interaction in a nursing home may be obligatory, such as visits related to medical care, assistance with daily living, housekeeping, delivery of meals, and family visits that may seem to be squeezed into one's day making any of the interactions feel less valuable (Kaiser et al., 2002). These same researchers found that non-obligatory visits from a person may be only as beneficial to residents as visits from a dog, though they also mentioned that a dog may be more readily able to meet the need for tactile comfort and ability to nurture. In addition to providing companionship, the attention provided by animals, as a basic element of social interactions, was a unique benefit in a busy world (Sellers, 2006).

Animals provide great social stimulation for those with more severe cases of dementia, as the animal does not require conversation or verbal interaction to socialize and does not have the same biases to the challenging or unpleasant manifestations of an advanced dementia that humans tend to hold. Therapy animals have the unique ability to show unconditional acceptance, being unphased by a person's physical appearance or speech idiosyncrasies, without the patient needing to fear being questioned or rejected for his or her difficulties (Barba, 1995). For someone who has aphasia or who cannot hold long conversations, the animal will be indifferent, while human visitors may signal reactions through their body language. For these patients, a non-demanding animal visit can provide benefit without requiring verbal communication (Barba, 1995). An animal's consistent availability, non-judgmental attention, tactile comfort, and need for love and nurturance are aspects of social support that are more easily provided via social interaction with animals than with humans (Kaiser et al., 2002).

Of course, using animals for social stimulation is not an option for everyone, as personal preferences, living arrangements, and allergies can interfere. If a person with dementia is living alone, there is risk of accidental over-feeding or under-feeding of a live-in animal, in which case an animal that self-regulates on food and can be left food by a caregiver is a better choice. For situations in which a live-in animal is not at all feasible, there are volunteer organizations that perform animal visits for patients and the elderly; if animals are not an option at all, even a robot dog has been shown to increase activity in patients with dementia during occupational therapy and in communication with other patients, though some patients preferred a motorized toy dog over the robot, most likely due to lack of familiarity with a robotic dog (Tamura et al., 2004). Adaptations can be made for many patients with dementia to provide the most beneficial and therapeutic social interventions as possible.

Conclusion

The convergence of epidemiologic, population-based, and experimental studies have garnered strong support for the associated benefits of socialization and social stimulation in both the prevention of cognitive decline and the amelioration of symptoms for those experiencing manifestations of the disease process. Not only can increased socialization be preventive and therapeutic, but greater socialization has also been associated with greater overall health, improved mood, greater connection with a greater sense of purpose in one's community, improved life satisfaction and enjoyment, and more robust coping strategies. These outcomes, in turn, collectively contribute to greater socialization opportunities and benefits in a mutually constitutive, reciprocal fashion. Individuals, loved ones, and treatment providers can provide greater attention to those opportunities available for increased social engagement, while future research can be directed at understanding the very nature and factors that improve the benefits of socialization, identifying the mediators that are associated with increased overall benefit. As research in this area continues to develop, emphasizing the importance of social activities and active engagement in cognition, emotion, and health outcomes in individuals with dementia continues to be important.

References

Aggarwal, N., Vass, A. A., Minardi, H. A., Ward, R., Garfield, C., & Cybyk, B. (2003). People with dementia and their relatives: Personal experiences of Alzheimer's and of the provision of care. *Journal of Psychiatric and Mental Health Nursing, 10*, 187-197.

Barba, B. E. (1995). The positive influence of animals: Animal-assisted therapy in acute care. *Clinical Nurse Specialist, 9*, 91-95.

Bassuk, S. S., Glass, T. A., & Berkman, L. F. (1999). Social disengagement and incident cognitive decline in community-dwelling elderly persons. *Annals of Internal Medicine 131*, 165-173.

Butters, M., Young, J., Lopez, O., Aizenstein, H., Mulsant, B., Reynolds, C., DeKosky, S., & Becker, J. (2008). Pathways linking late-life depression to persistent cognitive impairment and dementia. *Dialogues of Clinical Neuroscience, 10*, 345-357.

Cohen-Mansfield, J. (2001). Nonpharmacologic interventions for inappropriate behaviors in dementia. *American Journal of Geriatric Psychiatry, 9*, 361-381.

Crooks, V. C., Lubben, J., Petitti, D. B., Little, D., & Chiu, V. (2008). Social network, cognitive function, and dementia incidence among elderly women. *American Journal of Public Health, 98*, 1221-1227.

Flatt, J. D., & Hughes, T. F. (2013). Participation in social activities in later life: Does enjoyment have important implications for cognitive health? *Aging Health, 9*, 149-158.

Franz, C. E., O'Brien, R. C., Hauger, R. L., Mendoza, S. P., Panizzon, M. S., Prom-Wormley, E., Eaves, L. J., Jacobson, K., Lyons, M. J., Lupien, S., Hellhammer, D., Xian, H., & Kremen, W. S. (2011). Cross-sectional and 35-year longitudinal assessment of salivary cortisol and cognitive functioning: The Vietnam era twin study of aging. *Psychoneuroendocrinology, 36*, 1040-1052.

Fratiglioni, L., Paillard-Borg, S., & Winblad, B. (2004). An active and socially integrated lifestyle in late life might protect against dementia. *Lancet Neurology, 3,* 343-353.

Gallacher, J., Bayer, A., & Ben-Shlomo, Y. (2005). Commentary: Activity each day keeps dementia away—does social interaction really preserve cognitive function? *International Journal of Epidemiology, 34,* 872-873.

Glei, D. A., Landau, D. A., Goldman, N., Chuang, Y-L., Rodríguez, G., & Weinstein, M. (2005). Participating in social activities helps preserve cognitive function: An analysis of a longitudinal, population-based study of the elderly. *International Journal of Epidemiology, 34,* 864-871.

Hendrie, H. C., Albert, M. S., Butters, M. A., Gao, S., Knopman, D. S., Launer, L. J., Yaffe, K., Cuthbert, B. N., Edwards, E., & Wagster, M. V. (2006). The NIH cognitive and emotional health project: Report of the critical evaluation study committee. *Alzheimer's and Dementia, 2,* 12-32.

House, J., Landis, K., & Umberson, D. (1988). Social relationships and health. *Science, 241,* 540-545.

Howlerda, T. J., Deeg, D. J., Beekman, A. T., van Tilburg, T. G., Stek, M. L., Jonker, C., & Schoevers, R. A. (2012). Feelings of loneliness, but not social isolation, predict dementia onset: Results from the Amsterdam study of the elderly (AMSTEL). *Journal of Neurology, Neurosurgery and Psychiatry,* doi:10.1136/jnnp-2012-302755

James, B. D., Wilson, R. S., Barnes, L. L. & Bennett, D. A. (2011). Late-life social activity and cognitive decline in old age. *Journal of International Neuropsychological Society, 17,* 1-8.

Kaiser, L., Spence, L. J., McGavin, L., Struble, L., & Keilman, L. (2002). A dog and a "happy person" visit nursing home residents. *Western Journal of Nursing Research, 24,* 671-683.

Karp, A., Paillard-Borg, S., Wang, H-X., Silverstein, M., Winblad, B., & Fratiglioni, L. (2006). Mental, physical and social components in leisure activities equally contribute to decrease dementia risk. *Dementia and Geriatric Cognitive Disorders, 21,* 65-73.

Kramer, A. F., Colcombe, S. J., McAuley, E., Scalf, P. E., & Erickson, K. I. (2005). Fitness, aging and neurocognitive function. *Neurobiology of Aging, 26*(Suppl.), 124-127.

Landes, A. M., Sperry, S. D., Strauss, M. E., & Geldmacher, D. S. (2001). Apathy in Alzheimer's disease. *Journal of the American Geriatrics Society, 49*, 1700-1707.

Lupien, S. J., McEwen, B. S., Gunnar, M. R. & Heim, C. (2009). Effects of stress throughout the lifespan on the brain, behaviour and cognition. *Nature Reviews Neuroscience, 10*, 434-445.

Macauley, B. L. (2006). Animal-assisted therapy for persons with aphasia: A pilot study. *Journal of Rehabilitation Research and Development, 43*, 357-366.

McCabe, B. W., Baun, M. M., Speich, D., & Agrawal, S. (2002). Resident dog in the Alzheimer's special care unit. *Western Journal of Nursing Research, 24*, 684-696.

Morgan, D. G., & Stewart, N. J. (1997). The importance of the social environment in dementia care. *Western Journal of Nursing Research, 19*, 740-761.

Palo-Bengtsson, L., Winblad, B., & Ekman, S-L. (1998). Social dancing: A way to support intellectual, emotional and motor functions in persons with dementia. *Journal of Psychiatric and Mental Health Nursing, 5*, 545-554.

Politis, A. M., Vozzella, S., Mayer, L. S., Onyike, C. U., Baker, A. S., & Lyketsos, C. G. (2004). A randomized, controlled, clinical trial of activity therapy for apathy in patients with dementia residing in long-term care. *International Journal of Geriatric Psychiatry, 19*, 1087-1094.

Richards, K. C., Beck, C., O'Sullivan, P. S., & Shue, V. M. (2005). Effect of individualized social activity on sleep in nursing home residents with dementia. *Journal of the American Geriatrics Society, 53*, 1510-1517.

Sampson, E. L., Bulpitt, C. J., & Fletcher, A. E. (2009). Survival of community-dwelling older people: The effect of cognitive impairment and social engagement. *Journal of the American Geriatrics Society, 57*, 985-991.

Seeman, T. E., Singer, B. H., Ryff, C. D., Dienburg Love, G., & Levy-Storms, L. (2002). Social relationships, gender, and allostatic load across two age cohorts. *Psychosomatic Medicine, 64,* 395-406.

Sellers, D. M. (2006). The evaluation of an animal assisted therapy intervention for elders with dementia in long-term care. *Activities, Adaptation and Aging, 30,* 61-77.

Simard, M., Hudon, C., & Van Reekum, R. (2009). Psychological distress and risk for dementia. *Current Psychiatry Reports, 11,* 41-47.

Singh-Manoux, A., Richards, M., & Marmot, M. (2003). Leisure activity and cognitive function in middle age: Evidence from the Whitehall II study. *Journal of Epidemiology and Community Health, 57,* 907-913.

Slaughter, S., Calkins, M., Eliasziw, M., & Reimer, M. (2006). Measuring physical and social environments in nursing homes for people with middle- to late-stage dementia. *Journal of the American Geriatrics Society, 54,* 1436-1441.

Smith, K., & Christakis, N. (2008). Social networks and health. *Annual Review of Sociology, 34,* 405-429.

Tamura, T., Yonemitsu, S., Itoh, A., Oikawa, D., Kawakami, A., Higashi, Y., Fujimooto, T., & Nakajima, K. (2004). Is an entertainment robot useful in the care of elderly people with severe dementia? *Journals of Gerontology, Series A: Medical Sciences, 59,* 83-85.

Wang, H-X., Karp, A., Winblad, B., & Fratiglioni, L. (2002). Late-life engagement in social and leisure activities is associated with a decreased risk of dementia: A longitudinal study from the Kungsholmen project. *American Journal of Epidemiology, 155,* 1081-1087.

Wilson, R., Evans, D., Bienias, J., Mendes de Leon, C., Schneider, J., & Bennett, D. (2003). Proneness to psychological distress is associated with risk of Alzheimer's disease. *Neurology, 61,* 1479-1485.

CHAPTER 5

Dementia and Sensory Stimulation

Charles J. Golden, Lisa Lashley, Anthony Andrews, Rebecca Fontanetta, and Katherine Hickok

Sensory stimulation may be a viable, non-pharmacological treatment for dementia, resulting in improved functioning (e.g., Collier, McPherson, Ellis-Hill, Staal, & Bucks, 2010). Non-pharmacological treatments of dementia typically focus on slowing disease progression, coping with symptoms, and improving quality of life. Treatment decisions are made on a case-by-case basis, depending on the form of dementia and patient history. Sensory disturbances are common with many forms of dementia, including Alzheimer's disease (AD), Parkinson's dementia, and Lewy body dementia (Bakker, 2003; Benarroch, 2010; Perriol et al., 2005). Sensory depreciation can contribute to acceleration of decline in patients with dementia and result in subsequent functioning detriments. This chapter will review sensory loss and sensory stimulation treatments for dementia, including mechanisms of action.

Our senses allow us interact and learn from our environment. We take in information, process it, and make decisions based on what we see, hear, smell, taste, and touch. This process begins when we are born and continues throughout the lifespan. Further, this process can largely occur outside of conscious awareness. We do not have to consciously choose to see images on the television, hear sounds the radio, or feel and smell freshly washed laundry. Few people ever consider how or why sensory systems are functioning until they fail. When this occurs and compensatory responses are not sufficient to make up for losses in sensation, reactions can include confusion, denial, and depression, among others.

There are multiple causes of sensory loss, and it is important to note that sensory loss can be a natural function of aging. By the time we reach our 60s, we do not sense the world the same way we did when we were younger, as anyone who has to wear reading glasses will attest. Unfortunately, because this process is insidious, patients are often unaware of the extent of their deficits, and they may even deny them or attribute perceptual errors to external sources. The informed clinician will consider these factors when working with elderly patients, regardless of the patient's medical history.

Overview of the Senses and Neural Plasticity

The somatosensory system can be divided into two overarching components. Position, vibration, and fine discriminatory touch information from the body is transmitted from the peripheral nervous system to the dorsal root ganglia, located in the spinal cord, and then to the sensory processing areas of the brain. In the head and neck, this information is transmitted by the trigeminal nerve and processed in the pons. Pain and temperature information from the body is transmitted via the spinothalamic tract, moving from the periphery, to the spinal cord, to the thalamus, and to the primary sensory processing areas of the brain.

Sensory information is processed in specific, specialized areas of cortex. For example, most auditory information is primarily processed in the auditory cortex of the temporal lobes, while most visual information is processed in the visual cortex of the occipital lobe. Location is important when considering sensory loss as it relates to dementia. Dementias do not all attack the same brain areas. For example, AD is associated with damage to the temporal lobes, leaving the occipital lobes relatively spared in early stages of the disease. On the other hand, individuals with Parkinson's dementia suffer damage in the substantia nigra (a brain structure that produces dopamine, responsible for voluntary movement), which is located anterior to the auditory and occipital lobes. Thus, patients diagnosed with dementia are likely to have different patterns of sensory involvement.

Plasticity is also an important factor in sensory loss and stimulation treatment. Plasticity refers to the ability of the nervous system structures to assume the function of diseased or injured areas. Plasticity has been defined as the extent to which one can improve his/her performance in a task after exposure to performance-enhancing conditions (Baltes & Singer, 2001). Plasticity is inversely related to aging; infants and young children have considerably more plasticity than older adults.

Sensory Loss: Causes and Associations with Dementia

Sensory loss in adults can be caused by a variety of factors. Trauma, disease, and the typical aging process all contribute to sensory loss. Further, as dementia progresses in severity, neuronal loss is associated with sensory processing deficits (Baker et al., 2001). Impairments in hearing, vision, olfaction, and touch are common.

Gradual decline in all sensory modalities is a normal part of the aging process. For audition, this type of hearing loss is called presbycusis, and it typically begins to affect people in their 60s. Hearing loss begins with higher-frequency sounds and progresses to mid-frequency and lower-frequency sounds over time (American Speech-Language-Hearing Association, 2013). Other conditions known to cause hearing loss include otosclerosis, Ménière's disease, autoimmune inner ear disease, very loud noise, and traumatic brain injury, among others. Hearing loss may precede dementia (Albers, 2012), and it has been associated with lower quality of life (Li-Korotky, 2012). Additionally, for patients with AD, auditory hallucinations may occur as a consequence of damage to the auditory cortex and hearing pathways in the brain (Jabeen, McKeith, Fairbairn, Perry, & Ferrier, 1992).

Vision is one of our most relied-upon senses. According to Prevent Blindness America (2008), conditions most commonly known to cause vision loss include macular degeneration, glaucoma, detached retina, diabetic retinopathy, and cataracts. According to Schiller, Lucas, and Peregoy (2012), people over the age of 75 years are greater than three times more likely to report vision problems than people 18 years to 44 years of age, as described in American Foundation for the Blind (2013). Poor vision is also associated with the development of dementia, according to Rogers and Langa (2010), who found that individuals with good vision were over 60% less likely to develop dementia than individuals with poor vision. Further, vascular dementia and Alzheimer's disease have been associated with lower visual acuity and contrast sensitivity (Lakshminarayanan, Lagrave, Kean, Dick, & Shankle, 1996).

Disruptions in the functioning of olfaction increases the susceptibility of a person to environmental safety hazards, such as toxic substances, interferes with a person's ability to monitor his or her nutritional intake, preventing the detection of early signs of rotting in foods, and leads to a generally impoverished quality of life (Mesholam, Moberg, Mahr, & Doty, 1998). Although there are many causes of impaired olfaction, about two-thirds of cases are associated with upper respiratory infections, acute sinusitis, or head trauma (Deems et al., 1991).

Neurodegenerative diseases, such as Huntington's chorea, Korsakoff's syndrome, and Pick's disease have also been associated with anosmia (Mesholam et al., 1998), and animal research suggests that AD is characterized by early and progressive olfactory decline (Wesson et al., 2011). Persons with early-stage AD have both low-level and high-level cognitive deficits in odor detection and quality discrimination, presumably due to disruption in the posterior piriform cortex (Li, Howard, & Gottfried, 2010). Further, Rahayel, Frasnelli, and Joubert (2012) found that individuals with AD have impairments with high-level olfactory functions; in contrast, olfactory deficits in patients with Parkinson's disease tend to be uniform and global.

Neural Plasticity and Recovery of Function

There are several mechanisms important for cortical plasticity. The first is that plasticity is believed to be use-dependent. Repeated stimulation of neurons and neural tracts is a prerequisite for plasticity-mediated changes to occur. Stimulation of cortical plasticity is thought to originate with a process referred to as excitatory diaschisis, whereby distal areas in the brain that are functionally related to an injured area become hyperexcited (Buchkremer-Ratzmann, August, Hagemann, & Witte, 1996). Sensory stimulation treatment may take advantage of neural plasticity to improve quality of life and functioning for individuals with dementia. However, since neural plasticity is dependent upon multiple neurotransmitters, which may themselves be destroyed by dementing processes, the success of sensory stimulation may depend, in part, on early intervention and also by the particular sense being stimulated.

Auditory Sensory Stimulation

Dementia often causes pathophysiological changes to the central nervous system that impair hearing and auditory memory. For example, patients with AD have been found to have altered activity in the auditory cortex, which leads to impaired encoding and poorer verbal recall than non-clinical controls (Dhanjal, Warren, Patel, & Wise, 2013). Because it is likely that conceptual memories are stored in the association cortices, dementias that impair the functioning of these areas (e.g., frontotemporal dementia and Alzheimer's disease) are of particular concern for memory encoding and retrieval (Bonner & Grossman, 2012). Auditory sensory stimulation techniques, such as music therapy (e.g., Raglio, 2011), have been used for years to promote auditory stimulation and have been found to have calming effects on elderly patients (Holmes, Knights, Dean, Hodkinson, & Hopkins, 2006).

A favorite song can bring to the mind images, memories, feelings, and desires that have not been experienced for many years. Auditory sensory stimulation has been shown to have functional benefits for patients with dementia, including improvements in environmental awareness and level of participation in activities (Wolfe, 1983); higher scores on the Mini-Mental State Examination; and improved social activity and mood (Lord & Gardner, 1993). Positive outcome associations in autobiographical memory have also been found.

For example, Foster and Valentine (2001) found improvements in remote memory for patients with mild and moderate dementia following exposure to familiar music. They described how cafeteria noise resulted in better autobiographical retrieval than silence, and music better autobiographical retrieval than cafeteria noise. No effects were noted for recent memory. Even patients with moderate to severe sensory impairments may benefit from auditory stimulation, as it can be modified depending on the patient's needs. For example, sounds can be amplified for individuals with hearing loss; for a dementia patient with impaired comprehension, clinicians can repeat sounds or incorporate additional sensory cues, such as pictures (Vozzella, 2007).

A recent study by Delphin-Combe, Rouch, Martin-Gaujard, Relland, and Krolak-Salmon (2013) found that a new product, Voix d'Or (Golden Voice), is a promising innovation in the area of auditory sensory stimulation. The product provides auditory sensory stimulation treatment using music therapy, reminiscence, relaxation, or reorientation in reality. The authors used random assignment to either the Golden Voice treatment condition or occupational therapy, as usual. Preliminary results suggested that this device may reduce anxiety levels in patients with AD as compared to patients treated without auditory sensory stimulation. Limitations of the study include a small sample size and a lack of a control group employing more general auditory stimulation.

Autobiographical memories are subjectively among the most important memories individuals have. Meilán García and colleagues (2012) found that the emotional tone of music might moderate autobiographical memory recall for patients with dementia. The authors played music that was happy, sad, lacking emotion, or ambient noise for 25 patients with AD and investigated the results on autobiographical memory retrieval. They found that the emotional tone of the music, rather than the sounds themselves, played a critical role in recall of semantic information. The authors also found that sad music enabled more recall than other types of emotional music and that emotional music enabled more recall than ambient noise.

In a broader study, Särkämö, Tervaniemi, and Huotilainen (2013) investigated the long-terms effects of music therapy on the cognitive abilities of patients with mild to moderate dementia. Patients were assigned to a singing coaching group, music-listening group, or usual care group and coached for 10 weeks. Neuropsychological and quality of life assessments were conducted at baseline, at the end of the intervention, and at a six-month follow up. The results suggest that individuals in the singing and listening groups improved on measures of mood, orientation, and episodic memory retrieval as compared to those in the control group. The authors also found that singing was more beneficial for short-term and working memory than for listening.

Music therapy also provides individuals diagnosed with moderate or severe dementia pleasurable experiences (Takahashi & Matsushita, 2006). Cevasco and Grant (2003) found that patients diagnosed with Alzheimer's disease responded to familiar music with hand clapping, finger or toe tapping, and singing. Live music may be especially beneficial, regardless of the severity of the dementia, according to Holmes and colleagues (2006). As with any treatment, certain precautions are indicated for music therapy and other forms of auditory stimulation interventions. For patients with severe dementia, music choice may be crucial for positive results (Cevasco & Grant, 2003). The choice between vocal and background music is important. Cevasco and Grant (2003) found that patients diagnosed with severe dementia stopped participating in their activities and instead sang along with the vocal music. In this manner vocal music can be distracting and detract from functioning.

While care providers have used music and other forms of auditory sensory stimulation for years, researchers have only recently begun investigating the specific mechanisms by which this type of sensory stimulation affects the brains of patients with dementia. The research that exists is limited by small sample sizes, lack of uniform procedures, and clear differentiation of disease progression. Further, more studies investigating the long-term effects of auditory sensory stimulation should be conducted. Despite these limitations, preliminary research suggests the use of auditory sensory stimulation in patients with dementia can result in improved mood, orientation, auditory comprehension, and improved sematic and episodic retrieval.

Tactile Sensory Stimulation

Many individuals diagnosed with dementia can be resistant to care. However, because individuals with moderate to severe dementia are often highly dependent on caregivers for self-care, methods to increase cooperation and strengthen rapport with caregivers are important areas of research. Tactile sensory stimulation has been investigated as a means to reduce resistant behavior. Touching is also an important means of nonverbal communication. For example, nurses and other caregivers often use touch as a means by which to comfort agitated or distressed patients. Skovdahl, Sorlie, and Kihlgren (2007) found that purposeful touching reduced agitation and improved mood in moderate-to-severely demented individuals in a nursing home facility. Similarly, Scherder, Bouma, and Steen (1998) found that patients with suspected Alzheimer's disease felt less depressed and anxious following tactile sensory stimulation. Further, the authors found that following tactile stimulation, the patients were more socially active and alert than at baseline. The effects were only short-term, however, and were not observed six weeks after the treatment.

Tactile input can also increase the quality of life for dementia patients in a variety of practical ways. For example, many older adults have impaired thermoregulation, and using heat lamps while assisting dementia patients with bathing has been shown to decrease negative feelings associated with the experience (Bakker, 2003). Hand massage, animal-assisted therapy, or even simply holding a stuffed animal can provide a therapeutic effect and sense of comfort (Bakker, 2003). Animal-assisted therapy has been shown to facilitate socialization and improve motivation as well as lessen agitation, apathy, and withdrawal (Gellis, McClive-Reed, & Brown, 2009).

Massage and touch are associated with decreased anxiety (Gellis et al., 2009) and stimulates brain areas associated with opioid pain-reducers (Lindgren et al., 2012). Massage decreases both agitation and anxiety and promotes relaxation in persons with dementia (Harris & Richards, 2010). Further, simple hand-to-hand contact has also been associated with improved quality of life in elderly patients (Suzuki et al., 2010).

Other researchers examined the effects of tactile massage on stress levels for in dementia patients. Suzuki and colleagues (2010) implemented a six-week intervention using tactile massage, a form of tactile sensory stimulation, to determine its ability to reduce stress levels in individuals with dementia. The authors tracked patients' chromagranin A (CgA) levels, a protein associated with high stress, to determine the effects of tactile massage on stress. Frequency of aggressive behavior was also observed. The authors found that compared to controls, the patients who were treated with tactile massage a total of 30 times within six weeks had lower CgA levels and were significantly less aggressive than at baseline. The control group demonstrated no reductions in CgA or aggressiveness.

In addition to improvements in mood, tactile stimulation also has cognitive benefits. Most nursing homes and assisted living facilities offer daily or weekly Bingo games for patients. Research supports its use. Sobel (2001) compared the effects of the game Bingo to physical activity in 50 community adult day care centers. Short-term memory, concentration, word retrieval, and word recognition were assessed. Participants in the treatment group performed significantly better on tasks of naming and word list recognition, suggesting that Bingo results in cognitive gains above and beyond daily physical activity.

The research investigating tactile sensory stimulation is supportive of its use with dementia patients. As people get older, the likelihood of dependency on others for self-care needs increases. For individuals with dementia, this type of touching can be perceived as invasive or confusing, and it often leads to resistant behavior. This can be especially problematic given that much of nonverbal communication is conveyed via touching. A reassuring pat on the back or shoulder rub, for example, can provide considerable positive reinforcement. Tactile sensory stimulation programs have been shown to reduce aggressive behavior and agitation in dementia patients as well as increase positive mood. Further, new technologies such as vibrating belts can make use of existing tactile sensory abilities to assist patients in a variety of daily living skills, such as navigation (Grierson, Zeleck, Lam, Black, and Carnahan, 2011).

Olfactory Sensory Stimulation

The olfactory senses combine both taste and smell and are often our first defense against ingesting or breathing in harmful substances. Impairments in smell often precede the onset of cognitive problems, such as memory loss (Li et al., 2010). Deficits in odor detection, identification, and recognition occur early in the progression of Alzheimer's disease (Kareken et al. 2001; Rahayel et al., 2012; Wesson et al., 2011). Olfactory loss is also common in other neurodegenerative diseases, such as idiopathic Parkinson's disease and Huntington's chorea (Mesholam et al., 1998). Impairment or depression in olfactory ability to identify odors occurs in 80% of persons of 80 years of age and older. Parkinson's disease shows discrete impairment in olfaction in 70% to 90% of patients (Ebihara et al. 2006; Hawkes, Shephard, & Daniel, 1997).

Olfactory deficits in AD appear to be linked to dysfunction in the primary olfactory cortex rather than impaired working memory or primary abnormalities in semantic memory and naming (Kareken et al., 2001).

Persons with early-stage Alzheimer's disease have low-level deficits in both odor detection and quality discrimination and high-level deficits in odor perception and disruptions of odor quality coding in the posterior piriform cortex (Li et al., 2010). The etiology of the olfactory dysfunction is different in Alzheimer's disease and Parkinson's disease, in that in Alzheimer's disease it appears as though the higher order olfactory functions are impaired; whereas, all olfactory tasks appear to be affected in Parkinson's disease (Rahayel et al., 2012).

Disruptions in the functioning of olfaction increases the susceptibility of a person to environmental safety hazards, such as toxic substances, interferes with a person's ability to monitor his or her nutritional intake, preventing the detection of early signs of rotting in foods, and leads to a generally impoverished quality of life (Mesholam et al., 1998). Olfaction deficits mean decreased abilities in both taste and smell, as they are related senses; those with dementia often have deficits in both, which puts them at risk for hazards such as food and carbon monoxide poisoning (Bakker, 2003).

Aromatherapy has been used throughout history and across cultures to assist in curing ailments, to provide calming environments, and to ward off negative energy. Unlike the use of medications, there is little need to worry about adverse side effects (Fujii et al., 2008). Aromatherapy, or the act of nasal inhalation of odorants, is relatively simple to utilize, across various levels of age, mental status, or level of consciousness. Even patients who have had a tracheostomy or use a nasogastric feeding tube were able to participate in aromatherapy (Ebihara et al., 2006).

A study by Burns, Byrne, Ballard, and Holmes (2002) showed an excellent tolerability of aromatherapy, as all trial participants were able to complete the course of treatment, in contrast to a typical 30% drop-out rate for pharmacological trials. Holmes and Ballard (2004) found that aromatherapy may have effects even if a patient lacks the psychological perception of the smell. This is important since many people with dementia are anosmic due to loss of olfactory neurons. A direct placebo effect from the aromatherapy is an unlikely explanation for the benefits shown, as most people with severe dementia have lost any meaningful sense of smell.

Infusing an environment with pleasant scents can be beneficial for both persons with dementia and their caregivers (Bakker, 2003). Aromatherapy is most commonly administered via oil burners, soaking the scents into pillows or tissues, or by massaging essential oils into the skin (Holmes & Ballard, 2004). Aromatherapy uses a vast array of scents for different purposes; lavender, lemon balm, chamomile, and many others have been used in settings to treat mental health problems, such as anxiety and depression (Holmes & Ballard, 2004). Lavender scent is one of the most commonly used scents in aromatherapy, given its properties as a relaxant (Fujii et al., 2008).

Administered in a stream, using an oil burner and small fan, lavender oil can be used to treat agitated behavior in persons with severe dementia. In dementia care, lavender and lemon balm are most commonly used because of their sedative and cognitive enhancing properties and continue to show signs of efficacy in upcoming clinical studies. Those treated with lemon balm essential oil showed behavioral improvement, improved quality of life, and greater participation in activities, with the strongest effects on reducing excessive motor behaviors coming from aromatherapy with massage. Improvements in sleep and decreased resistance to care in persons with dementia have also been found following aromatherapy (Holmes & Ballard, 2004). Fujii et al. (2008) showed that behavioral problems were so quickly subdued by lavender aromatherapy, that simply testing for recognition of the smell improved agitated behavior.

Aromatherapy has also been shown to be beneficial in improving physical problems in persons with dementia. Olfactory stimulation using black pepper oil has been shown as a possible remedy for treatment of persons at high risk for pneumonia, a leading cause of death in older people, as it stimulates the insular cortex to improve swallowing in people with dysphagia (Ebihara et al., 2006).

Holmes and Ballard (2004) explain that personalization and tailoring of care is particularly important with aromatherapy in persons with dementia. They note that there are individual differences in what scents individuals may find more or less favorable and to what degree the scents can be best tolerated. Not only preference, but also past associations with an odor, can influence treatment outcomes, as scent is often strongly tied to memory.

Visual Sensory Stimulation

Many people experience vision loss as they grow older. There can be a number of changes in one's visual abilities, such as problems with depth perception, glare, visual misinterpretation, all of which can be worse for someone experiencing cognitive deterioration or disorders. As memory declines in dementia, people may forget to wear their glasses or forget to go in for check-ups and update their prescriptions (Bakker, 2003). Elderly populations also typically spend less time outdoors or exposed to bright light, and this is even more true of older adults with dementia (Mishima et al., 1994). These populations also often have disrupted sleep patterns, displaying irregular sleep-wake rhythms with frequent awakenings during the night and naps in the day (Mishima et al., 1994).

The inability to maintain circadian rest-activity rhythmicity can exacerbate sleep disruption and contribute to behavioral disturbances and cognitive dysfunction in persons with dementia (Etcher, Whall, Kumar, Devanand, & Yeragani, 2012). Impaired sleep, though common in older people and nearly universal in persons with AD, can cause lower daytime function, risk of mood disorders, lessened quality of life, impaired immune system, risk of falls or injury, need for more physician visits, and higher healthcare costs (Sloane et al., 2007). These problems in sleep can also contribute to increased daytime somnolence, which prevents the ability or availability to participate in socializing or activities (Dowling et al., 2008).

Visual stimulation for the benefit of people with dementia can come in many forms, ranging from looking at pictures of loved ones or trips from one's past to using bright light to help regulate one's circadian rhythm. Sloane et al. (2007) explained that light therapy may be used to regulate circadian rhythms. The use of high-intensity ambient lighting through the day, especially in the morning to decrease daytime drowsiness, increases nighttime sleep (Sloane et al., 2007). Since bright light is well tolerated and is not known to cause any adverse effects, it is generally recommended that the rooms individuals will be using during the daytime be remodeled or simply further equipped with more lighting to allow passive light exposure and eliminate the need for use of light therapy stations, such as those used for Seasonal Affective Disorder (Sloane et al., 2007). Morning bright light and melatonin in the evening, in a study by Dowling et al. (2008), was shown to result in more daytime activity, less daytime somnolence, and a more normal sleep-wake cycle.

Currently, there is no accepted standardization for light therapy, so the intensity, duration, and timing of bright light exposure will more likely be worked out to individual preference and results (Dowling et al., 2008). It would be a good idea for individual living settings to determine a person's sleep onset and duration preference before deciding on the best times for bright light exposure (Dowling et al., 2008).

Art therapy is another increasingly common form of visual sensory stimulation that does not often require much outside motivation to encourage people to participate. It can involve media based on a person's preferences and skill sets, such as clay, paint, collage, or pencils. Art therapy provides for meaningful stimulation, a chance for social interaction if done in groups or pairs, and a chance to assert one's personal choice and independence, while also providing pleasure and improving one's mood (Gellis et al., 2009). Art therapy combines visual therapy with tactile therapy as well as the cognitive satisfaction of creating something.

Multi-Sensory Stimulation

Multi-sensory therapy provides stimulation to the senses of touch, sight, hearing, smell, and taste as well as vestibular and proprioceptive stimulation (Baillon, van Dipen, & Prettyman, 2002). It is hypothesized that by enhancing sensory signals, the demand on the central nervous system would be reduced, therefore improving performance in such areas as balance, communication, mood, cognition and behavior. *Snoezelen*, developed in the Netherlands in the 1960s, was one of the first types of multi-sensory stimulation. It involves activity in a dusky, attractively lit room with soft music and may include objects pertaining to the five senses. *Snoezelen* requires a resident-oriented attitude, knowledge, and skills in order for the individual's caregiver to incorporate the personal attributes in order to achieve a state of well-being (van Weert, van Dulman, Spreeuwenberg, Ribbe, & Bensing, 2005a). This allows the caregiver to continue to treat the individual with cognitive impairments with dignity, by showing empathy and attending to the person's individual background and needs. For example, if a patient with dementia desires to spend his/her time outside or does not feel comfortable in enclosed rooms, one could accommodate the sensory stimuli for outside settings. Similarly, if a patient prefers a certain style of music or has cultural or religious restrictions to certain tasks or objects, these again can be personalized.

Multi-sensory stimulation may be an appropriate tool to communicate with severely demented individuals, since intellectual capabilities are not directly involved (Finnema, Dröes, Ribbe, & Van Tilburg, 2000; van Weert, van Dulman, Spreeuwenberg, Ribbe, & Bensing, 2005b). Multi-sensory environments contain a variety of equipment to stimulate the senses and control the number of competing visual, auditory, olfactory, gustatory, and tactile stimuli and intensity of stimulation. Interventions in multi-sensory, environment-based therapy may include music, light, touch, massage and aromatherapies intended both to stimulate and relax/soothe individuals with dementia (Klages, Zecevic, Orange, & Hobson, 2011; Sánchez, Millán-Calenti, Lorenzo-López, & Maseda, 2013; Ward-Smith, Llanque, & Curran, 2009). Specific devices involved may include mirror balls, colored spotlights, bubble tubes, projectors, fiber-optic sprays or curtains, music players, aromatherapy diffusers, panels with interactive knobs and switches to activate lights and sounds, handheld/vibrating objects, swinging chairs, and food (Baillon et al., 2002; Klages et al., 2011).

Multi-sensory therapy usually occurs in a room designed to create a feeling of comfort and safety, in which the individual is meant to relax and enjoy the surrounding stimulation (Baillon et al., 2002). Multi-sensory environments may vary in their color, layout, equipment, etc. in order to fit the needs of the specific individuals for whom the room is equipped (Baillon et al., 2002). For example, the color of the walls may be altered to prevent extraneous light from entering, specific music may be played for a clientele of a certain age, soft cushions or couches may be used for those who are not fully ambulatory or experience joint pain. These environments provide an activity-based intervention in order to combat the imbalance in sensory stimulation by balancing sensory-stimulating activities with sensory calming activities in order to assist with confusion and behavior changes in dementia (Collier et al., 2010; Sánchez et al., 2013).

Multi-sensory stimulation environments are implemented in a one-to-one setting using a nondirective approach, allowing for individuality in treatment. This may be advantageous to patients, since they will be receiving individual attention and appropriate reinforcements by the caregiver. Additionally, as mentioned above, the specific modalities and contexts of treatment can be specifically tailored to the patients. It should be noted that some individuals with dementia might become more agitated or distressed from multi-sensory stimulation; therefore, it is important for the medical professional administering the therapy to be sensitive to the individual's reaction to the environment to allow this therapy to be minimally distressing.

Finnema et al. (2000) reviewed a number of studies, which largely demonstrated short-term positive effects for both mood and behavior of multi-sensory stimulation; however, these studies were typically limited by small sample sizes and unblinded study designs. Sánchez et al. (2013) conducted a review of multi-sensory stimulation environments in individuals with dementia. Overall, results indicated that multi-sensory stimulation environments led to some improvements in behavior, mood, cognition, communication, and functional status; however, most of these gains were short-lived.

Staal et al. (2007) reported that adults with dementia who received multi-sensory behavior therapy, in which non-contingent reinforcement was utilized, showed reduced levels of agitation, apathy, and increased independence in activities of daily living. Ward-Smith et al. (2009) found that incidences of psychotic behaviors were reduced in individuals with Alzheimer's disease who received multi-sensory behavior therapy. Robichaud, Hebert, and Desrosiers (1994) found that sensory integration decreased the frequency of disruptive behavior and increased independence of patients as well as improved the caregiver's reactions disruptive behaviors. Baker et al. (2003) demonstrated limited short-term improvements from multi-sensory stimulation in behavior and cognition (i.e. memory) in adults with dementia. Collier et al. (2010) found a significant improvement in motor and process skills in individuals with dementia who received multi-sensory, environment-based therapy. Klages et al. (2011) provided evidence that unstructured Snoezelen room sessions were unsuccessful in reducing falls or enhancing balance. A structured Snoezelen room, however, catered to the individual needs of the patient, especially focusing on promoting head and eye movement and vibration, may prove more successful for treating balance. Aromatherapy and bright light treatment have been shown to improve agitation, quality of life, restlessness, and sleep disturbance (Burns et al., 2002).

Van Weert et al. (2005b) observed improvements in both verbal and nonverbal communication in dementia patients residing in a nursing home by implementing Snoezelen's principles of rapport-building nonverbal behavior, such as affective touch and smiling, and decreasing negative communication, such as disapproval. Congruent with these results, individuals with dementia displayed decreased levels of apathetic behavior, negativism, reluctance, loss of decorum, rebellious behavior, aggressive behavior, boredom, inactivity, and depression as the result of Snoezelen (van Weert et al., 2005a). Additionally, these residents displayed higher levels of happiness and enjoyment, showed stronger rapport with their nurses, displayed greater responsive to communication, and spoke more frequently in full sentences.

While the evidence supporting the use of this therapy is both mixed and limited, multi-sensory stimulation can certainly be a helpful tool for some individuals with dementia to mitigate their symptoms and allow the relationships and interactions between patients and caregivers/family to be more pleasant and calm, including increasing staff morale in residential care facilities. Overall improvements have been noted in the areas of independence, behavior, mood, cognition, communication, sleeping, restlessness and agitation. Multi-sensory stimulation environments can be created relatively easily (e.g. bedside) and inexpensively and have potential to benefit both individuals afflicted with dementia and those who care for them. Further research should be conducted to evaluate the effectiveness of multi-sensory, environment-based therapy due to lack of studies with control conditions and sufficient numbers of subjects included.

Conclusion

Sensory stimulation offers several positive features to the treatment of dementia. In addition to maintaining sensory skills with practice and stimulation, or at lease reducing the degree and rate of decline of sensory skills, the stimulation provides positive social interactions and cognitive stimulation. It is useful in reducing the impact of anxiety, depression, and fear on the individual's functioning, leading to a stronger ability to interact appropriately with the environment. Even in the absence of dementia, the lack of sensory stimulation can lead to cognitive and emotional impairment, elevated levels of fatigue, and higher levels of interpersonal withdrawal. By using a variety of stimulation techniques, as discussed in the chapter, the impact of the restricted environments that individuals living with dementia often face given limitations imposed on them by their disease can be minimized, thus improving overall quality of life and functioning.

References

Albers, K. (2012). Hearing loss and dementia: New insights. *Minnesota Medicine, 95*, 52-54.

American Foundation for the Blind. (2013). *Special report on aging and vision loss.* Retrieved September 26, 2013, from http://www.afb.org/section.aspx?SectionID=15&DocumentID=4423 American Speech-Language-Hearing Association. (2013). Hearing loss and the audiologist. Retrieved September 15, 2013, from http://www.asha.org/careers/professions/hla/

Baillon, S., van Diepen, E., & Prettyman, R. (2002). Multi-sensory therapy in psychiatric care. *Advances in Psychiatric Treatment, 8*, 444-450.

Baker, R., Bell, S., Baker, E., Holloway, J., Pearce, R., Dowling, Z., Thomas, P., Assey, J., & Wareing, L-A.. (2001). A randomized controlled trial of the effects of multi sensory stimulation (MSS) for people with dementia. *British Journal of Clinical Psychology, 40*, 81-96.

Baker, R., Holloway, J., Holtkamp, C. C. M., Larsson, A., Hartman, L. C., Pearce, R., Scherman, B., Johansson, S., Thomas, P. W., Wareing, L. A., & Owens, M. (2003). Effects of multi-sensory stimulation for people with dementia. *Journal of Advanced Nursing, 43*, 465-477.

Bakker, R. (2003). Sensory loss, dementia, and environments. *Generations, 27*, 46-52.

Baltes, P. B., & Singer, T. (2001). Plasticity and the ageing mind: An exemplar of the bio-cultural orchestration of brain and behaviour. *European Review, 1*, 59-76.

Benarroch, E. E. (2010). Olfactory system: Functional organization and involvement in neurodegenerative disease. Neurology, 75, 1104-1109. Bonner, M. F., & Grossman, M. (2012). Gray matter density of auditory association cortex relates to knowledge of sound concepts in primary progressive aphasia. *Journal of Neuroscience, 32*, 7986-7991.

Buchkremer-Ratzmann, I., August, M., Hagemann, G., & Witte, O. W. (1996). Electrophysiological transcortical diaschisis after cortical photothrombosis in rat brain. *Stroke, 27*, 1105-1011.

Burns, A., Byrne, J., Ballard, C., & Holmes, C. (2002). Sensory stimulation in dementia: An effective option for managing behavioural problems. *BMJ, 325*, 1312-1313.

Cevasco, A. M., & Grant, R. E. (2003). Comparison of different methods for eliciting exercise-to-music for clients with Alzheimer's disease. *Journal of Music Therapy, 40*, 41-56.

Collier, L., McPherson, K., Ellis-Hill, C., Staal, J., & Bucks, R. (2010). Multisensory sensory stimulation to improve functional performance in moderate to severe dementia—interim results. *American Journal of Alzheimer's Disease and Other Dementias, 25*, 698-703.

Deems, D. A., Doty, R. L., Settle, R. G., Moore-Gillon, V., Shaman, P., Mester, A. F., Kimmelman, C. P., Brightman, V. J., & Snow, J. B. Jr. (1991). Smell and taste disorders, a study of 750 patients from the University of Pennsylvania Smell and Taste Center. *Archives of Otolaryngology-Head and Neck Surgery, 117*, 519-528.

Delphin-Combe, F., Rouch, I., Martin-Gaujard, G., Relland, S., & Krolak-Salmon, P. (2013). Effect of a non-pharmacological intervention, Voix d'Or®, on behavior disturbances in Alzheimer disease and associated disorders. *Gériatrie et Psychologie Neuropsychiatrie du Vieillissement, 11*, 323-330.

Dhanjal, N. S., Warren, J. E., Patel, M. C., & Wise, R. S. (2013). Auditory cortical function during verbal episodic memory encoding in Alzheimer's disease. *Annals of Neurology, 73*, 294-302.

Dowling, G. A., Burr, R. L., Van Someren, E. J. W., Hubbard, E. M., Luxenberg, J. S., Mastick, J., & Cooper, B. A. (2008). Melatonin and bright-light treatment for rest-activity disruption in institutionalized patients with Alzheimer's disease. *Journal of the American Geriatrics Society, 56*, 239-246.

Ebihara, T., Ebihara, S., Maruyama, M., Kobayashi, M., Itou, A., Arai, H., & Sasaki, H. (2006). A randomized trial of olfactory stimulation using black pepper oil in older people with swallowing dysfunction. *Journal of the American Geriatrics Society, 54*, 1401-1406.

Etcher, L., Whall, A., Kumar, R., Devanand, D., & Yeragani, V. (2012). Nonlinear indices of circadian changes in individuals with dementia and aggression. *Psychiatry Research, 199*, 77-78.

Finnema, E., Dröes, R. M., Ribbe, M., & Van Tilburg, W. (2000). The effects of emotion-oriented approaches in the care for persons suffering from dementia: A review of the literature. *International Journal of Geriatric Psychiatry, 15*, 141-161.

Foster, N. A., & Valentine, E. R. (2001). The effect of auditory stimulation on autobiographical recall in dementia. *Experimental Aging Research, 27*, 215-228.

Fujii, M., Hatakeyama, R., Fukuoka, Y., Yamamoto, T., Sasaki, R., Moriya, M., Kanno, M., & Sasaki, H. (2008). Lavender aroma therapy for behavioral and psychological symptoms in dementia patients. *Geriatrics and Gerontology International, 8*, 136-138.

Gellis, Z. D., McClive-Reed, K. P., & Brown, E. (2009). Treatments for depression in older persons with dementia. *Annals of Long-Term Care, 17*, 29-36.

Grierson, L. M., Zelek, J., Lam, I., Black, S. E., & Carnahan, H. (2011). Application of a tactile way-finding device to facilitate navigation in persons with dementia. *Assistive Technology, 23*, 108-115.

Harris, M., & Richards, K. C. (2010). The physiological and psychological effects of slow-stroke back massage and hand massage on relaxation in older people. *Journal of Clinical Nursing, 19*, 917-926.

Hawkes, C. H., Shephard, B. C., & Daniel, S. E. (1997). Olfactory dysfunction in Parkinson's disease. *Journal of Neurology, Neurosurgery and Psychiatry, 62*, 436-446.

Holmes, C., & Ballard, C. (2004). Aromatherapy in dementia. *Advances in Psychiatric Treatment, 10*, 296-300.

Holmes, C., Knights, A., Dean, C., Hodkinson, S., & Hopkins, V. (2006). Keep music live: Music and the alleviation of apathy in dementia subjects. *International Psychogeriatrics, 18*, 623-630.

Jabeen, S., McKeith, I. G., Fairbairn, A. F., Perry, R. H., & Ferrier, I. (1992). Psychotic symptoms in Alzheimer's disease. *International Journal Of Geriatric Psychiatry, 7*, 341-345.

Kareken, D. A., Doty, R. L., Moberg, P. J., Mosnik, D., Chen, S. H., Farlow, M. R., & Hutchins, G. D. (2001). Olfactory-evoked regional cerebral blood flow in Alzheimer's disease. *Neuropsychology, 15*, 18-29.

Klages, K., Zecevic, A., Orange, J. B., & Hobson, S. (2011). Potential of Snoezelen room multisensory stimulation to improve balance in individuals with dementia: A feasibility randomized controlled trial. *Clinical rehabilitation, 25*, 607-616.

Lakshminarayanan, V., Lagrave, J., Kean, M., Dick, M., & Shankle, R. (1996). Vision in dementia: Contrast effects. *Neurological Research, 18*, 9-15.

Li, W., Howard, J. D., & Gottfried, J. A. (2010). Disruption of odour quality coding in piriform cortex mediates olfactory deficits in Alzheimer's disease. *Brain, 133*, 2714-2726.

Li-Korotky, H. (2012). Age-related hearing loss: Quality of care for quality of life. *The Gerontologist, 52*, 265-271.

Lindgren, L., Westling, G., Brulin, C., Lehtipalo, S., Andersson, M., & Nyberg, L. (2012). Pleasant human touch is represented in pregenual anterior cingulate cortex. *NeuroImage, 59*, 3427-3432.

Lord, T. R., & Garner, J. E. (1993). Effects of music on Alzheimer patients. *Perceptual and Motor Skills, 76*, 451-455.

Meilán García, J. J., Iodice, R., Carro, J., Sánchez, J. A., Palmero, F., & Mateos, A. M. (2012). Improvement of autobiographic memory recovery by means of sad music in Alzheimer's disease type dementia. *Aging Clinical and Experimental Research, 24*, 227-232.

Mesholam, R. I., Moberg, P. J., Mahr, R. N., & Doty, R. L. (1998). Olfaction in neurodegenerative disease: A meta-analysis of olfactory functioning in Alzheimer's and Parkinson's diseases. *Archives of Neurology, 55*, 84-90.

Mishima, K., Okawa, M., Hishikawa, Y., Hozumi, S., Hori, H., & Takahashi, K. (1994). Morning bright light therapy for sleep and behavior disorders in elderly patients with dementia. *Acta Psychiatrica Scandinavica, 89*, 1-7.

Perriol, M-P., Dujardin, K., Derambure, P., Marcq, A., Bourriez, J-L., Laureau, E., Pasquier, F., Defebvre, L., & Destee, A. (2005). Disturbance of sensory filtering in dementia with Lewy bodies: Comparison with Parkinson's disease dementia and Alzheimer's disease. *Journal of Neurology, Neurosurgery and Psychiatry, 76*, 106-108.

Prevent Blindness America. (2008). Vision problems in the *U.S.: Prevalence of adult vision impairment and age-related eye disease in America* (update to the 4th ed.). Schaumburg, IL: Prevent Blindness America.

Raglio, A. (2011). Music therapy in dementia. *Non-Pharmacological Therapies in Dementia, 1*, 3-16.

Rahayel, S., Frasnelli, J., & Joubert, S. (2012). The effect of Alzheimer's disease and Parkinson's disease on olfaction: A meta-analysis. *Behavioural Brain Research, 231*, 60-74.

Robichaud, L., Hébert, R., & Desrosiers, J. (1994). Efficacy of a sensory integration program on behaviors of inpatients with dementia. *American Journal of Occupational Therapy, 48*, 355-360.

Rogers, M., & Langa, K. (2010). Untreated poor vision: A contributing factor to late-life dementia. *American Journal of Epidemiology, 171*, 728-735.

Sánchez, A., Millán-Calenti, J. C., Lorenzo-López, L., & Maseda, A. (2013). Multisensory stimulation for people with dementia: A review of the literature. *American Journal of Alzheimer's Disease and Other Dementias, 28,* 7-14.

Särkämö, T., Tervaniemi, M., & Huotilainen, M. (2013). Music perception and cognition: Development, neural basis, and rehabilitative use of music. *WIREs Cognitive Science, 4,* 441-451.

Scherder, E., Bouma, A., & Steen, L. (1998). Effects of peripheral tactile nerve stimulation on affective behavior of patients with probable Alzheimer's disease. *American Journal of Alzheimer's Disease and Other Dementias, 13,* 61-69.

Schiller, J. S., Lucas, J. W., & Peregoy, J. A. (2012). Summary health statistics for U.S. adults: National Health Interview Survey, 2011. National Center for Health Statistics. *Vital Health Statistics, 10*(256).

Skovdahl, K., Sörlie, V., & Kihlgren, M. (2007). Tactile stimulation associated with nursing care to individuals with dementia showing aggressive or restless tendencies: An intervention study in dementia care. *International Journal of Older People Nursing, 2,* 162-170.

Sloane, P. D., Williams, C. S., Mitchell, C. M., Preisser, J. S., Wood, W., Barrick, A. L., Hickman, S. E., Gill, K. S., Connell, B. R., Edinger, J., & Zimmerman, S. (2007). High-intensity environmental light in dementia: Effect on sleep and activity. *Journal of the American Geriatrics Society, 55,* 1524-1533.

Sobel, B. P. (2001). Bingo vs. physical intervention in stimulating short-term cognition in Alzheimer's disease patients. *American Journal of Alzheimer's Disease And Other Dementias, 16,* 115-120.

Staal, J., Sacks, A., Matheis, R., Collier, L., Calia, T., Hanif, H., & Kofman, E. (2007). The effects of Snoezelen (multi-sensory behavior therapy) and psychiatric care on agitation, apathy, and activities of daily living in dementia patients on a short term geriatric psychiatric inpatient unit. *International Journal of Psychiatry in Medicine, 37,* 357-370.

Suzuki, M., Tatsumi, A., Otsuka, T., Kikuchi, K., Mizuta, A., Makino, K., Kimoto, A., Fujiwara, K., Abe, T., Nakagomi, T., Hayashi, T., & Saruhara, T. (2010). Physical and psychological effects of 6-week tactile massage on elderly patients with severe dementia. *American Journal of Alzheimer's Disease and Other Dementias, 25*, 680-686.

Takahashi, T., & Matsushita, H. (2006). Long-term effects of music therapy on elderly with moderate/severe dementia. *Journal of Music Therapy, 43*, 317-333.

van Weert, J. C. M., van Dulmen, A. M., Spreeuwenberg, P. M. M., Ribbe, M. W., & Bensing, J. M. (2005a). Behavioral and mood effects of Snoezelen integrated into 24-hour dementia care. *Journal of the American Geriatrics Society, 53*, 24-33.

van Weert, J., van Dulmen, A. M., Spreeuwenberg, P. M., Ribbe, M. W., & Bensing, J. M. (2005b). Effects of snoezelen, integrated in 24h dementia care, on nurse-patient communication during morning care. *Patient Education and Counseling, 58*, 312-326.

Vozzella, S. (2007). Sensory stimulation in dementia care: Why it is important and how to implement it. *Topics in Geriatric Rehabilitation, 23*, 102-113.

Ward-Smith, P., Llanque, S. M., & Curran, D. (2009). The effect of multisensory stimulation on persons residing in an extended care facility. *American Journal of Alzheimer's Disease and Other Dementias, 24*, 450-455.

Wesson, D. W., Borkowski, A. H., Landreth, G. E., Nixon, R. A., Levy, E., & Wilson, D. A. (2011). Sensory network dysfunction, behavioral impairments, and their reversibility in an Alzheimer's -amyloidosis mouse model. *Journal of Neuroscience, 31*, 15962–15971.

Wolfe, J. R. (1983). The use of music in a group sensory training program for regressed geriatric patients. *Activities, Adaptation and Aging, 4*, 49-62.

CHAPTER 6

Dietary Intake for Neuroprotection and Improved Neurocognitive Functioning
Samuel T. Gontkovsky and Robert M. Nevels

The body of the average adult human contains approximately 30 trillion cells, from which all tissues and organs, including the brain, are comprised. In order to function properly, cells within the body require, among other things, nutrients derived from food intake. Nutrients provide the raw materials necessary for cell production, energy, and protection. Although it has long been known that cell damage and associated malfunctioning may lead to various health problems, it is only relatively recently that research has begun to explore the manner in which the influence of dietary factors may detrimentally affect health, in particular brain health. Indeed, empirical evidence from the past decade suggests that several neurological diseases and disorders, including Alzheimer's disease (AD), may be associated with diet. The purpose of this chapter is to discuss the key elements of diet in relation to brain health and to briefly review the scientific literature examining the relationship between dietary intake and neurological illness.

Obesity

Obesity in the United States has increased dramatically during the past two decades and continues to do so. Indeed, it is regarded by some researchers as an epidemic. Obesity is a particular problem for individuals over the age of 50 years and increases the risk for developing heart disease, diabetes mellitus, stroke, and Alzheimer's disease (Small & Vorgan, 2011). Obesity often is associated with hypertension, elevated triglycerides, low high-density lipoprotein (HDL) cholesterol, and elevated fasting glycemia, which contribute to the cluster of symptoms collectively referred to as the metabolic syndrome (Grundy et al., 2004). According to Raffaitin et al. (2009), individuals with metabolic syndrome are at an increased risk for developing vascular dementia, and those with diabetes mellitus or elevated triglycerides are at an increased risk for developing Alzheimer's disease and vascular dementia. Research also has demonstrated that a higher body mass index, even among healthy individuals, is associated with greater cognitive decline over time (Cournot et al., 2006). Further, it has been reported that obesity at midlife is strongly predictive of both Alzheimer's disease and vascular dementia in later life (Whitmer, Gunderson, Quesenberry, Zhou, & Yaffe, 2007). This evidence suggests that maintaining a healthy body weight may delay onset of cognitive decline as well as development of various forms of dementia (Small & Vorgan, 2011), and some research has indicated that the dietary factors that reduce the risks of health problems, such as diabetes mellitus and cardiovascular disease, likewise appear to reduce risks for cognitive decline and dementia.

Cell Energy Production and Free Radicals

As cells within the body utilize oxygen and nutrients to produce energy, a small percentage of the oxygen molecules are released in the form of reactive oxygen species (ROS), commonly referred to as free radicals and resulting in a condition of oxidative stress. Free radical molecules are reactive oxidants, which can have harmful effects on cells, including causing damage to deoxyribonucleic acid (DNA) as well as to the various proteins, fats, and enzymes required for healthy cell functioning. As a result of this oxidative damage, ROS have been associated with accelerated aging, in general, as well as to the development of a number of specific medical conditions, including cancer, lung disease, cochlear impairment, diabetes mellitus, cataracts, osteoarthritis, and vascular disease.

The brain is especially susceptible to free radical-induced oxidative damage due to its high content of readily oxidized fatty acids, high use of oxygen, low levels of antioxidants, and high levels of iron (Tuppo & Forman, 2001); evidence has emerged that this damage may play a role in the development of neurological pathology, including AD (Markesbery, 1999; Pratico & Delanty, 2000) and vascular dementia (Bennett, Grant, & Aldred, 2009). In Alzheimer's disease, increased amyloid beta results in elevated ROS production and associated vulnerability of brain cells to damage from free radicals (Butterfield, 1996; Munch, Simm, Double, & Rieder, 1996; Tuppo & Forman, 2001). Oxidative stress within the body's vascular system may lead to vascular disease secondary to inflammation and ischemic injury, thereby resulting in vascular dementia. That increased oxidative stress is present in both AD and vascular dementia has led some researchers to propose that the conditions are two extremes of a single disease process (Bennett et al., 2009).

Within the context of a healthy internal environment, cells defend themselves against the onslaught of free radicals by utilizing antioxidants and various enzymes derived primarily from dietary intake; the body is therefore protected from the negative effects of oxidative stress. With poor nutrition, however, the amount of free radicals exceeds the protective capability of cells, leaving them vulnerable to damage and the body susceptible to various health conditions and diseases (Charlton, Rabinowitz, Geffen, & Dhansay, 2004).

Dietary Recommendations for Cell Protection and Improved Brain Functioning

There exists no consensus as to the most effective dietary approaches for promoting brain health and protecting the body against the development of harmful internal environments that may lead to diseases, including dementia. This lack of consensus is understandable from a neurological perspective, given that the underlying causes of most central nervous system diseases, such as Alzheimer's disease and multiple sclerosis, remain unknown. Nevertheless, research has yielded substantial evidence to support various recommendations with respect to diet that provide for cell protection and improved brain functioning.

The Mediterranean Diet

Inspired by the traditional eating habits of the Greek, Spanish, and southern Italian cultures, the Mediterranean diet emphasizes the primary consumption of plant-based foods, including fruits, vegetables, whole grains, nuts, and legumes, while limiting the consumption of red meat and substituting unhealthy saturated fats (e.g., butter) with healthy unsaturated fats (e.g., olive oil). Additional elements of the Mediterranean diet include using herbs/spices rather than salt for flavoring food, as well as eating fish and poultry at least two times per week. Key to this diet is the consumption of foods that are low in saturated fat and relatively high in monounsaturated fat and fiber. Moderate consumption of red wine also may be considered in light of the fact that it contains flavonoids, which are plant secondary metabolites with powerful antioxidant properties.

Strong evidence exists in the literature suggesting that the Mediterranean diet is associated with a decreased risk for a number of vascular complications, including hypertension, dyslipidemia, and coronary heart disease (Chrysohoou, Panagiotakos, Pitsavos, Das, & Stefanadis, 2004; de Lorgeril et al., 1999; Esposito et al., 2004; Psaltopoulou et al., 2004; Singh et al., 2002). Further, Nordmann et al. (2011) concluded after conducting a meta-analytic review of the literature comparing Mediterranean and low-fat diets that the former appears to be more effective in inducing clinically relevant and positive long-term modifications in various cardiovascular risk factors and inflammatory markers.

Although not entirely conclusive, a number of scientific investigations also have revealed that adherence to the Mediterranean diet may be associated with a trend for reduced risk of developing mild cognitive impairment (MCI), a lower risk for developing Alzheimer's disease, and a reduced risk of conversion from MCI to AD (Hu et al., 2013; Lourida et al., 2013; Scarmeas, Stern, Mayeux, & Luchsinger, 2006; Scarmeas et al., 2009; Scarmeas, Stern, Tang, Mayeux, & Luchsinger, 2006; Solfrizzi et al., 2011). Given the previously mentioned positive effects of the Mediterranean diet on hypertension, dyslipidemia, and coronary heart disease in conjunction with the apparent link between AD and heart disease and between AD and vascular dementia, it may well be that the Mediterranean diet will prove beneficial for lowering the risk of developing vascular dementia, as well; additional research is needed to examine this hypothesis, and no conclusions can be made about this potential association at this time.

It remains unclear as to whether one or more specific components of the Mediterranean diet are yielding the aforementioned positive effects on aspects of health, in general, and brain functioning, specifically, or whether the diet, as a whole, is producing these beneficial results.
Beyond the specifics of the Mediterranean diet, the range of nutrients recommended for healthy bodily functioning, as specified by the United States Department of Agriculture, generally may be obtained through consumption of a varied and balanced diet. For individuals failing to consume appropriate nutrients through diet as a consequence of unhealthy patterns of eating, persons living with health conditions (e.g., diabetes mellitus, celiac disease, Crohn's disease) that preclude or restrict the

consumption of certain foods, and individuals who have a decreased ability to process certain nutrients (e.g., reduced ability of elderly individuals to absorb vitamin B12 from foods), dietary supplements often are typically recommended. The remainder of this chapter will be devoted to a discussion of more specific dietary components, such as specific foods or properties/elements of foods, as well as dietary supplements that may promote improved brain functioning and may be helpful in delaying the onset of dementia and/or slowing the cognitive decline of individuals who have been diagnosed with dementia.

Antioxidants and Flavonoids

Antioxidants are molecules that inhibit oxidation of other molecules. Antioxidants are critical in protecting cells in the body because they bind directly to and destroy the free radicals associated with oxidative stress, which can cause a variety of detrimental effects on health. In this light, foods rich in antioxidants generally are recommended to promote brain functioning and stave off dementia. Most berries, including blueberries, raspberries, strawberries, blackberries, cranberries, acai berries, and elderberries possess a high content of flavonoids, which function as potent antioxidants (Isaacson & Ochner, 2013). For example, findings from a recent study reported that greater long-term intake of flavonoids, in particular anthocyanidins, primarily from blueberries and strawberries was associated with slower rates of cognitive decline in older adults (Devore, Kang, Breteler, and Grodstein, 2012). Other fruits and vegetables rich in antioxidants that may promote brain health and offer neuroprotection include cherries, pomegranates, red grapes, oranges, grapefruits, apples, carrots, broccoli, beets, spinach, kale, cabbage, artichokes, greens, and tomatoes, especially cooked tomatoes (Isaacson & Ochner, 2013). As an example, animal research has suggested that consumption of pomegranate juice may improve cognitive functioning as well as reduce amyloid deposition in key areas of the brain associated with AD (Hartman et al., 2006). Dark chocolates with a cocoa content of 70% or greater as well as various teas also serve as good dietary sources of flavonoids and thus function as antioxidants.

Minerals

Various enzymes can also function to protect cells in an antioxidant manner by disabling the free radicals resulting from energy production. In order to operate properly, these enzymes require minerals, including selenium, copper, and manganese, which can be obtained through dietary intake of whole grains. Other foods rich in minerals that help to produce specific protective enzymes include broccoli, cauliflower, and garlic. Although several specific minerals are required for the human body to function properly, most are necessary only in small amounts and are toxic in larger quantities. For example, many minerals (e.g., iron, manganese, and copper) are metals, referred to in chemistry and medicine as heavy metals. Ongoing exposure to heavy metals may lead to higher than normal or toxic levels of these elements in the body, potentially resulting in inflammation as well as antioxidant depletion and associated increased free radical generation (Fife, 2011).

A substantial amount of research has examined the potential contributions of heavy metals, in particular aluminum, in the development of the various neurological conditions that may cause dementia, and autopsy studies have detected small deposits of aluminum in the damaged brain areas of individuals with Alzheimer's disease (Small & Vorgan, 2011). The possible neurotoxic effects of aluminum have been demonstrated in the literature. Aluminum exposure in adults can lead to age-related, neurological deficits resembling those found in Alzheimer's disease, and as noted above, aluminum has been found in brain areas demonstrating AD pathology (Shaw & Tomljenovic, 2013). The characteristics of aluminum bioavailability, however, are complex, and its potential role in the development of AD remains to be convincingly established (Kawahara & Kato-Negishi, 2011).

Vitamins

Vitamins are organic compounds, which are considered essential nutrients and required in limited amounts in order for cells to function properly. Thirteen vitamins, primarily B vitamins, are universally recognized at this time and are classified according to their biological and chemical activity as opposed to their structure. Vitamins are either water soluble or fat soluble. Water-soluble vitamins, such as vitamins B and C, are absorbed and eliminated quickly by the body and therefore must be replaced continually. In contrast, fat soluble vitamins, such as vitamins A, D, and E, are stored in the liver and fatty tissues and are absorbed much more slowly by the body (Isaacson & Ochner, 2013). A comprehensive discussion of all vitamins and their nutritional importance to the human body is beyond the scope of this chapter; however, we will provide an overview of the key vitamins that are thought to be important for general brain health and potentially beneficial for individuals with dementia.

B Vitamins comprise 8 of the 13 universally-accepted vitamins and, although chemically distinct from one another, often exist in the same foods. Certain B vitamins have been shown to be potentially effective in lowering elevated plasma homocysteine concentrations. Homocysteine is a non-protein amino acid created as a byproduct of protein digestion and removed from the body through complex processes requiring vitamins B6, B9 (folic acid), and B12. Several conditions, including dietary intake of large amounts of protein in conjunction with decreased levels of these B vitamins, can result in elevated levels of homocysteine in the blood, which has been implicated in risk for a number of health issues, including cognitive impairment and dementia (Clarke, 2008; Smith, 2006). Consequently, these B vitamins are being studied for their potential effects on brain health. Although research in this area is in the early stages, de Jager, Oulhaj, Jacoby, Refsum, and Smith (2012) reported that daily doses of B vitamins relative to placebo appear to slow the cognitive decline in individuals with mild cognitive impairment, in particular those persons with elevated homocysteine. More recently, Douaud et al. (2013) reported that dietary supplementation with B vitamins can slow the cerebral atrophy of specific gray matter regions, including the medial temporal lobe, which are particularly vulnerable to Alzheimer's disease.

Vitamin B1 (thiamin) assists cells in converting carbohydrates into energy and is essential for proper functioning of the muscles and nerves. A deficiency of thiamin in the body, commonly associated with alcoholism, can produce a variety of symptoms, including weakness, fatigue, psychosis, and confusion. If diagnosed early, a thiamin deficiency generally can be treated successfully with vitamin B1 supplements, a balanced and healthy diet, and abstinence from alcohol. If left untreated, a severe thiamin deficiency may result in brain damage in the form of Wernicke's encephalopathy and Korsakoff's syndrome.

Vitamin D deficiencies have been associated with a number of physical and mental health issues, including cardiovascular disease, diabetes mellitus, osteoporosis, and depression, all of which are considered risk factors for dementia (Grant, 2009). Multiple studies have now been published showing an association between low blood levels of vitamin D and neurocognitive impairment and describing the potential neuroprotective effects of vitamin D in several neurological illnesses that may lead to dementia, including multiple sclerosis, Parkinson's disease, and Alzheimer's disease (Evatt et al., 2008; Hayes, 2000; Hayes, Cantorna, & DeLuca, 1997; Llewellyn, Langa, & Lang, 2009; Przybelski & Binkley, 2007).

Vitamins C and E have antioxidant properties and therefore are being studied for their potential beneficial effects against Alzheimer's disease and other forms of dementia. Following a critical review of the literature concerning the role of vitamin C in the development of dementia, Harrison (2012) concluded that maintaining healthy levels of vitamin C may have a protective function against age-related cognitive decline and AD; however, avoiding vitamin C deficiencies in the first place through a healthy diet is likely to be more beneficial than is taking supplements in response to a deficiency. Mangialasche et al. (2010) reported that high plasma levels of vitamin E were associated with a reduced risk of AD in advanced age, though the authors noted that the neuroprotective effects appeared related to a combination of different forms of the vitamin. Not all research supports a neuroprotective effect of antioxidant vitamins, however. Luchsinger, Tang, Shea, and Mayeux, (2003) stated that dietary, supplemental, or total intake of carotenes or vitamin C and E was not associated with a decreased risk of developing Alzheimer's disease over a four-year span in a sample of elderly participants. Other researchers have pointed out the potential risks associated with high supplemental doses of vitamins C and E and recommend against their routine use for neuroprotection (Boothby & Doering, 2005). Although the evidence concerning vitamin C and E supplementation as a means for promoting brain health remains unclear, a natural diet high in these vitamins appears beneficial in most cases. Citrus fruits and many vegetables are good sources of vitamin C; almonds and hazelnuts have long been known to be especially good sources of vitamin E.

Proteins

Proteins are large molecules consisting of one or more chains of amino acids that are responsible for carrying out numerous responsibilities in the body, including functioning as enzymes that catalyze chemical reactions, repairing damaged DNA within cells, and, in conjunction with lipids/fats, maintaining the integrity of cell membranes. Though a comprehensive description of the role of proteins in cellular function is beyond the scope of this chapter, it suffices to state that, from a dietary perspective, the appropriate intake of proteins is essential for good health. All proteins are not equal, however. While complete protein sources, or high quality proteins, provide all of the essential amino acids, incomplete protein sources are low in one or more of the essential amino acids. Most animal-based foods, including red meat, poultry, fish, eggs, milk, and cheese are considered complete protein sources. Incomplete sources of protein generally are derived from plant-based foods, such as dry beans and rice.

The biological value of proteins derived from different foods is based on a number of factors. For example, some complete protein sources are high in saturated fats, which generally are viewed as unhealthy and associated with an increased risk for developing various health problems, including cardiovascular disease. Similar to proteins, fats are essential for the body to function properly, but some fats appear to be better for health than others, as will be discussed below. In choosing dietary sources of proteins, it is necessary to weigh the positives and negatives of each.

From a neurological perspective, some studies have reported an association between dietary intake favoring protein derived from fish, poultry, and nuts, as opposed to that derived from red meat, in reducing the risk of AD and other forms of dementia (Gu, Nieves, Stern, Luchsinger, & Scarmeas 2010); this is consistent with the previously discussed recommendations of the Mediterranean diet. Although nuts are relatively high in fat, the fat is unsaturated, generally considered healthier than saturated fat. Further, some nuts also are high in other nutrients, such as antioxidants, that appear to promote improved brain health and functioning. Similarly, fish are high in protein, but many species also function as a good source of omega-3 fatty acids. Although red meats are high in saturated fats, they are sources of complete proteins and contain other important vitamins and minerals. If red meat is consumed, it is generally recommended to consume it in moderation and to choose the leanest cuts of meat. Other experts argue that whey, soy, and egg-white proteins are the best forms of proteins (Isaacson & Ochner, 2013). Milk, yogurt, and cheese also contain all of the essential amino acids, though fat content and other dietary considerations should also be kept in mind (Small & Vorgan, 2011).

Lipid, Fats, Oils, and Cholesterol

The term "lipids" describes a class of fats and fat-like substances within the body. Fats, oils, and cholesterols are subsets of lipids comprised of varying compounds that are generally insoluble in water and soluble in organic solvents. Lipids provide a number of functions within the body, such as storing energy and acting as structural components of cell membranes. Fats also function to improve the availability and absorption of many vitamins and minerals and are essential for properly absorbing fat-soluble nutrients, including vitamins A, D, E, and K (Fife, 2011). The primary distinction between fats and oils is that at room temperature, the former is a solid and the latter is a liquid.

Cholesterol is the principal sterol synthesized by animals; it is produced by the liver and is required for the biosynthesis of steroid hormones, bile acids, and vitamin D (Hanukoglu, 1992). Cholesterol is transported in the blood by molecules known as lipoproteins. Low density lipoprotein (LDL) transports cholesterol from the liver to the various cells of the body. It is generally referred to as unhealthy cholesterol because excess levels may increase the risk for various health problems, including vascular disease. High density lipoprotein (HDL) transports cholesterol from the various cells of the body back to the liver, where it is broken down or expelled from the body as waste. It generally is considered healthy cholesterol and may function to prevent vascular disease. Finally, triglycerides are the chemical forms in which the majority of fats exist in the body as well as in foods; in conjunction with cholesterol, they comprise the plasma lipids. Plasma triglycerides originate from fats consumed in foods or are generated within the body from energy sources, such as proteins and carbohydrates. Calories from food consumption that are not immediately utilized by the body are converted to triglycerides and stored in fat cells to be used for energy at a later time. Alcohol increases the production and plasma levels of triglycerides.

With respect to dietary intake, edible animal fats include fish oil, butter, and lard; edible plant fats include peanut, sesame, coconut, olive, and sunflower oils. Fats may be classified in several ways. For the purposes of this chapter, an emphasis will be placed on saturated versus unsaturated fats. Unsaturated fats generally are considered healthy fats, in part because they contribute to the increase of HDL cholesterol levels. In contrast, saturated fats generally are considered unhealthy fats because they raise LDL cholesterol levels. Dietary consumption of excess fat may lead to obesity, which, as noted previously, increases the risk for the development of various health issues, including cognitive decline and dementia. Unhealthy fats, such as the omega-6 fatty acids found in red meats and most processed and fried foods promote inflammation and contribute to neuronal damage and memory impairment if chronically consumed in excess (Small & Vorgan, 2011). Further, Hanson et al. (2013) recently reported that the lipidation states of apolipoproteins and amyloid beta peptides in the brain may be modulated by dietary intake, with a high-fat, high-glycemic-index diet increasing the concentrations in the brain of proteins linked to Alzheimer's disease and a low-fat, low-glycemic-index diet yielding the opposite effect. Research is not entirely consistent or conclusive, however, as Siri-Tarino, Sun, Hu, and Krauss (2010) recently published a report in which it was suggested that the link between high dietary levels of saturated fats and increased risk of coronary heart disease or cardiovascular disease remains controversial.

Nevertheless, most current research advocates limiting the dietary intake of omega-6 fatty acids while maximizing the dietary intake of omega-3 fatty acids. A substantial percentage of the essential fatty acids in phospholipids is comprised of omega-3 fatty acids, in particular docosahexanoic acid (DHA), which is the most abundant omega-3 fatty acid in the brain; further, it plays a critical role in both cognitive and emotional functioning. According to Cole and Frautschy (2010), DHA may slow pathogenesis of both AD and vascular dementia through suppression of neuroinflammation and oxidative damage that contribute to synaptic loss and neuronal dysfunction. Omega-3 fatty acids also have been shown to potentially lower blood levels of the amyloid beta protein related to Alzheimer's disease (Gu, Schupf, Cosentino, Luchsinger, & Scarmeas, 2012) and may offer neuroprotection against the accumulation of hyperphosphorylated tau proteins in intraneuronal neurofibrillary tangles associated with AD (Small & Vorgan, 2011). Finally, DHA increases brain levels of the neuroprotective brain-derived neurotrophic factor and reduces the fatty acid arachidonate and its prostaglandin metabolites that have been implicated in promoting AD. Clinical trials suggest that DHA, or fish oil alone, may slow early stages of AD progression but that these effects may be apolipoprotein E genotype specific (Cole & Frautschy, 2010). In contrast, Quinn et al. (2010) reported that dietary supplementation with DHA as compared with placebo failed to slow the rate of cognitive and functional decline in a sample of patients with mild to moderate AD. Nonetheless, the bulk of the scientific evidence appears to support a diet rich in omega-3 fatty acids, especially DHA. Good dietary sources of omega-3 essential fatty acids include flaxseed oil, walnuts, and fish, in particular wild-caught tuna and salmon, although herring, mackerel, anchovies, and sardines are good sources, as well.

Another promising avenue of related investigation involves the dietary intake of coconut oil as a means for promoting brain health and neuroprotection. Coconut oil has shown promise in having a range of beneficial health effects, including acting as a defense against infections and environmental toxins, increasing HDL cholesterol, and alleviating symptoms associated with diabetes mellitus and insulin resistance, among other things. Although research is required to explore the potential effects of coconut oil with respect to its effects on cognitive functioning as well as prevention and treatment of dementia, many experts already are recommending it as a dietary supplement for improving brain health (Fife, 2011).

Carbohydrates

Carbohydrates are organic compounds that, similar to the previously discussed nutrients, perform a number of important roles within the human body, including assisting with energy storage, plasma coagulation, and coenzyme formation. Relative to the rest of the human body, the brain requires considerable energy, a major source of which is provided by carbohydrates consumed in the diet. Carbohydrates may be classified in several ways; however, for the purposes of this chapter, we will consider carbohydrates as either simple or complex. Simple carbohydrates consist primarily of sugar, have a high glycemic index, and are absorbed and digested rapidly. Examples of foods containing simple carbohydrates include, candy, cookies, honey, jam, and white bread. In comparison to simple carbohydrates, complex carbohydrates generally contain more starch, have a lower glycemic index, are absorbed and digested more slowly, and often contain fiber. Examples of foods containing complex carbohydrates include whole grain breads and cereals, brown rice, oatmeal, and various vegetables, such as spinach, beans, zucchini, and yams.

Many experts suggest that foods high in whole grains and fiber promote brain health, assist in weight control, lower blood pressure, and reduce the risk for stroke, diabetes mellitus, and heart disease and therefore recommend a higher consumption of complex carbohydrates relative to simple carbohydrates (Isaacson & Ochner, 2013; Park, Subar, Hollenbeck, & Schatzkin, 2011; Small & Vorgan, 2011). Other experts advocate for diets that are high in fats, relatively high in proteins, and low in carbohydrates, such as the ketogenic diet, which results in the brain relying on ketones, as opposed to glucose converted from carbohydrates, for supplying the vast majority of its energy requirements (Fife, 2011). Ketones are water-soluble, biochemicals that are produced as by-products when fatty acids are broken down in the liver for energy. The ketogenic diet has been used as a treatment for refractory epilepsy in children for many years (Freeman, Kossoff, & Hartman, 2007), and some researchers suggest that ketones possess potent neuroprotective properties that may help in reducing the risk for and treating various neurological illness, including dementia (Hartman & Vining, 2007; Fife, 2011). Others researchers argue the diets high in carbohydrates, especially simple carbohydrates, and relatively low in proteins, fats, and fiber may result in spikes in blood glucose levels that result in significant stress on the body, especially the pancreas, and that over time may lead to systemic insulin-resistance diseases, such as obesity and type 2 diabetes mellitus, which consequently may promote neurodegeneration (De La Monte, 2012; Fife 2012). Indeed, Alzheimer's disease has been referred to by some as type 3 diabetes mellitus.

Caffeine

Several studies have demonstrated the potential beneficial effects of caffeine and coffee on brain health. For example, Eskelinen and Kivipelto (2010) reported that consumption of three to five cups of coffee per day at midlife was associated with a 65% lower rate of developing AD and dementia in later life. Daily consumption of coffee also may reduce the risk for developing Parkinson's disease and diabetes mellitus (Small & Vorgan, 2011). Additional studies are required to clarify whether the apparent beneficial effects of coffee consumption on neurocognitive functioning are mediated by caffeine or other mechanisms, such as antioxidant capacity and increased insulin sensitivity (Eskelinen & Kivipelto, 2010). Although excessive consumption of caffeine may result in problematic issues, including irritability and insomnia, coffee consumption in moderation generally is considered acceptable, and sometimes recommended, as part of a brain healthy diet (Isaacson & Ochner, 2013; Small & Vorgan, 2011).

Alcohol

The effects of alcohol on neurocognitive functioning depends largely on the frequency of consumption as well as the amount consumed. Without question, chronic and heavy alcohol use can be harmful, if not toxic, to the brain, possibly resulting in permanent neurocognitive dysfunction. Further, because alcoholism often is associated with a poor diet, it can contribute to a thiamin deficiency, which may lead to Wernicke's encephalopathy and Korsakoff's syndrome. In addition, research has suggested that binge drinking in midlife is associated with an increased risk for development of dementia in later life (Järvenpää, Rinne, Koskenvuo, Räihä, & Kaprio, 2005).

Light to moderate alcohol consumption, however, has been shown to have several potential beneficial effects on health, including a decreased risk of developing cardiovascular problems and certain forms of cancer. With respect to neurological functioning, Virtaa et al. (2010) reported evidence suggesting that individuals whose dietary intake during midlife included light to moderate alcohol consumption showed a reduced risk for cognitive impairment in later life as compared with individuals whose dietary during midlife included no alcohol consumption or heavy alcohol consumption. Further, Anstey, Mack, and Cherbuin (2009) found that light to moderate alcohol consumption in later life appears to be associated with a reduced risk for developing dementia, particularly Alzheimer's disease. Xu et al. (2009) reported similar findings in a sample of people diagnosed with mild cognitive impairment, suggesting that those patients who consumed light to moderate levels of alcohol had a decreased risk of developing dementia as compared with those patients who abstained from alcohol consumption or who consumed high levels of alcohol. It should be noted, however, that patients with MCI who consumed high levels of alcohol were at an increased risk for developing dementia as compared with those who abstained from alcohol consumption.

According to Small and Vorgan (2011), beer, wine, and hard liquor all appear to be associated with a reduced risk for developing AD, and the antioxidant properties in any of these forms of alcohol may have neuroprotective effects. Despite the potential beneficial influences of light to moderate alcohol consumption on brain health, most experts do not recommend that nondrinkers initiate alcohol use as a means for preventing dementia. Alcohol has additive and synergistic drug interactions with many medications, especially benzodiazepines and opioids; further, significant injuries and death can occur from various alcohol-related accidents, including falls and vehicular crashes (Preston, Tagliana, & O'Neal, 2010).

Ginkgo Biloba

Ginkgo biloba is a unique species of tree whose leaf extracts have been purported to have numerous health benefits, including anti-inflammatory, antifungal, and antibacterial effects. Extracts of ginkgo leaves also contain flavonoids, which, as noted previously, act to produce strong antioxidant effects. In this light, ginkgo can be used as a dietary supplement as a potential means for enhancing concentration and memory. Although ginkgo biloba has been reported to significantly improve attention in healthy individuals (Elsabagh, Hartley, Ali, Williamson, & File, 2005; Kennedy, Scholey, & Wesnes, 2000), results regarding its effects on the neurocognitive functioning of individuals with dementia have been inconclusive. While some research suggests that gingko is superior to placebo in the treatment of mild to moderate dementia (Ihl et al., 2010, and may improve aspects of cognitive performance and social functioning among individuals with AD or vascular dementia (Le Bars et al., 1997), most studies report that gingko biloba as a dietary supplement is neither effective in preventing the development of Alzheimer's disease and dementia nor helpful in treating the cognitive symptoms following the onset of dementia (Schneider, 2012; Vellas et al., 2012). Research also has begun to explore the potential use of gingko in improving the cognition of individuals with various other diseases that may lead to dementia, such as vascular pathology and multiple sclerosis, but the findings similarly remain inconclusive. Overall, research findings suggest that ginkgo biloba appears to be more effective than placebo in improving the cognitive functioning of individuals with dementia, but with unclear clinical relevance. Further research is needed to clarify the various inconsistencies in methodologies and findings across studies before any firm recommendations can be made regarding its routine use as a dietary supplement in such cases.

Medical Foods

Medical foods are foods developed for consumption or administration under the supervision of a physician designed for the dietary management of a disease or condition that, based on scientific research, has established nutritional requirements. Medical foods are subject to the labeling requirements of the Federal Food, Drug, and Cosmetic Act. Examples of common illnesses for which medical foods have been developed include metabolic syndrome, diabetes mellitus, chronic fatigue syndrome, inflammatory bowel disease, osteoarthritis, and many allergies. Research investigating the use of medical foods for individuals with Alzheimer's disease has yielded positive findings. For example, Scheltens et al. (2010) reported improved memory functioning in persons with mild AD after 12 weeks of dietary supplementation with Souvenaid. A subsequent study by Scheltens et al. (2012) supported the findings of the prior investigation and provided additional evidence that Souvenaid effects functional connectivity in the brain, thereby supporting the hypothesis of modified synaptic activity. Although these results are quite promising, additional clinical trials examining the effects of medical foods in individuals with dementia are necessary before firm conclusions and recommendations can be made.

Conclusion

This chapter illustrates the established link that exists between dietary intake and brain heath and describes the manner in which various nutrients may, individually or collectively, promote improved cognitive functioning, assist in delaying onset of dementia through neuroprotective mechanisms, and/or potentially slow the progression of cognitive and functional decline in individuals who have been diagnosed with MCI or dementia. It is important to note that this chapter is not exhaustive in its coverage of the empirical literature in this area. There exist many other avenues of scientific exploration with respect to the relationship between nutrients and brain health, and ongoing research continues to explore the myriad dietary factors that may offer neuroprotection, improve neurocognitive functioning, and assist in treatment of the neurological illnesses that may cause dementia.

As we attempted to point out throughout the chapter, results of studies examining the associations among diet, brain health, cognitive functioning, and neurological illness are neither entirely consistent nor conclusive. Regarding the potential uses and benefits of the specific nutrients and dietary factors discussed in this chapter, many of the published scientific investigations contradict one another. Further, professional experts often have differing opinions, which may be influenced, in part, by their experience as practicing healthcare professionals. This ambiguity in the scientific literature reflects the inherent difficulty in conducting clinical nutrition studies. As discussed by Myers (2008), dietary exposure to various nutrients generally is estimated based on questionnaires completed by study participants, which may be inaccurate. Although biomarkers of nutrient consumption may provide more reliable data, they usually are unavailable and/or unaffordable. Secondly, consumption of a particular food (e.g., fish or poultry) generally results in non-consumption of another food (e.g., beef or pork), thereby posing methodological challenges in differentiating the effects of foods being consumed from those not being consumed. Long-term dietary interventions also are inconvenient for people, and compliance with study protocols requires extreme effort from participants. Finally, randomized, controlled clinical trials are virtually impossible to conduct in this area of investigation secondary to the difficulty in blinding study participants as to their diet (Myers, 2008). Hu et al. (2013) also note the difficulty in examining the individual influences of nutrients due to the fact that they are correlated with one another. This being the case, the understanding of nutritional factors in neurocognitive functioning must derive from research involving observation, brief clinical investigations, and animal intervention studies (Myers, 2008).

Although many nutrients have been supported through empirical investigations to yield beneficial effects on brain health among healthy individuals as well as persons with dementia, specific recommendations for dietary intake largely remain elusive at present. Based on the current literature, however, general recommendations in this regard with respect to diet include maintaining a healthy weight and avoiding obesity. Eating habits that minimize inflammation and provide a steady supply of fuel generally are considered ideal. Increasing dietary intake of whole foods, while limiting dietary intake of fast foods, fried foods, packaged foods, and processed foods is recommended. From a broader standpoint, diets, such as the Mediterranean diet, which emphasize complex carbohydrates over simple carbohydrates, unsaturated fats over saturated fats, and omega-3 fatty acids over omega-6 fatty acids, appear to be the most beneficial with respect to neuroprotection and brain health. Generally speaking, limiting the consumption of red meat and obtaining proteins from other sources, such as fish, poultry, and nuts is recommended. When red meat is consumed, it is best if it is lean. In addition to being a source of protein, many nuts, such as pistachios, have been reported to reduce LDL cholesterol and have beneficial antioxidants effects. Fish is a good source of protein, and many species also are rich in omega-3 fatty acids. Replacing butter with olive oil and eating an array of fruits and vegetables across the color spectrum rich in vitamins, minerals, and antioxidants will help to counteract the effects of oxidative stress. As noted previously, berries appear to be especially beneficial in promoting brain health. Teas also are quite beneficial and periodic treats of dark chocolates, unless otherwise contraindicated, can be considered for neuroprotection. Finally, consumption of coffee and alcohol, in moderation, may have brain and overall health benefits that warrant further research.

It is ideal to procure nutrients through regular dietary consumption of foods, as the value of many dietary supplements in promoting brain health remains debated. Supplemental nutrient intake clearly is beneficial in deficiency conditions (Julien, Advokat, & Comaty, 2011). In well-nourished populations, however, the use of supplements, typically as a means to prevent against chronic diseases, remains controversial. Results of epidemiologic studies assessing supplement use, mortality, and morbidity risk have been inconsistent, and the long-term effects of dietary supplements generally remain unknown. It also seems apparent that many, if not most, supplemental nutrients can produce detrimental effects in some individuals, especially if taken in excess. Readers also should understand that since dietary supplements are not regulated by the Food and Drug Administration, little control exists as to claims that can be made by manufacturers of these products.

In closing, a critical caveat for consideration is that individuals should not implement dietary changes without first consulting with their physicians. As alluded to previously, not all foods and dietary supplements are necessarily appropriate or safe for individuals with certain medical conditions or persons being prescribed certain medications, and thus diligent consultation with medical professionals before undertaking any changes in diet is necessary.

References

Anstey, K. J., Mack, H. A., & Cherbuin, N. (2009). Alcohol consumption as a risk factor for dementia and cognitive decline: Meta-analysis of prospective studies. *American Journal of Geriatric Psychiatry, 17*, 542-555.

Bennett, S., Grant, M. M., & Aldred, S. (2009). Oxidative stress in vascular dementia and Alzheimer's disease: A common pathology. *Journal of Alzheimer's Disease, 17*, 245-257.

Boothby, L. A., & Doering, P. L. (2005). Vitamin C and vitamin E for Alzheimer's disease. *Annals of Pharmacotherapy, 39*, 2073-2080.

Butterfield, D. A. (1996). Alzheimer's disease: A disorder of oxidative stress. *Alzheimer's Disease Review, 1*, 68-70.

Charlton, K. E., Rabinowitz, T. L., Geffen, L. N., & Dhansay, M. A. (2004). Lowered plasma vitamin C, but not vitamin E, concentrations in dementia patients. *Journal of Nutrition, Health, and Aging, 8*, 99-107.

Chrysohoou, C., Panagiotakos, D. B., Pitsavos, C., Das, U. N., & Stefanadis, C. (2004). Adherence to the Mediterranean diet attenuates inflammation and coagulation process in healthy adults: The ATTICA study. *Journal of the American College of Cardiology, 44*, 152-158.

Clarke, R. (2008). B-vitamins and prevention of dementia. *Proceedings of the Nutrition Society, 67*, 75-81.

Cole, G. M., & Frautschy, S. A. (2010). DHA may prevent age-related dementia. *Journal of Nutrition, 140*, 869-874.

Cournot, M., Marquie, J. C., Ansiau, D., Martinaud, C., Fonds, H., Ferrieres, J., & Ruidavets, J. B. (2006). Relation between body mass index and cognitive function in healthy middle-aged men and women. *Neurology, 67*, 1208-1214.

de Jager, C. A., Oulhaj, A., Jacoby, R., Refsum, H., & Smith, A. D. (2012). Cognitive and clinical outcomes of homocysteine-lowering B-vitamin treatment in mild cognitive impairment: A randomized controlled trial. *International Journal of Geriatric Psychiatry, 27,* 592-600.

De La Monte, S. M. (2012). Metabolic derangements mediate cognitive impairment and Alzheimer's disease: Role of peripheral insulin-resistance diseases. *Panminerva Medica, 54,* 171-178.

de Lorgeril, M., Salen, P., Martin, J. L., Monjaud, I., Delaye, J., & Mamelle, N. (1999). Mediterranean diet, traditional risk factors, and the rate of cardiovascular complications after myocardial infarction: Final report of the Lyon diet heart study. *Circulation, 99,* 779-785.

Devore, E. E., Kang, J. H., Breteler, M. M., & Grodstein, F. (2012). Dietary intakes of berries and flavonoids in relation to cognitive decline. *Annals of Neurology, 72,* 134-143.

Douaud, G., Refsum, H., de Jager, C. A., Jacoby, R., Nichols, T. E., Smith, S. M., & Smith, A. D. (2013). Preventing Alzheimer's disease-related gray matter atrophy by B-vitamin treatment. *Proceedings of the National Academy of Sciences, 110,* 9523-9528.

Elsabagh, S., Hartley, D. E., Ali, O., Williamson, E. M., & File, S. E. (2005). Differential cognitive effects of Ginkgo biloba after acute and chronic treatment in healthy young volunteers. *Psychopharmacology, 179,* 437-446.

Eskelinen, M. H., & Kivipelto, M. (2010). Caffeine as a protective factor in dementia and Alzheimer's disease. *Journal of Alzheimer's Disease, 20,* S167-S174.

Esposito, K., Marfella, R., Ciotola, M., Di Palo, C., Giugliano, F., Giugliano, G., D'Armieto, M., D'Andrea, F., & Giugliano, D. (2004). Effect of a Mediterranean-style diet on endothelial dysfunction and markers of vascular inflammation in the metabolic syndrome: A randomized trial. *JAMA, 292,* 1440-1446.

Evatt, M. L., Delong, M. R., Khazai, N. Rosen, A., Triche, S., & Tangpricha, V. (2008). Prevalence of vitamin D insufficiency in patients with Parkinson disease and Alzheimer disease. *Archives of Neurology, 65,* 1348-1352.

Fife, B. (2011). *Stop Alzheimer's now! How to prevent and reverse dementia, Parkinson's, ALS, multiple sclerosis, and other Neurodegenerative disorders.* Colorado Springs, CO: Piccadilly.

Freeman, J. M., Kossoff, E. H., & Hartman, A. L. (2007). The ketogenic diet: One decade later. *Pediatrics, 119,* 535-543.

Grant, W. B. (2009). Does vitamin D reduce the risk of dementia? *Journal of Alzheimer's Disease, 17,* 151-159.

Grundy, S. M., Brewer, H. B. Jr., Cleeman, J. I., Smith, S. C. Jr., & Lenfant, C. for the Conference Participants. (2004). NHLBI/AHA conference proceedings: Definition of metabolic syndrome: Report of the National Heart, Lung, and Blood Institute/American Heart Association conference on scientific issues related to definition. *Circulation, 109,* 433-438.

Gu, Y., Nieves, J. W., Stern, Y., Luchsinger, J. A., & Scarmeas, N. (2010). Food combination and Alzheimer's disease risk: A protective diet. *Archives of Neurology, 67,* 699-706.

Gu, Y., Schupf, N., Cosentino, S. A., Luchsinger, J. A., & Scarmeas, N. (2012). Nutrient intake and plasma B-amyloid. *Neurology, 78,* 1832-1840.

Hanson, A. J., Bayer-Carter, J. L., Green, P. S., Montine, T. J., Wilkinson, C. W., Baker, L. D., Watson, G. S., Bonner, L. M., Callaghan, M., Leverenz, J. B., Tsai, E., Postupna, N., Zhang, J., Lampe, J., & Craft, S. (2013). Effect of apolipoprotein E genotype and diet on apolipoprotein E lipidation and amyloid peptides: Randomized clinical trial. *JAMA Neurology, 70,* 972-980.

Hanukoglu, I. (1992). Steroidogenic enzymes: Structure, function, and role in regulation of steroid hormone biosynthesis. *Journal of Steroid Biochemistry and Molecular Biology, 43,* 779-804.

Harrison, F. E. (2012). A critical review of vitamin C for the prevention of age-related cognitive decline and Alzheimer's disease. *Journal of Alzheimer's Disease, 29,* 711-726.

Hartman, R. E., Shah, A., Fagan, A. M., Schwetye, K. E., Parsadanian, M., Schulman, R. N., Finn, M. B., & Holtzman, D. M. (2006). Pomegranate juice decreases amyloid load and improves behavior in a mouse model of Alzheimer's disease. *Neurobiology of Disease, 24*, 506-515.

Hartman, A. L., & Vining, E. P. G. (2007). Clinical aspects of the ketogenic diet. *Epilepsia, 48*, 31-42.

Hayes, C. E. (2000). Vitamin D: A natural inhibitor of multiple sclerosis. *Proceedings of the Nutrition Society, 59*, 531-535.

Hayes, C. E., Cantorna, M. T., & DeLuca, H. F. (1997). Vitamin D and multiple sclerosis. *Proceedings of the Society for Experimental Biology and Medicine, 216*, 21-27.

Hu, N., Yu, J-T., Tan, L., Wang, Y-L., Sun, L., & Tan, L. (2013). Nutrition and the risk of Alzheimer's disease. *BioMed Research International*, 524820. doi:org/10.1155/2013/524820.

Ihl, R., Bachinskaya, N., Korczyn, A. D., Vakhapova, V., Tribanek, M., Hoerr, R., & Napryeyenko, O. (2010). Efficacy and safety of a once-daily formulation of ginkgo biloba extract EGb 761 in dementia with neuropsychiatric features: A randomized controlled trial. *International Journal of Geriatric Psychiatry, 26*, 1186-1194.

Isaacson, R. S., & Ochner, C. N. (2013). *The Alzheimer's diet: A step-by-step nutritional approach for memory loss prevention and treatment*. Miami Beach, FL: AD Education Consultants.

Järvenpää, T., Rinne, J. O., Koskenvuo, M., Räihä, I., & Kaprio, J. (2005). Binge drinking in midlife and dementia risk. *Epidemiology, 16*, 766-771.

Julien, R. M., Advokat, C. D., & Comaty, J. E. (2011). A primer of drug action (12th ed.) New York: Worth.

Kawahara, M., & Kato-Negishi, M. (2011). Link between aluminum and the pathogenesis of Alzheimer's disease: The integration of the aluminum and amyloid cascade hypotheses. *International Journal of Alzheimer's Disease*, 276393. doi:10.4061/2011/276393.

Kennedy, D. O., Scholey, A. B., & Wesnes, K. A. (2000). The dose-dependent cognitive effects of acute administration of Ginkgo biloba to healthy young volunteers. *Psychopharmacology, 151*, 416-423.

Le Bars, P. L., Katz, M. M., Berman, N., Itil, T. M., Freedman, A. M., & Schatzberg, A. F. (1997). A placebo-controlled, double-blind, randomized trial of an extract of gingko biloba for dementia: North American EGb study group. *JAMA, 278*, 1327-1332.

Llewellyn, D. J., Langa, K. M., & Lang, I. A. (2009). Serum 25-hydroxyvitamin D concentration and cognitive impairment. *Journal of Geriatric Psychiatry and Neurology, 22*, 188-195.

Lourida, I., Soni, M., Thompson-Coon, J., Purandare, N., Lang, I. A., Ukoumunne, O. C., & Liewellyn, D. J. (2013). Mediterrean diet, cognitive function, and dementia: A systemic review. *Epidemiology, 24*, 479-489.

Luchsinger, J. A., Tang, M. X., Shea, S., & Mayeux, R. (2003). Antioxidant vitamin intake and risk of Alzheimer disease. *Archives of Neurology, 60*, 203-208.

Mangialasche, F., Kivipelto, M., Mecocci, P., Rizzuto, D., Palmer, K., Winblad, B., & Fratiglioni, L. (2010). High plasma levels of vitamin E forms and reduced Alzheimer's disease risk in advanced age. *Journal of Alzheimer's Disease, 20*, 1029-1037.

Markesbery, W. R. (1999). The role of oxidative stress in Alzheimer's disease. *Archives of Neurology, 56*, 1449-1452.

Munch, G., Simm, A., Double, K. L., & Rieder, P. (1996). Oxidative stress and advanced glycation end products—parts of a vicious circle in neurodegeneration? *Alzheimer's Disease Review, 1*, 71-74.

Myers, N. (Ed.). (2008). *Environmental threats to healthy aging: With a closer look at Alzheimer's & Parkinson's disease.* Brookline, MA: Greater Boston Physicians for Social Responsibility and Science and Environmental Health Network.

Nordmann, A. J., Suter-Zimmermann, K., Bucher, H. C., Shai, I., Tuttle, K. R., Estruch, R., & Briel, M. (2011). Meta-analysis comparing Mediterranean to low-fat diets for modification of cardiovascular risk factors. *American Journal of Medicine, 124,* 841-851.

Park, Y., Subar, A. F., Hollenbeck, A., & Schatzkin, A. (2011). Dietary fiber intake and mortality in the NIH-AARP diet and health study. *JAMA Internal Medicine, 171,* 1061-1068.

Pratico, D., & Delanty, N. (2000). Oxidative injury in diseases of the central nervous system: Focus on Alzheimer's disease. *American Journal of Medicine, 109,* 577-585.

Preston, J., O'Neal, J. H., & Talaga, M. C. (2013). *Handbook of clinical psychopharmacology for therapists* (7th ed.). Oakland, CA: New Harbinger.

Przybelski, R. J., & Binkley, N. C. (2007). Is vitamin D important for preserving cognition? A positive correlation of serum 25-hydroxyvitamin D concentration with cognitive function. *Archives of Biochemistry and Biophysicis, 460,* 202-205.

Psaltopoulou, T., Naska, A., Orfanos, P., Trichopoulos, D., Mountokalakis, T., & Trichopoulou, A. (2004). Olive oil, the Mediterranean diet, and arterial blood pressure: The Greek European prospective investigation into cancer and nutrition (EPIC) study. *American Journal of Clinical Nutrition, 80,* 1012-1018.

Quinn, J. F., Raman, R., Thomas, R. G., Yurko-Mauro, K., Nelson, E. B., Van Dyck, C., Galvin, J. E., Emond, J., Jack, C. R. Jr., Weiner, M., Shinto, L., & Aisen, P. S. (2010). Docosahexaenoic acid supplementation and cognitive decline in Alzheimer disease: A randomized trial. *JAMA, 304,* 1903-1911.

Raffaitin, C., Gin, H., Empana, J. P., Helmer, C., Berr, C., Tzourio, C., Portet, F., Dartigues, J. F., Alpérovitch, A., & Barberger-Gateau, P. (2009). Metabolic syndrome and risk for incident Alzheimer's disease or vascular dementia: The three-city study. *Diabetes Care, 32,* 169-174.

Scarmeas, N., Stern, Y., Mayeux, R., & Luchsinger, J. A. (2006). Mediterranean diet, Alzheimer disease, and vascular mediation. *Archives of Neurology, 63,* 1709-1717.

Scarmeas, N., Stern, Y., Mayeux, R., Manly, J. J., Schupf, N., & Luchsinger, J. A. (2009). Mediterranean diet and mild cognitive impairment. *Archives of Neurology, 66,* 216-225.

Scarmeas, N., Stern, Y., Tang, M. X., Mayeux, R., & Luchsinger, J. A. (2006). Mediterranean diet and risk for Alzheimer's disease. *Annals of Neurology, 59,* 912-921.

Scheltens, P., Kamphuis, P. J., Verhey, F. R., Olde Rikkert, M. G., Wurtman, R. J., Wilkinson, D., Twisk, J. W., & Kurz, A. (2010). Efficacy of a medical food in mild Alzheimer's disease: A randomized, controlled trial. *Alzheimer's and Dementia, 6,* 1-10.

Scheltens. P., Twisk, J. W., Blesa, R., Scarpini, E., von Arnim, C. A., Bongers, A., Harrison, J., Swinkels, S. H., Stam, C. J., de Waal, H., Wurtman, R. J., Wieggers, R. L., Vellas, B., & Kamphuis, P. J. (2012). Efficacy of Souvenaid in mild Alzheimer's disease: Results from a randomized, controlled trial. *Journal of Alzheimer's disease, 31,* 225-236.

Schneider, L. S. (2012). Ginkgo and AD: Key negatives and lessons from GuidAge. *The Lancet Neurology, 11,* 836-837.

Shaw, C. A., & Tomljenovic, L. (2013). Aluminum in the central nervous system (CNS): Toxicity in humans and animals, vaccine adjuvants, and autoimmunity. *Immunologic Research, 56,* 304-316.

Singh, R. B., Dubnov, G., Niaz, M. A., Ghosh, S., Singh, R., Rastogi, S. S., Manor, O., Pella, D., & Berry, E. M. (2002). Effect of an Indo-Mediterranean diet on progression of coronary artery disease in high risk patients (Indo-Mediterranean Diet Heart Study): A randomised single-blind trial. *Lancet, 360,* 1455-1461.

Siri-Tarino, P. W., Sun, Q., Hu, F. B., & Krauss, R. M. (2010). Meta-analysis of prospective cohort studies evaluating the association of saturated fat with cardiovascular disease. *American Journal of Clinical Nutrition, 91,* 535-546.

Small, G., & Vorgan, G. (2011). *The Alzheimer's prevention program: Keep your brain healthy for the rest of your life*. New York: Workman.

Smith, A. D. (2006). Prevention of dementia: A role for B vitamins? *Nutrition and Health, 18*, 225-226.

Solfrizzi, V., Frisardi, V., Seripa, D., Logroscino, G., Imbimbo, B. P., D'Onofrio, G., Addante, F., Sancarlo, D., Cascavilla, L., Pilotto, A., & Panza, F. (2011). Mediterranean diet in predementia and dementia syndromes. *Current Alzheimer Research, 8*, 520-542.

Tuppo, E. E., & Forman, L. J. (2001). Free radical oxidative damage and Alzheimer's disease. *Journal of the American Osteopathic Association, 101*, S11-S15.

Vellas, B., Coley, N., Ousset, P. J., Berrut, G., Dartigues, J. F. O., Dubois, B., Grandjean, H. L. N., Pasquier, F., Piette, F. O., Robert, P., Touchon, J., Garnier, P., Mathiex-Fortunet, H. L. N., & Andrieu, S., for the GuidAge Study Group. (2012). Long-term use of standardised ginkgo biloba extract for the prevention of Alzheimer's disease (GuidAge): A randomised placebo-controlled trial. *The Lancet Neurology 11*, 851-859.

Virtaa, J. J., Järvenpää, T., Heikkilä, K., Perola, M., Koskenvuo, M., Räihä, I., Rinne, J. O., & Kaprio, J. (2010). Midlife alcohol consumption and later risk of cognitive impairment: A twin follow-up study. *Journal of Alzheimer's Disease, 22*, 939-948.

Whitmer, R. A., Gunderson, E. P., Quesenberry, C. P. Jr., Zhou, J., & Yaffe, K. (2007). Body mass index in midlife and risk of Alzheimer disease and vascular dementia. *Current Alzheimer's Research, 4*, 103-109.

Xu, G., Liu, X., Yin, Q., Zhu, W., Zhang, R., & Fan, X. (2009). Alcohol consumption and transition of mild cognitive impairment to dementia. *Psychiatry and Clinical Neurosciences, 63*, 43-49.

CHAPTER 7

Exercise and Physical Activity in Dementia
Kimberly R. Willis, Aaron W. Powell, and Samuel T. Gontkovsky

According to Blair (2009), there is overwhelming evidence that regular exercise has important health benefits, including reduced risk of heart disease, type 2 diabetes mellitus, and some cancers. Lack of physical activity is one of the most important health problems of the 21st century, associated with 16% of all deaths for men and women. For those adults participating in regular exercise during midlife, there is a lower risk of dementia later in life (Lautenschlager, Cox, & Cyarto, 2012). Friedland et al. (2001) found that individuals who are relatively inactive, cognitively or physically, in early and midlife have a 250% increased risk of developing Alzheimer's disease (AD). They note the low prevalence of AD in developing countries, such as India or Nigeria, where people typically live more active lifestyles. Exercise for the elderly and those who are ill is as important as it is for persons who are young and healthy. The elderly, particularly those who already have some form of cognitive or physical disability, however, are at an increased risk of a sedentary lifestyle and its associated health consequences, including death (Blair, 2009). Further contributing to the disparities, the elderly, disabled, and other the demographic groups at higher risk of a sedentary lifestyle and dementia also have relatively less access to health promotion programs related to physical activity (Singh, 2002).

Though terms exercise and physical activity often are used interchangeably in much of the literature, there are important distinctions between these two constructs. According to Caspersen, Powell, and Christenson (1985), physical activity can be defined as bodily movement produced by the skeletal muscles resulting in energy expenditure and can be categorized into occupational, sports, household, and other activities. In contrast, exercise is a subset of physical activity that is structured, planned, and repetitive, with improvement of maintenance of physical fitness as a final or immediate objective. Examples of exercise include weight training and cycling. For those people who have difficulty ambulating, seated activities are available (e.g., rowing, recumbent biking, or using upper extremity ergometer). Much of the following research is actually referring to some form of exercise, though the term physical activity is being used. In general, physical activity is encouraged as certainly being beneficial, but more rigorous, structured exercise is prescribed because it is a more measurable goal. Irrespective of age, health, and physical abilities, the elderly tend to benefit across various life domains by incorporating some form of exercise into their daily lives. Given the myriad benefits, from reducing depressive symptomatology to improving various domains of cognitive functioning, it is not surprising that physicians are recommending more rigorous and structured exercise regimens for their elderly patients.

Aside from the more obvious, functional barriers to exercise associated with physical and cognitive disabilities, there are also psychological barriers, including depression, reduced self-efficacy, and social isolation that typically coincide with declines in mobility (Singh, 2002). It is common for care providers and family members of elderly individuals or individuals with cognitive impairments to express reservations in encouraging exercise due to concerns over risk of adverse effects or injury. Another barrier may be a belief that individuals with various health complications simply will no longer benefit exercise. The elderly and individuals with dementia, however, can continue to experience many of the same benefits from exercise as younger, healthy individuals. In fact, the literature generally demonstrates the safety of exercise programs, even for people who have multiple preexisting functional impairments or disabilities (Singh, 2002). Many times, the elderly and persons with dementia can even participate in rigorous activity, including relatively intense aerobic exercise or strength training. These interventions should be pursued responsibly and with consultation with a medical professional in order to ensure that the appropriate type and level of activity is chosen to optimize health benefits (Lautenschlager et al., 2012).

Functional decline is a major factor affecting quality of life for the elderly and individuals with dementia, particularly the reduced ability to perform activities of daily living (Andersen, Wittrup-Jensen, Lolk, Andersen, & Kragh-Sørensen, 2004). There is mounting evidence that exercise has multiple benefits for people with dementia. Many studies suggest that exercise may slow cognitive impairment and functional decline associated with Alzheimer's disease, thereby improving agility, dynamic balance, ambulation, and ability to perform activities of daily living, in addition to reducing risk for falls and incidence of disability and dependent care (Lucia & Ruiz, 2011). Indeed, the majority of clinicians (78%) advise clients with cognition difficulties to pursue exercise (Roberts, Karlawish, Uhlmann, Petersen, & Green, 2010).

Do Exercise and Physical Activity Positively Impact Cognitive and Functional Abilities?

It should be noted that the research concerning exercise and physical activity among individuals with cognitive deficits is by no means conclusive, nor is there always consensus. More studies are needed that include larger sample sizes, better control groups, longer periods of intervention, and greater consistency with respect to exercise programs and assessments (Lautenschlager et al., 2012). A review sponsored by the Cochrane Collaboration (Forbes et al., 2008) found insufficient evidence of exercise programs having a significant impact in improving cognition, function, behavior, or mood in people with dementia. The authors used exceptionally strict criteria for inclusion of trials, however, basing their conclusion on the limited review of only two trials. Several studies and reviews have underlined the importance of two factors in the findings. First, while the positive effects of exercise may seem small in some cases, when one considers that the control groups often experience declines in this same duration, the positive impact of exercise becomes more impressive. Second, while the interventions themselves often limited to only a few weeks or months, the positive effects can be long lasting, and all indications seem to be that physical activity can improve functioning at every stage of dementia (Lautenschlager et al., 2008; Thom & Clare, 2011).

An additional review of non-demented subjects followed for 1-12 years found that 3,210 out of 33,816 individuals showed cognitive decline over time (Sofi et al., 2011). Those who had a high level of physical activity were significantly protected (38%) against cognitive deterioration. Further, even low to moderate levels of exercise showed significant protection (35%) against cognitive decline. People with Alzheimer's disease who exercise with their caregivers are generally more active and have improved functioning and mood (Pérez & Cancela Carral, 2008). A more recent, systematic review by Pitkälä, Savikko, Poysti, Strandberg, and Laakkonen (2013) considered the efficacy of exercise in 20 randomized, controlled trials to explore improvements in functional impairments and mobility limitations among older individuals with dementia. Almost half of the trials reviewed were determined to be of high quality, with exercise improving mobility and decreasing functional limitations. The authors concluded that with intense exercise on a regular basis, improvements could be made in various functional domains.

Functional dependence increases with the progression of dementia, thereby increasing both hospitalization and institutionalization. Functional independence is crucial for maintaining a sense of self-efficacy and quality of life (Rolland et al., 2007; Yu, Kolanowski, Strumpf, & Eslinger, 2006). Research indicates a direct relationship between cognition and functional decline and the benefits of exercise for both (Yu et al., 2006). According to Thom and Clare (2011), cognitive training and physical exercise should not be mutually exclusive. Multi-modal interventions, combining exercise with cognitive activities, generally have shown the greatest chance of enhancing functional performance.

Cognitive Benefits

Exercise has proven to play a role in improving cognition among seniors without dementia. For example, Cassilhas et al. (2007) found significantly improved cognitive performance in elderly study participants on measures of memory and verbal reasoning following six months of moderate-intensity or high-intensity resistance training. Similarly, Liu-Ambrose et al. (2008) reported significantly improved executive functioning among seniors with a recent history of falls after six months of participation in an individualized, home-based program of balance and strength training. Liu-Ambrose and Donaldson (2009) describe the following three beneficial factors of resistance training for cognitive functioning:

- moderation of the development of sarcopenia, which is associated with increased falls and fracture risk as well as physical disability,

- reduction of serum homocysteine, which is associated with impaired cognitive performance, AD, and cerebral white matter lesions, and

- increased concentrations of insulin-like growth factor 1, which improves cognitive performance and promotes neuronal growth, survival, and differentiation.

Evers, Klusmann, Schwarzer, and Heuser (2011) examined the cognitive effects of participating in either physical exercise or cognitive interventions for six months in a sample of healthy elderly women. The exercise group had 30 minutes of endurance training followed by 60 minutes of strength, balance, flexibility and coordination training. The cognitive group had a computer course and learned how to operate common software for writing, calculating, surfing the Web, emailing, drawing, and image editing. Composite cognitive scores were significantly better for both groups, while the control group's scores declined. The positive impacts were most pronounced for individuals with lower baseline scores.

According to Honea et al. (2009), the hippocampal region of the brain suffers atrophy in early stage Alzheimer's disease, and cardiovascular fitness can counteract this problem, increasing volume within the medial temporal and parietal cortices. Most studies focus on the more common exercise intervention of aerobic activity. Erickson and Kramer (2009) reviewed the literature in this area, including studies of elderly participants with dementia, and found that there is sufficient evidence to defend the use of moderate levels of aerobic exercise as an intervention to produce significant improvement in cognitive function, particularly executive abilities, which often have the greatest rate of decline. For example, Kramer et al. (1999) demonstrated improved executive function with six months of aerobic walking as compared to a control group who completed only stretching and toning. According to Colcombe and Kramer (2003), greater changes to cognition occurred with a combination of aerobic exercise and cognitive tasks as compared to only aerobic or non-aerobic activities alone. Other studies reviewed reported retention of neural plasticity and even reversal of decay in varying regions of the brain. Colcombe et al. (2006) determined that those who are more fit, relative to persons who are less fit, had greater grey matter volume in multiple regions of the brain including the frontal and temporal lobes. Additionally, Burns et al. (2008) found that individuals with AD who were more fit demonstrated less whole brain atrophy, suggesting that exercise may be a factor that moderates the disease process.

According to Pérez and Cancela Carral (2008), exercise may decrease the extracellular amyloid beta plaques that are associated with Alzheimer's disease. Exercise can increase cerebral blood flow in older adults, thus enhancing cerebral perfusion, or a potential healing effect for damaged areas of brain tissue, and also may result in enhanced nitric oxide levels, which can have an indirect impact on degrading amyloid beta plaques. Aerobic exercise causes the release of brain-derived neurotrophic factor, which acts to promote growth of new brain cells and improve existing connections (Heidrich, 2005). One study examined the effect of exercise in a mouse model of Alzheimer's disease and found a decrease in amyloid beta plaque levels in the brain, with preliminary data suggesting that long-term running enhanced the rate of learning in the animals (Adlard, Perreau, Pop, & Cotman, 2005). These results were thought to be consistent with other studies proposing that exercise stimulates plasticity-related processes, which in turn facilitate the encoding of information. In their literature review, Yu et al. (2006) found that "exercise stimulates gene expressions of nerve growth factors important for the neurogenesis, production and function of neurotransmitters, and synaptogenesis, especially in the hippocampal region where AD pathology is severe" (p. 362).

Thurm and colleagues (2011) found improved cognitive functioning in a small trial with very frail participants with dementia. Their positive results are important because of the moderate exercise intervention, only twice per week for 45 minutes, mostly in a sitting position, and because of the brevity of the intervention, as it was only 10 weeks. The exercise focused on strengthening, coordination, balance, flexibility, and stamina.

There is some evidence of exercise having a stronger effect on women. Baker et al. (2010) found that over a six-month period of high-intensity aerobic exercise for participants with mild cognitive impairment (MCI), there were improvements with executive function. Despite comparable gains in cardiovascular fitness for both genders, women demonstrated significantly stronger improvements in cognition. The authors argue that this could have resulted from changes to synthesis of glucose and effects related to insulin sensitivity. Also, women showed decreased levels of cortisol, though men presented with the opposite effect. Higher levels of cortisol are a known predictor of more rapid disease progression. A study by Erickson and Kramer (2009) also found that postmenopausal women who were more fit, regardless of taking hormone replacement therapy, demonstrated improved cognition and brain volume.

Lautenschlager et al. (2008) examined 138 participants randomly assigned to an education and usual care group or a 24-week home-based program of physical activity, with an 18-month follow-up. Participants had subjective and objective MCI. Each week, the exercise group was expected to perform 150 minutes of moderate-intensity physical activity. Primarily, this involved walking, but 12 participants included some strength training, as well. Participants recorded their own physical activity at close to 80% compliance. At six months, the exercise group was walking 9000 steps a week more than the control group. Assessments of cognitive function were completed at 6, 12, and 18 months. Exercise participants showed significantly better cognitive scores throughout the trial, with better delayed recall and improved clinical dementia ratings. Differences were small, in some cases, but important given the modest levels of exercise. An important finding in the study was that the benefits persisted even at one-year follow up.

According to Yu et al. (2006), the cognitive processes of memory, executive functioning, and visuospatial functioning often work together to organize the completion of many advanced functional skills, such as preparing meals or managing finances. Memory organizes past experiences, which are arranged into specific behaviors through executive functioning that subsequently allows a skilled task to be completed safely via visuospatial processing. The authors believe that executive function may have more of an effect on changes in function than memory and visuospatial functioning. Farias, Harrell, Neumann, and Houtz (2003) suggest that cognitive dysfunction accounts for 25% to 50% of variance in instrumental activities of daily living (IADLs), while the specific domain of executive dysfunction has independently explained 43% of this variance (Royall, Chiodo, & Polk, 2000). IADLs versus basic ADLs are the first to decline in mild stages of AD, the latter being preserved until later severity stages of the disease (Yu et al., 2006). The authors concluded that delaying a decline in ADLs may be possible by improving executive function through exercise.

A recent literature review of studies examining the effect of aerobic exercise on neurocognitive performance (Smith et al., 2010) was able to differentiate the impact on specific cognitive domains, including attention and processing speed, executive functioning, working memory, and memory. Most studies had subjects participating in an intense walking or jogging program, though some incorporated strength training into their respective protocols. Improvements in all domains except working memory occurred with exercise, though studies that combined walking with strength training had the best results in attention and processing speed as well as working memory. Only one domain, working memory, appeared to be mediated by age, with older participants making larger improvements than their younger counterparts. Additionally, level of impairment was associated with executive functioning and memory, with those people who were mildly impaired making the most improvements. The review concluded that a mixture of exercises, both aerobic and resistance training, can be more beneficial overall, and that even mild, or low intensity, exercise can be helpful. Those who are more severely impaired would be expected to demonstrate greater improvement with executive function, while who are more mildly impaired would be expected to exhibit greater improvements in long-term memory.

Physical Benefits

The benefits of exercise, in general, arguably can also extend to the elderly and cognitively impaired, according to Pérez and Cancela Carral (2008). There is a reduced risk of falls secondary to increased balance control. There also is the benefit of increased appetite and, subsequently, nutrition. Improved sleep and bone density also are demonstrated. There is a decline in the secondary risk factors associated with dementia, such as vascular disease or hypertension. A decline in the ability to perform basic ADLs is a major factor precipitating declines in quality of life and greater burden of care, which can result in the individual requiring placement in an institution or skilled care facility (Rolland et al., 2007). Over the period of a year, 134 participants were to exercise for one hour, twice per week, incorporating 30 minutes of brisk walking and a combination of aerobic, lower extremity strength training, flexibility, and standing balance training in order to determine whether or not exercise could reduce decline in ADLs. Compliance was generally low, so the researchers saw a decline in ADL performance for both the exercise and control group, but the exercise group declined only one third as much as the control group (Rolland et al., 2007). This is a fairly large difference for the exercise group, despite their low level of participation, further highlighting that even some exercise appears to have health benefits. Arkin (2003) reported positive results of improved stamina and agility with exercise twice per week for 60 minutes when aerobics were combined with upper body and lower body strengthening. Participants also improved their distance in the six-minute walk by an average of 267 feet in 10 weeks. Teri et al. (2003) studied 153 people with Alzheimer's disease who were in either an exercise group or a control group. While the participants in the control group who received routine medical care showed declines across various domains, the exercise group demonstrated an improvement in physical function and affective status after a three-month exercise program, with follow-up at two years. There was also a reduction in restricted activity days for the exercise group, but not for the control group. This investigation also included behavioral management interventions, with caregivers assisting with the intervention.

Another study of 150 people, who were at a high risk for a decline in mental function, highlighted the importance of self-management and self-directed thinking in a program conducted only once per week for three months, 90 minutes each session, which consisted of 30 minutes of individualized walking and 60 minutes of group participation (Maki et al., 2012). Participants were expected to set weekly short-term goals, use a pedometer to measure their walking distance, and write self-assessments on daily activities. The control group received lectures on nutrition and healthcare. The researchers performed myriad cognitive and functional assessments and found that the exercise group experienced significant improvements both in function and quality of life.

A study of a community-based, caregiver-supervised, exercise program for people with Alzheimer's disease found that after four months of daily walking and balance/strength training, participants showed improvement in cognition and function (Vreugdenhil, Cannell, Davies, & Razay, 2012). Regular walking in the neighborhood was found to be particularly enjoyable for the participants, since it seemed to offer an opportunity for social stimulation. Other findings included improved depressive symptomatology for those receiving the intervention as well as a sense of improved well-being for many of the caregivers who assisted the participants with their activities.

Psychological Benefits

Pérez and Cancela Carral (2008) call attention to the up to 23% incidence of depression among individuals diagnosed with Alzheimer's disease and argue the same benefit of exercise for ameliorating depression for people without dementia is also experienced among people with dementia. Exercise improves mood, raising dopamine and serotonin levels, and contributes to improved attention and learning (Heidrich, 2005). According to Babyak et al. (2000), exercise has been shown to be as effective as medication in the treatment of depression. Banjaree et al. (2013) concluded that routine provision of antidepressants is not indicated for the treatment of depression for those people with dementia. Arkin (2003) argues that physical fitness is an area in which persons diagnosed with AD can make meaningful improvements, thus increasing self-esteem. Exercise may provide such individuals with a sense of purpose, and a benefit of a regularly performed activity has a calming effect on mood. After a multi-modal, student-led, exercise intervention consisting of 16-20 sessions per semester over a period of two to eight semesters, Arkin found continued significant improvements in mood at two, three, and four years.

The authors argue that the incidence of depression in patients with AD is much higher than the reported 23%, possibly greater than 80%. Many studies of exercise and physical activity highlight positive effect on general mood or depression symptoms. Williams and Tappen (2008) reviewed the literature on exercise interventions for depression and found that while there is clear evidence exercise is effective in fending off depression for the elderly, little research with the cognitively impaired groups, particularly those with advanced Alzheimer's disease, has been conducted. This population has a decreased ability to participate in speech therapies and is more at risk of being prescribed antidepressant medications. Their study categorized the reviewed interventions into the three categories of comprehensive exercise, supervised walking, and social conversation. Sessions were five days per week for 16 weeks, with the length of each session progressively increased to 30 minutes. The comprehensive exercise group participated in ten minutes of upper and lower extremity strengthening and standing balance activities, progressively increasing in repetitions followed by a walking component which progressed to 20 minutes. For the walking group, pace was individualized and progressed to 30 minutes. The participants ambulated with assistive devices, as needed, with help provided from a caregiver who utilized a gait belt for safety purposes. The control group had 30 minutes of casual conversation, which was not therapeutically oriented. The researchers found no significant differences across treatment groups in age, gender, length of stay, or scores on depression assessments at pre-intervention testing. They found that while all the groups showed significant improvement in depressive symptoms and mood, the exercise group demonstrated the greatest improvements.

Other Factors

Enriched environments are multi-dimensional and include varying components of social interaction, mental activity, and exercise (Myers, 2008). Some studies recommend a combined approach, with exercise combined with cognitive and social activity. Thom and Clare (2011) argue that multi-modal interventions, particularly when incorporating the learning of new skills, have demonstrated optimal gains in improved functioning. For example, Heidrich (2005) encourages the employment of new ways to do old things, such as using a different hand for a routine task or learning a new language or musical instrument. She also argues that dance lessons or Tai Chi are triply beneficial in that they activate cognition with learning a new skill, provide exercise for increased circulation to the brain, and contribute to socialization and social skills. Further, Thom and Clare (2011) state that combined aerobic training and cognitive training in healthy older adults seems to result in equal or greater effects when combining the training types than when undertaking them separately; they further suggest that multi-modal interventions have the following key benefits:

- Improving the likelihood that activities will continue to be performed after the program has ended,
- Increasing processing speed,
- Facilitating more difficult movements and improving overall wellbeing, and
- Promoting a more engaged lifestyle.

Thom and Clare (2011) also highlight that older people with dementia have an increased risk for falls up to eight times greater than those without dementia. They argue that cognitive impairment is associated with the increased rate of falls, but that greater physical activity has been shown to protect against falls in this population. Interventions that include high doses of exercise and high level balance activities were reported by Wesson et al. (2013) as having the greatest reduction in falls (42%) among the elderly. Currently, little research has been conducted with respect to fall prevention in those with dementia, though this group tends to have a high fall rate with associated injuries and other adverse outcomes. The small pilot study completed by Wesson et al. (2013) demonstrated the feasibility of this type intervention to decrease fall rates. Further research into this area, particularly including participants with different types and stages of dementia, is recommended.

One area that receives little attention in the literature is the important role of care providers in the lives of individuals with dementia, either family members or professional caregivers. There has been interest in recent years in exploring the role of exercise interventions in not only lessening the burden on caregivers but also societal burden (i.e., the monetary costs related to considerable resources required to manage the care for elderly with dementia). Improvements in functional decline are often found to be associated with reductions in caregiver burden (Canonici et al., 2012). Many caregivers are family members who often are elderly themselves and possess their own health issues and physical limitations. Education is a key element in preparing these caregivers as well as healthcare providers to deal with people with dementia. Positive reinforcement and encouragement by the caregiver(s) are effective ways to facilitate participation with an activity (Yao, Giordani, Algase, You, & Alexander, 2013). Further, the general health and mood of caregivers can be very important variables contribution to the quality of interactions that take place with persons with dementia and their willingness to engage in exercise.

The care providers may need their own set of interventions or training in order to be better prepared for those interventions implemented with clients. For example, Teri et al. (2003) educated caregivers on modification recommendations for specific, unwanted behaviors in addition to an exercise program with comparison to a control group who received regular medical treatment only. The treatment group involved 12 one-on-one sessions completed by healthcare providers with the caregiver and the patient. Frequency of the initial twice-weekly sessions decreased to bi-weekly over a three-month period. After this intervention component was assessed, four follow-up interviews were completed regularly during the next two years. The purpose of this study was to determine if education of caregivers on behavior modification in conjunction with an exercise program could decrease burden of care. At the initial three-month assessment, the intervention group demonstrated better functioning as compared to the control group. This positive trend continued over the following two years. The researchers argued that the success of such programs would depend largely on caregivers' abilities and preparedness to carry out the interventions beyond the training.

Conclusion

Those individuals presenting with most limited cases of mobility at baseline typically demonstrate the greatest improvements (Roach, Tappen, Kirk-Sanchez, Williams, & Loewenstein, 2011). This finding, however, should not discourage early or preventive exercise interventions, which also hold significant promise for improved quality of life and overall functioning. Good fitness or health should not preclude one from exercising. Though research typically demonstrates greater gains among those who show more severe cognitive and functional impairments, this can be a function of there simply being greater variability in the scores and greater room for improvement, and thus larger effect sizes. Moreover, Smith et al. (2010) reported significant improvements in memory scores among individuals with even mild degrees of impairment. A combination of the following four common components should be incorporated into an exercise program: strength, flexibility, balance, and endurance (Roach et al., 2011). According to Singh et al. (2002), resistance/strength training can improve limitations in mobility and increase overall morale, which have, in turn, been associated with improved overall functioning. The combination of strength and balance training can help with gait stability, demonstrate a decreased incidence of falls, and may be required to prepare individuals for aerobic exercise, which can improve quality of life through improved psychological, pain, and disability outcomes. Additionally, Singh et al. (2002) found no evidence to support the idea that flexibility or range of motion exercises alone reduce disability, yet, stretching is often the only modality prescribed.

Physical and cognitive interventions need not be mutually exclusive, as people typically do not exercise without cognitive operatives or social stimuli of some kind. A challenge with this research is the difficulty isolating these specific variables for their impact on cognitive or functional improvement. Further, attempts to isolate these variables typically do not generalize to real world settings where exercise activities are multi-dimensional, calling upon various cognitive and physical domains. In one case, a social control group with no exercise increased the six-minute walk distance by 10% over 16 weeks (Roach et al., 2011). In another study, Arkin (2003) incorporated memory and language stimulation activities during exercise sessions for optimal gains.

There is an overall consensus that an exercise program generally should include varying levels of intensity of aerobic exercise, balance activities, strength training, and range of motion exercises. Thom and Clare (2011) argue that a variety of activities leads to an improved ability to participate in routine tasks. They also emphasize a dose-response relationship –generally, the more the exercise, the greater the improvement. High-intensity resistance exercise has been demonstrated to be as safe as low-intensity exercise in most cases and is also considered more effective for improvements across functional measures. High-intensity resistance exercise is also generally more efficient.

Lucia and Ruiz (2011) believe that preventing the risk of cognitive decline may be possible with daily, moderate-intensity, aerobic exercise at a minimum of 30 minutes per session or with greater than or equal to 20 minutes of high-intensity exercise for three days each week. According to Roach et al. (2011), however, there is evidence that there is less benefit in unsystematic, unplanned exercise routines as compared to exercises in which activity specificity, intensity, and duration are considered. In their study, gains in transfer ability were observed in the activity-specific exercise group, while declines were seen in the walking-only group and the control group. Singh (2002) echoes the argument that exercise prescriptions should be specific on modality, frequency, duration, and intensity. Perz and Cancela Carral (2008) recommend aerobic exercise, specifically dual tasks of talking while ambulating at least 30 minutes per day for the majority of the week or completing 20 minutes of moderate-level cycling three times per week. They advocate that this should be completed in conjunction with strength training three times per week on alternating days to demonstrate the greatest improvements mood, cognition, and speech. For more severe cases of dementia, Netz, Axelrod, and Argov (2007) recommended 45-minute morning sessions of smaller groups, with no more than 15 participants, 2-3 times per week. They recommend that music may be used intermittently, depending on participants' ability to focus on instructor interactions. Low-intensity sessions may initially be completed in a seated position, but as able, the participants should progress to performing these in a standing position. Incorporating balance activities into the sessions is also recommended and should be activity-specific (e.g., sit to stand or ambulation with periodic changes in direction) and focused on past leisure activities (e.g., incorporating basketball passes while in a standing position for a person who previously played basketball). Initially, more interaction should be expected between the instructor and participant for certain activities; however, progression to the pairing of participants to work with each other should be the ultimate goal. Lastly, all sessions generally should have short warm-up and cool-down periods incorporated.

Singh (2002) suggests that practical implementation solutions and behavior support systems are essential factors for motivation and success and should be customized to the special needs of the elderly and cognitively/functionally impaired. For those with multiple co-morbidities, the American College of Sports Medicine (2010) recommends evaluation by a physician prior to the initiation of an exercise program for acquisition of specific safety tips and guidelines for exercises. Lautenschlager et al. (2012) emphasize the importance of a support system to help with the initial exercise program development and provide input regarding progress. Because persons with dementia often are impaired in their ability to learn or remember new information, it is advisable to incorporate into the program exercises related to or including familiar activities (Arkin, 2003; Roach et al., 2011). The simpler the exercise is to complete, the greater ease with which it is facilitated by a care provider or family member. Thom and Clare (2011) argue that the use of exercise professionals to deliver interventions may achieve more beneficial results, and some researchers even suggest this as a requirement to ensure that the exercise intensity is optimal. People diagnosed with dementia should not be excluded from participating in exercise. Dementia is not a contraindication to exercise; rather, individuals with dementia stand to make particularly beneficial gains across multiple areas of functioning, including cognition.

References

Adlard, P. A., Perreau, V. M., Pop, V., & Cotman, C. W. (2005). Voluntary exercise decreases amyloid load in a transgenic model of Alzheimer's disease. *Journal of Neuroscience, 25*, 4217-4221.

American College of Sports Medicine. (2010). *ACSM'S guidelines for exercise testing and prescription* (8th ed.). Lippincott Williams & Wilkins.

Andersen, C. K., Wittrup-Jensen, K. U., Lolk, A., Andersen, K., & Kragh-Sørensen, P. (2004). Ability to perform activities of daily living is the main factor affecting quality of life in patients with dementia. *Health and Quality of Life Outcomes, 2*: 52. doi:10.1186/1477-7525-2-52

Arkin, S. M. (2003). Student-led exercise sessions yield significant fitness gains for Alzheimer's patients. *American Journal of Alzheimer's Disease and Other Dementias, 18*, 159-170.

Babyak, M., Blumenthal, J. A., Herman, S., Khatri, P., Doraiswamy, M., Moore, K., Craighead, W. E., Baldewicz, T. T., & Krishnan, K. R. (2000). Exercise treatment for major depression: Maintenance of therapeutic benefit at 10 months. *Psychosomatic Medicine, 62*, 633-638.

Baker, L. D., Frank, L. L., Foster-Schubert, K., Green, P. S., Wilkinson, C. W., McTierman, A., Plymate, S. R., Fishel, M. A., Watson, G. S., Cholerton, B. A., Dunca, G. E., Mehta, P. D., & Craft, S. (2010). Effects of aerobic exercise on mild cognitive impairment: A controlled trial. *Archives of Neurology, 67*, 71-79.

Banerjee, S., Hellier, J., Romeo, R., Dewey, M., Knapp, M., Ballard, C., Baldwin, R., Bentham, P., Fox, C., Holmes, C., Katona, C., Lawton, C., Lindesay, J., Livingston, G., McCrae, N., Moniz-Cook, E., Murray, J., Nurock, S., Orrell, M., O'Brien, J., Poppe, M., Thomas, A., Walwyn, R., Wilson, K., & Burns, A. (2013). Study of the use of antidepressants for depression in dementia: The HTA-SADD trial-a multicentre, randomised, double-blind, placebo-controlled trial of the clinical effectiveness and cost-effectiveness of sertraline and mirtazapine. *Health Technology Assessment, 17*, 1-166. doi:10.3310/hta1707

Blair, S. N. (2009). Physical inactivity: The biggest public health problem of the 21st century. *British Journal of Sports Medicine, 43,* 1-2.

Burns, J. M., Cronk, B. B., Anderson, H. S., Donnelly, J. E., Thomas, G. P., Harsha, A., Brooks, W. M., & Swerdlow, R. H. (2008). Cardiorespiratory fitness and brain atrophy in early Alzheimer's disease. *Neurology, 71,* 210-216.

Canonici, A.P., Andrade, L. P., Gobbi, S., Santos-Galduroz, R. F., Gobbi, L. T., & Stella, F. (2012). Functional dependence and caregiver burden in Alzheimer's disease: A controlled trial on the benefits of motor intervention. *Psychogeriatrics, 12,* 186-192.

Caspersen, C. J., Powell, K. E., & Christenson, G. M. (1985). Physical activity, exercise, and physical fitness: Definitions and distinctions for health-related research. *Public Health Reports, 100,* 126-131.

Cassilhas, R. C., Viana, V. A. R., Grassmann, V., Santos, R. T., Santos, R. F., Tufik, S., & Mello, M. T. (2007). The impact of resistance exercise on the cognitive function of the elderly. *Medicine and Science in Sports and Exercise, 39,* 1401-1407.

Colcombe, S. J., Erickson, K. I., Scalf, P. E., Kim, J. S., Prakash, R., McAuley, E., Elavsky, S., Marquez, D. X., Hu, L., & Kramer, A. F. (2006). Aerobic exercise training increases brain volume in aging humans. *Journals of Gerontology, Series A: Medical Sciences, 61,* 1166-1170.

Colcombe, S. J., & Kramer, A. F. (2003). Fitness effects on the cognitive function of older adults: a meta-analytic study. *Psychological Science, 14,* 125-130.

Erickson, K. I., & Kramer, A. F. (2009). Aerobic exercise effects on cognitive and neural plasticity in older adults. *British Journal of Sports Medicine, 43,* 22-24.

Evers, A., Klusmann, V., Schwarzer, R., & Heuser, I. (2011). Improving cognition by adherence to physical or mental exercise: A moderated mediation analysis. *Aging and Mental Health, 15,* 446-455.

Farias, S. T., Harrell, E., Neumann, C., & Houtz, A. (2003). The relationship between neuropsychological performance and daily functioning in individuals with Alzheimer's Disease: Ecological validity of neuropsychological tests. *Archives of Clinical Neuropsychology, 18,* 655-672.

Forbes, D., Forbes, S., Morgan, D. G., Markle-Reid, M., Wood, J., & Culum, I. (2008). Physical activity programs for persons with dementia. *Cochrane Database of Systematic Reviews, 16,* CD006489. doi: 10.1002/14651858.CD006489.pub2.

Friedland, R. P., Fritsch, T., Smyth, K. A., Koss, E., Lerner, A. J., Chen, C. H., Petot, G. J., & Debanne, S. M. (2001). Patients with Alzheimer's disease have reduced activities in midlife compared with healthy control-group members. *Proceedings of the National Academy of Sciences, 98,* 3440-3445.

Heidrich, R. (2005). Senior fitness: *The diet and exercise program for maximum health and longevity.* New York: Lantern.

Honea, R., Thomas, G. P., Harsha, A., Anderson, H. S., Donnelly, J. E., Brooks, W. M., & Burns, J. M. (2009). Cardiorespiratory fitness and preserved medial temporal lobe volume in Alzheimer's Disease. *Alzheimer disease and associated disorders, 23,* 188-197.

Kramer, A. F., Hahn, S., Cohen, N. J., Banich, M. T., McAuley, E., Harrison, C., R., Chason, J., Vakil, E., Bardell, L., Boileau, R. A., & Colcombe, A. (1999). *Ageing, fitness, and neurocognitive function. Nature, 400,* 418-419.

Lautenschlager, N. T., Cox, K., & Cyarto, E. V. (2012). The influence of exercise on brain aging and dementia. *Biochimica et Biophysica Acta-Molecular Basis of Disease, 1822,* 474-481.

Lautenschlager, N. T., Cox, K. L., Flicker, L., Foster, J. K., Van Bockxmeer, F. M., Xiao, J., Greenop, K. R., & Almeida, O. P.. (2008). Effect of physical activity on cognitive function in older adults at risk for Alzheimer disease: *A randomized trial. JAMA, 300,* 1027-1037.

Liu-Ambrose, T., & Donaldson, M. G. (2009). Exercise and cognition in older adults: Is there a role for resistance training programmes? *British Journal of Sports Medicine, 43,* 25-27.

Liu-Ambrose, T., Donaldson, M. G., Ahamed, Y., Graf, P., Cook, W. L., Close, J., Lord, S. R., & Khan, K. M. (2008). Otago home-based strength and balance retraining improves executive functioning in older fallers: A randomized controlled trial. *Journal of the American Geriatrics Society, 56,* 1821-1830.

Lucia, A., & Ruiz, J. R. (2011). Exercise is beneficial for patients with Alzheimer's disease: A call for action. *British Journal of Sports Medicine, 45,* 468-469.

Maki, Y., Ura, C., Yamaguchi, T., Murai, T., Isahai, M., Kaiho, A., Yamagami, T., Tanaka, S., Miyamae, F., Sugiyama, M., Awata, S., Takahashi, R., & Yamaguchi, H. (2012). Effects of intervention using a community-based walking program for prevention of mental decline: A randomized controlled trial. *Journal of the American Geriatrics Society, 60,* 505-510.

Myers, N. (Ed.). (2008). *Environmental threats to healthy aging: With a closer look at Alzheimer's & Parkinson's disease.* Brookline, MA: Greater Boston Physicians for Social Responsibility and Science and Environmental Health Network.

Netz, Y., Axelrad, S., & Argov, E. (2007). Group physical activity for demented older adults–feasibility and effectiveness. *Clinical Rehabilitation, 11,* 977-986.

Pérez, C. A., & Cancela Carral, J. M. (2008). Benefits of physical exercise for older adults with Alzheimer's disease. *Geriatric Nursing, 29,* 384-391.

Pitkälä, K., Savikko, N., Poysti, M., Strandberg, T., & Laakkonen, M. L. (2013). Efficacy of physical exercise intervention on mobility and physical functioning in older people with dementia: A systematic review. *Experimental Gerontology, 48,* 85-93.

Roach, K. E., Tappen, R. M., Kirk-Sanchez, N., Williams, C. L., & Loewenstein, D. (2011). A randomized controlled trial of an activity specific exercise program for individuals with Alzheimer disease in long-term care settings. *Journal of Geriatric Physical Therapy, 34*, 50-56.

Roberts, J., Karlawish, J., Uhlmann, W., Petersen, R., & Green, R. (2010). Mild cognitive impairment in clinical care: A survey of American Academy of Neurology members. *Neurology, 75*, 425-431.

Rolland, Y., Pillard, F., Klapouszczak, A., Reynish, E., Thomas, D., Andrieu, S., Rivière, D., & Vellas, B, (2007). Exercise program for nursing home residents with Alzheimer's disease: A 1-year randomized, controlled trial. *Journal of the American Geriatrics Society, 55*, 158-165.

Royall, D. R., Chiodo, L.K., & Polk, M. J. (2000). Correlates of disability among elderly retirees with 'subclinical' cognitive impairment. *Journals of Gerontology, Series A: Medical Sciences, 55*, M541-M546.

Singh, M. A. F. (2002). Exercise Comes of Age Rationale and Recommendations for a Geriatric Exercise Prescription. *The Journals of Gerontology, Series A: Medical Sciences, 57*, M262–M282.

Smith, P. J., Blumenthal, J. A., Hoffman, B. M., Cooper, H., Strauman, T. A., Welsh-Bohmer, K., Browndyke, J. N., & Sherwood, A. (2010). Aerobic exercise and neurocognitive performance: A meta-analytic review of randomized controlled trials. *Psychosomatic Medicine, 72*, 239-252.

Sofi, F., Valecchi, D., Bacci, D., Abbate, R., Gensini, G. F., Casini, A., & Macchi, C. (2011). Physical activity and risk of cognitive decline: A meta-analysis of prospective studies. *Journal of Internal Medicine, 269*, 107-117.

Teri, L., Gibbons, L. E., McCurry, S. M., Logsdon, R. G., Buchner, D. M., Barlow, W. E., Kukull, W. A., LaCroix, A. Z., McCormick, W., & Larson, E. R. (2003). Exercise plus behavioral management in patients with Alzheimer disease: A randomized controlled trial. *JAMA, 290*, 2015-2022.

Thom, J. M., & Clare, L. (2011). Rationale for combined exercise and cognition-focused interventions to improve functional independence in people with dementia. *Gerontology, 57*, 265-275.

Thurm, F., Scharpf, A., Liebermann, N., Kolassa, S., Elbert, T., Luchtenberg, D., Woll, A., & Kolassa, I-T. (2011). Improvement of cognitive function after physical movement training in institutionalized very frail older adults with dementia. *GeroPsych, 24*, 197-208.

Vreugdenhil, A., Cannell, J., Davies, A., & Razay, G. (2012). A community-based exercise programme to improve functional ability in people with Alzheimer's disease: A randomized controlled trial. *Scandinavian Journal of Caring Sciences, 26*, 12-19.

Wesson, J., Clemson, L., Brodaty, H., Lord, S., Taylor, M., Gitlin, L., & Close, J. (2013). A feasibility study and pilot randomised trial of a tailored prevention program to reduce falls in older people with mild dementia. *BMC Geriatrics, 13*: 89. doi:10.1186/1471-2318-13-89.

Williams, C. L., & Tappen, R. M. (2008). Exercise training for depressed older adults with Alzheimer's disease. *Aging and Mental Health, 12*, 72-80.

Yao, L., Giordani, B. J., Algase, D. L., You, M., & Alexander, N. B. (2013). Fall risk-relevant functional mobility outcomes in dementia following dyadic tai chi exercise. *West Journal of Nursing Research, 35*, 281-296.

Yu, F., Kolanowski, A. M., Strumpf, N. E., & Eslinger, P. J. (2006). Improving cognition and function through exercise intervention in Alzheimer's disease. *Journal of Nursing Scholarship, 38*, 358-365.

CHAPTER 8

Psychological Stress and Behavioral Issues in Dementia

R. Lauren Whitehead, Charles J. Golden, and Kelly McCormick

There is a growing body of research exploring the role of stress in the acceleration of cognitive decline and dementia. These findings point to the importance of effective stress management to potentially prevent or delay the onset of cognitive decline. Chronic activation of the "stress circuit" releases hormones that can contribute to degenerative changes in the brain. Difficulty in successfully managing common life stressors is being increasingly linked to elevated risk for dementia. A recent longitudinal study found that more frequent and constant psychological stress was associated with increased risk of developing dementia, particularly Alzheimer's disease, later in life (Johansson et al., 2013). In this study, the most frequently reported stressors included mental illness in a relative or spouse, social problems in a spouse, and alcohol abuse in a sibling.

Work-related stress, especially that which is characterized by a perceived lack of control to meet job expectations, also has been linked to an increased risk for developing dementia, particularly Alzheimer's disease (Wang, Wahlberg, Karp, Winblad, & Fratiglioni, 2012). Further speaking to the role of myriad job-related variables in this complex relationship, the study also found that less frequent social support in the work setting, in addition to the perceived lack of control, was associated with an increased risk of dementia, particularly vascular dementia. Whereas Wang et al. did not find vascular disease to be associated with increased risk, other research suggests that impaired cardiovascular functioning may indeed accelerate dementia onset (Andel et al., 2012).

Research consistently suggests that the behavioral and psychological symptoms of stress are found in a majority of patients with a dementia diagnosis. Behavioral and psychological symptoms of dementia (BPSD), agitation, behavioral symptoms, challenging behaviors, behavioral disturbances, and neuropsychiatric symptoms are all labels that have been used to describe the presence of behaviors that complicate the presentation and course of dementia. Researchers differ in how they label and examine specific subtypes of BPSD. Whereas some studies have measured BPSD as a broad and heterogeneous collection of complicating factors associated with dementia, others have attempted to isolate specific symptoms or behaviors often co-occurring with dementia, including agitation, aggression, mood disorders, psychosis, sexual disinhibition, eating dysfunction, and abnormal vocalizations.

For the purposes of this chapter, specific symptoms of BPSD will be described in regard to their presentation, identification, and treatment in patients with dementia. This format is not meant to imply that these symptoms occur in isolation, but rather allows for a better evaluation of each problem. There is considerable overlap in the ways in which these symptoms may present in any individual. In this chapter, except where otherwise noted, the term "dementia" is used broadly and includes multiple etiologies and levels of severity of the disease.

Overall Incidence

In an epidemiological study comparing BPSD using the Neuropsychiatric Inventory (discussed below) in elderly residents with and without dementia, the authors found that over 61% of dementia patients reported disturbance in at least one of the measured domains; dementia patients also scored higher than individuals without dementia in every domain (Lykestos et al., 2000). Apathy was most common, observed in 27% of patients, followed by depression (24%) and agitation/aggression (24%). Agitation/aggression became more prevalent in later stages of dementia.

Irritability was demonstrated in 20% of the participants, closely followed by delusions (19%). Anxiety was reported in 17% of patients with dementia. Aberrant motor behaviors were more frequent in later stages of dementia and present within 14% of participants. Disinhibition (9%) and elation (1%) were less prevalent BPSD found in this study. The authors also found that patients with different types of dementia expressed similar rates of BPSD, though patients with Alzheimer's disease were more likely to experience delusions than were patients with vascular dementia. Patients with vascular dementia were more likely to exhibit depressive symptomatology than were patients with Alzheimer's dementia (Lykestos et al., 2000).

Assessment Procedures

Several measures are available for identifying BPSD. Proper assessment may help distinguish symptoms and therefore help target interventions designed to improve the patient's functioning. These measures include broad inventories of psychopathology as well as measures specific to certain types of symptoms, which are reviewed later in this chapter. The broad measures herein discussed are not an exhaustive list of available assessments, but rather are offered as examples. Clinicians are encouraged to consult test manuals and other sources before deciding which assessment is appropriate for use with a particular patient and whether the clinician is qualified to use it.

The Neuropsychiatric Inventory (NPI) is a psychological battery that has been used widely in research settings to measure BPSD in ten domains, including delusions, hallucinations, dysphoria, anxiety, agitation/aggression, euphoria, disinhibition, irritability/lability, apathy, and aberrant motor activity (Cummings et al., 1994). Ratings of frequency and severity of behaviors, as well as resultant stress on caregivers, are obtained based on caregiver report following inquiry with screening questions to determine if a particular symptom may be present (Seigournel, Kunik, Snow, Wilson, & Stanley, 2008). There are also two alternate forms of the NPI, namely the short-form NPI-Q (Kaufer et al., 2000), and the caregiver assessment CGA-NPI (Kang et al., 2004).

The Behavioral Pathology in Alzheimer's Disease (BEHAVE-AD) is another symptom battery that assesses the following seven behavioral domains: paranoid and delusional ideation, hallucinations, activity disturbances, aggressiveness, diurnal rhythm disturbances, affective disturbance, and anxieties and phobias (Reisberg, Borenstein, Salob, & Ferris, 1987). This caregiver rating scale of behavioral presence and severity also has been adapted into a clinician observer rating scale, the Empirical BEHAVE-AD (E-BEHAVE-AD; Auer, Monteiro, & Reisberg, 1996).

Several formal measures are available to assess depression in patients with dementia. The Cornell Scale for Depression in Dementia (CSDD; Alexopolous, Abrams, Young, & Shamoian, 1988) is one such tool used by clinicians to gather information from patients as well as caregivers regarding the presence and severity of symptoms of major depression observed within the past week. The CSDD measures depressive symptoms in the following five clusters: mood related signs, behavioral disturbance, physical signs, cyclic functions, and ideational disturbance.

Numerous measures are also available for evaluating apathy in patients with dementia. Proper assessment may help distinguish those for whom apathy may be mistaken for depression or resistance to treatment, and therefore help target interventions designed to improve the patient's functioning. These measures include the psychopathology inventories previously mentioned as well as measures specific to symptoms of apathy. Again, clinicians are cautioned to educate themselves and determine whether an instrument is appropriate for use with a particular client.

The Irritability/Apathy Scale (IAS) is a brief informant rating scale that asks the rater about the severity and frequency of behaviors and traits reflecting irritability or apathy (Burns, Folstein, Brandt, & Folstein, 1990). In contrast, the Apathy Evaluation Scale (AES) focuses specifically on apathy and its associated behaviors; it is available in three forms for use depending on whether the rater is a clinician, other informant, or the patient (Marin, Biedrzycki, & Firinciogullari, 1991). In completing apathy scales, the rater is encouraged to consider both the person's premorbid level of motivation and cultural expectations regarding appropriate level of activity (Landes, Sperry, Strauss, & Geldmacher, 2001). Furthermore, it is recommended that raters distinguish motivation from ability and focus on behaviors the patient is able to perform in light of cognitive and physical limitations (Landes et al., 2001).

In addition to the inventories discussed above, there are several measures that are specific to the assessment of anxiety in dementia. The Worry Scale is a self-report form for patients with mild dementia (LaBarge, 1993). Despite its name, however, The Worry Scale contains items indicative of other BPSD and is highly correlated with measures of depression and anger (Seigournel et al., 2008). The Rating Anxiety in Dementia (RAID) enables clinicians to include data from direct observations and information collected from patients, caregivers, and medical records to identify Generalized Anxiety Disorder (GAD) among patients with dementia (Shankar, Walker, Frost, & Orrell, 1999).

In their 2008 critique of measures of anxiety in dementia, Seigournel and colleagues offered several standards that can be used to evaluate the BEHAVE-AD, NPI, RAID, and The Worry Scale. These standards included the assessment of anxiety as an independent construct, the inclusion of symptoms less likely to be affected by dementia (e.g., concentration), the incorporation of multiple sources of information, and established psychometrics. Their comparison suggested that while no one instrument stood out as a gold standard assessment of anxiety in dementia, the NPI, BEHAVE-AD, and RAID were considered preferred measures, depending on the specific goals of the assessment (Seigournel et al, 2008).

Types of BPSD

Depression

Depression and apathy both have been reported to be the psychological symptoms most frequently comorbid with dementia. Research suggests that depression and apathy are qualitatively different constructs that should be distinguished to better inform treatment. While apathy is characterized by lack of motivation and emotional responsiveness, depression is characterized by sadness, guilt, self-criticism, helplessness, and hopelessness (Landes et al., 2001). Like other features of BPSD, however, depression and apathy can and often do occur together. In a study using the NPI to assess BPSD in patients with Alzheimer's dementia, 43% of patients were found to be apathetic and 37% were found to have apathy and depression (Levy, Cummings, & Fairbanks, 1998). Given differential symptoms and features associated with each construct, depression and apathy are herein discussed separately.

Research examining the relationship between depression and dementia has included the study of clinical depression as well as the impact of depressive symptoms, which can be present even if an individual does not meet full diagnostic criteria for clinical depression. Depression and depressive symptomatology have been shown to be associated with multiple complications of dementia, including more severely impaired daily functioning and quality of life, accelerated cognitive decline (Masterman, 2003), and increased risk of behavioral disturbances, suicide, and mortality (Hudon, Voyer, Tremblay, Tardif, &Carmichael, 2010). Increased caregiver burden and greater

187

likelihood of hospitalization also have been associated with depression in dementia (Douglas, James, & Ballard, 2004).

Prevalence rates of diagnosable depression in nursing home patients with dementia range from 9% to 30%, though depressive symptoms are found in up to two-thirds of this population (Gruber-Baldini et al., 2005). Despite this frequency, however, the diagnosis is often overlooked and undertreated in nursing homes, particularly in patients with dementia. It has been reported that less than half of nursing homes involve mental health professionals in the identification and treatment of depression, though nursing home patients have been reported to be significantly more likely to have mental health professionals involved in their care than residential care/assisted living facility patients (Gruber-Baldini et al., 2005). In Gruber-Baldini and colleague's 2005 study of 347 nursing home and residential care/assisted living facility residents with dementia, 25% were rated by nurse supervisors as having symptoms consistent with depression, as measured by a modified administration of the CSDD, with similar prevalence rates noted in both settings (24% in residential care/assisted living facilities and 27% in nursing homes). Feeling anxious and easily annoyed were the most frequently endorsed symptoms on the CSDD. Among those identified as depressed in the study, only 42% had been previously diagnosed as having depression. Furthermore, patients found to be depressed also were more likely to manifest an increased severity of cognitive impairment, to demonstrate more frequent behavioral symptoms, and to endorse pain than their non-depressed counterparts. Behavioral symptoms were more likely to be manifested by patients in residential care/assisted living facilities than in nursing homes.

Research strongly suggests that dementia increases the risk of depression and that depressive symptoms can exacerbate cognitive decline. Even in non-demented patients, developmental changes in the brain increase vulnerability to depression with aging (Tiemeier, 2003). Depression can impact the progression and severity of cognitive impairment in patients with dementia. A history of depression has been associated with a 150% greater likelihood of developing dementia in individuals over age 65 (Brommelhoff et al., 2009). Furthermore, twin studies revealed that depressed twins were three times more likely to develop dementia than their non-depressed twin siblings. The authors indicated that these findings suggest that depression may be a prodromal feature of dementia (Brommelhoff et al., 2009).

Hudon and colleagues (2010) studied the pattern of cognitive impairment in 150 hospital or nursing home patients with either Alzheimer's, vascular, or undifferentiated dementia. Results indicated that both depressed and non-depressed subjects showed moderate to severe impairment on tasks of attention and memory, calculation, and spatio-constructive skills. Language skills were moderately impaired in both the depressed and non-depressed groups, and both groups demonstrated mild to moderate impairment on tasks of perception, voluntary movements, and primitive reflexes/motor skills. Depressed patients, however, performed worse on almost all measured composites, but the disparity between groups was significant with regard to perception, attention and memory, calculation, and language. Furthermore, behavioral disturbances also were correlated with almost all measured cognitive composites. Notably, the 70.5% of the sample showing agitation and the 44.0% showing motor retardation performed significantly worse on cognitive measures. Interestingly, patients with ideational disturbances, including pessimism, self-deprecation, suicidal ideation, and mood congruent delusions performed better on almost all cognitive measures, especially the spatio-constructive tasks. Further research is necessary to further explore these relationships and potential mediators.

Apathy

Apathy has been defined as loss of motivation characterized by reduction in the following behaviors: initiation, persistence, interest, social engagement, emotional responsiveness, and insight (Landes et al., 2001). These features have been associated with increased caregiver stress and earlier need for institutionalization. Apathy has been reported to be the most common change in Alzheimer's disease, present in up to 92% of patients (Landes et al., 2001). Despite its prevalence, it is suspected that apathy is often mistaken for depression or oppositional behavior.

Apathy has been differentiated from depression in that the prominent emotional manifestation is indifference as opposed to sadness (Landes et al., 2001). Neuropsychological test findings have been shown to distinguish apathy from depression. In a 2001 study, Landes et al. reported that that patients categorized as apathetic but not depressed, based on psychiatric assessments, demonstrated more impaired performance on tasks of naming, word list learning, verbal fluency, and set-shifting; contrastingly, patients who were both apathetic and depressed performed worse on only one measure of cognitive functioning, specifically abstract reasoning. Furthermore, greater apathy and cognitive impairment have been associated with lack of awareness of cognitive deficits and less depression (Landes et al., 2001).

Effective treatment of apathy is dependent on its accurate identification and diagnosis. Treatment interventions have focused on adjustments in caregiving, including education, use of verbal and visual prompts, and implementation of routines. Caregivers are also encouraged to promote patients exhibiting apathy to initiate activities of which they are capable, regardless of how well they can be performed (Landes, et al. 2001).

Anxiety

The prevalence of anxiety disorders comorbid with dementia has been reported in the range of 5% to 21% (Starkstein, Jorge, Petracca, & Robinson, 2007), while presence of anxiety symptoms in dementia ranges between 8% and 71% (Lykestos, et al., 2001). Seigournel and colleagues (2008) reported that anxiety is more prevalent in both vascular dementia and frontotemporal dementia than in Alzheimer's dementia; also, anxiety is less prevalent in the later stages of dementia. It is possible that increased severity of dementia leads to a declining awareness of deficits, which in turn leads to reduced anxiety. Age, education, and gender are not strongly associated with the development of anxiety in dementia (Seigournel et al., 2008). There have also been demographic variables associated with the prevalence of anxiety, with individuals of Asian and Hispanic descent reporting higher rates of anxiety than dementia subjects of African American or Caucasian ethnicity (Seigournel et al., 2008).

Anxiety in dementia is associated with myriad adverse behavioral symptoms, decreased functional competence and quality of life, and more impaired neuropsychological performance (Seigournel et al., 2008). Anxiety may be difficult to detect in patients with dementia for several reasons. First, the prominent worry characteristic of anxiety is an internal experience that may be difficult for dementia patients with language impairments to communicate (Seigournel et al., 2008). Secondly, the observable aspects of anxiety, including difficulty concentrating, restlessness, and being easily fatigued can be attributed to symptoms of dementia. Research, however, has distinguished anxiety in individuals with dementia from GAD by showing that symptoms including excessive worry, fears, irritability, muscle tension, and respiratory symptoms were independently associated with GAD (Starkstein et al., 2007). Anxiety also may be mistaken for depression or agitation (Seigournel et al., 2008).

As with the assessment of other BPSD, evaluation of anxiety in dementia should not rely solely on caregiver report. As mentioned above, dementia patients, particularly those with language impairments, may not be able to verbally express their fears and worries. These considerations speak to the need to examine multiple sources of information in order to accurately identify anxiety.

Agitation, Anger and Aggression

The term "agitation" has been used both generally as synonymous with BPSD as well as more narrowly to describe specific behavior, including anger and aggression (also referred to in research as hostility and irritability). Agitation also has been reported as a psychotic feature of dementia (Ujkaj et al., 2012); however, anger and aggression are not necessarily indicative of psychosis and may be characteristic of other BPSD. Often used as a last resort when other treatments have been ineffective, electroconvulsive therapy has been shown to be safe and effective in the treatment of agitation and aggression in dementia (Ujkaj et al., 2012). The most common side effect was a period of confusion immediately following the treatment, which typically resolved within two days.

Sleep Dysfunction

Dementia can lead to disrupted patterns of sleep including insomnia, daytime napping, and sundowning, a syndrome marked by nocturnal agitation, confusion, and wandering (Masterman, 2003). Sleep problems have been associated with decreased alertness and more impaired cognitive functioning in Alzheimer's disease, resulting in increased distress to caregivers. Research suggests that non-pharmacological treatment of sleep dysfunction, including limiting time spent in bed at night and waking up at a consistent time, reducing daytime napping, and limiting the amount of fluids consumed in the evenings may be effective in alleviating problems in this area. Light therapy to promote regulation of the body's circadian rhythm also has been proposed as a non-pharmacological treatment for sleep dysfunction in patients with dementia (Masterman, 2003).

Psychosis

Psychotic symptoms, including delusions and hallucinations, are more common in advanced stages of dementia (Cohen-Mansfield, Taylor, & Werner, 1998; Lykestos et al., 2000). Delusions are reportedly more common than hallucinations, with frequently reported delusions including thoughts that others are stealing, beliefs that caregivers are impersonators, and fears around infidelity and abandonment by a loved one. Though associations between delusions and demographic variables such age, race, and marital status have not been demonstrated, gender has been found to be significantly correlated; women are more likely than men to experience delusions (Cohen-Mansfield et al., 1998). Impaired vision has also been found to be associated with a higher prevalence of delusions and hallucinations (Cohen-Mansfield et al., 1998).

Delusions and hallucinations are strongly associated with the presence of other BPSD. Patients demonstrating verbally and physically nonaggressive behaviors were more frequently reported to have delusional beliefs (Cohen-Mansfield et al., 1998). A statically significant correlation between psychotic symptoms and depression in dementia was not found, though depressed patients appeared more likely to have delusional beliefs. The 1998 finding of Cohen-Mansfield and colleagues suggesting that patients with Alzheimer's disease have the highest rates of delusions and hallucinations compared to other dementia etiologies has been supported by subsequent research (Lykestos et al., 2000).

Less Common Behavioral and Psychological Symptoms of Dementia Mania, eating dysfunction, and sexual disinhibition are less commonly reported BPSD. While sexual disinhibition has been reported as moderately common in clinical settings (International Psychogeriatric Association, 1998, 2002), research has given seemingly little attention to the association between dementia and sexual disinhibition independent from other impulsive behaviors. Accordingly, indications for how to reduce this behavior are scarce; however, Masterman (2003) recommends redirecting unwanted sexual attention by encouraging more appropriate expressions of affection.

Treatment Considerations

Person-Centered

Studies of treatment efficacy in patients with BPSD consistently suggest the need for therapeutic approaches that are individualized, taking into account the biological, psychosocial, and environmental factors of BPSD relevant to an individual (Cohen-Mansfield, 2000; Masterman, 2003). Biological factors include comorbid health problems and medical conditions, as well as the possibility of acute toxic and metabolic changes, superimposed delirium, and pharmacological contributors (Masterman, 2003). The selection of appropriate intervention also should take into account the etiology of the dementia and severity of cognitive impairment, as these factors may limit participation in treatment. Assessment of psychosocial functioning should consider the patient's emotional and behavioral symptoms, stressors, coping skills, and quality of social interactions. Individuals' living environments and access to appropriate health care may be important considerations as well.

There are several models informing the identification and individualized intervention of BPSD. Learned behavior models posit that behaviors are preceded by triggers and reinforced by consequences. Also known as the Antecedent-Behavior-Consequence, or ABC model, this theory suggests that antecedents and consequences to behavioral disturbances be identified and modified in order to change a target behavior (Cohen-Mansfield, 2001).

Cohen-Mansfield's "unmet needs" model for agitation is another theory underlying individualized treatment (2000). This model posits that behaviors can serve to meet an unmet need or communicate a need. In identifying the function of a behavioral symptom, interventions can be targeted to meet or eliminate the need rather than focusing solely on extinguishing the behavior. For example, providing an activity (intervention) to an individual with dementia who wanders (behavior) may meet the need for stimulation.

Systemic

The value of systemic treatment approaches involving interdisciplinary teams of families, caregivers, and treatment providers is are supported by dementia treatment research (Douglas et al., 2004). In a study in which patients' family members and residential care staff collaborated in evaluation and individualized treatment planning using primarily social interventions, 42% of patients in residential care showed a reduction in the frequency of BPSD (Bird, Llewellyn-Jones, & Korten, 2009). Lending further support for the implementation of individualized evaluation and treatment, Bird and colleagues (2009) also found that 65.9% of interventions were successful at reducing BPSD regardless of severity of cognitive impairment and medication status. It is important to identify the treatment goals in patients with dementia and BPSD. Depending on whether treatment aims are to improve cognition or to improve mood and behavioral symptoms, different interventions may be indicated or contraindicated (Douglas et al., 2004).

Non-Pharmacological Treatments

There are strong trends in the literature suggesting that non-pharmacological treatments should be considered as primary interventions in patients with dementia before pharmacological agents are recommended (Douglas at al., 2004; Masterman, 2003). Despite this trend, prescription medications are often the first-line intervention in clinical settings. In addition to concerns associated with high placebo effects in studies of the effectiveness of some medications, pharmacological treatment of elderly patients raises special concerns regarding dosing, side effects, and drug interaction effects (Masterman, 2003). Some neuroleptic medications have been shown to accelerate cognitive decline and impair overall wellbeing (Douglas et al., 2004). Atypical neuroleptics used in the treatment of agitation and psychosis in dementia have been reported to result in complicating side effects including sedation, which can paradoxically increase confusion and agitation (Masterman, 2003). Benzodiazepines, while shown to be efficacious in the treatment of anxiety in non-demented patients, also are contraindicated for treatment of BSPD due to potential side effects including sedation, cognitive impairment, and memory disturbance (Masterman, 2003). The efficacy and risks of pharmacological treatment of dementia are further discussed in Chapter 2.

Behavioral Therapy. Behavioral therapy, also known as behavior modification treatment, is a person-centered approach that seeks to identify the underlying causes of BPSD on an individual level by identifying variables that activate the symptoms and potential sources of reinforcement within the person's environment. Though research in this area is ongoing, there is support for the use of behavioral therapy for its efficacy in reducing verbal and physical aggression (Masterman, 2003) as well as improving wandering and incontinence (Douglas et al., 2004). Masterman (2003) also reported that behavior modification treatment showed efficacy for improving self-care and socialization. Behavioral therapy has been tailored for patients with moderate to severe dementia (Wilkins, Kiosses, & Ravdin, 2010). An approach designed to teach caregivers to assist patients with problem solving and participation in pleasurable activities was reported to reduce problematic symptoms at six-month follow up (Teri, Logsdon, Uomoto, & McCurry, 1997).

Cognitive Behavioral Therapy. Much like behavioral therapy, cognitive behavioral therapy (CBT) seeks to identify the individual factors underlying a behavior but includes identification and reframing of the cognitions that perpetuate maladaptive behaviors. CBT has been adapted for treatment of depression in patients with dementia to include neuropsychological testing to identify the individual's strengths and weaknesses (Teri & Gallagher-Thompson, 1991). This form of CBT is reported to be effective in early stage Alzheimer's disease (Douglas et al., 2004; Teri & Gallagher-Thompson, 1991); however, its efficacy for use with patients in later stages or different etiologies of dementia is unclear.

Problem Adaptation Therapy. An approach incorporating both person-centered and systemic features, Problem Adaptation Therapy (PATH) is considered to be a type of Problem Solving Therapy (PST), a form of CBT. PATH is a brief (12 weeks) home-based intervention designed to treat depression in patients with mild to moderate dementia that has been shown to be superior to supportive therapy in symptom reduction (Kiosses, Teri, Velligen & Alexopolous, 2011). PATH focuses on use of memory aids in the patient's environment and involves caregivers in engaging patients in pleasurable activities (Wilkins et al., 2010).

Interpersonal Psychotherapy. Interpersonal Psychotherapy (IPT) is a brief psychodynamic psychotherapy developed in response to CBT to treat Major Depressive Disorder and co-occurring disorders (Weissman, Markowitz, & Klerman, 2007). It is based on the assumption that depression occurs in response to an interpersonal loss, which may include loss of identity due to necessary role transitions given an individual's dementia status. Also an individualized approach, its goals include symptom reduction and improved interpersonal experiences. Though IPT has shown some success in depressed older adults, it has not been well researched in older adults with dementia (Douglas et al., 2004).

Reality Orientation. This intervention seeks to improve memory and orientation by using environmental cues and memory aids. The intervention is appropriate for use with individuals and groups. It is noteworthy, however, that this treatment focuses on improving the cognitive symptoms of dementia. BPSD, including decline in mood, have been reported in association with use of this treatment, perhaps because it reminds patients of their change in functioning. Reality orientation therapy has demonstrated little long-term effects in its administration as an individual or group intervention (Douglas et al., 2004).

Validation Therapy. In contrast to reality orientation, validation therapy is more targeted toward improving emotional rather than cognitive symptoms in individuals with dementia. This treatment model encourages the clinician to focus on the emotional aspects of the patient's speech content and to validate their experience of identified feelings. Though its efficacy is not yet proven, case studies suggest that validation therapy improves mood and reduces BPSD (Douglas et al., 2004).

Reminiscence Therapy. Reminiscence therapy is a multi-modal intervention designed to encourage patients to recall positive and meaningful experiences in order to be reminded of their premorbid personality. This intervention can be administered to an individual or group and used in the context of other treatments, such as art or music therapy. Though no significant findings relating to symptom improvement have been reported for this treatment modality, some studies suggest a trend toward reduced BPSD and improved self-care and social functioning (Douglas et al., 2004).

Pet Therapy. There is limited research regarding the efficacy of pet therapy for treatment of BPSD. Cohen-Mansfield (2001) reported that allowing hospital patients, two thirds of whom had dementia, to spend one hour a day for five days with a dog resulted in a trend toward improvement. In another small study, the author also reported that having a pet in the home was associated with decreased verbal aggression in individuals with dementia (Cohen-Mansfield, 2001).

Bright Light Therapy. Light therapy has been proposed as a treatment to improve sleep dysfunction in patients with dementia (Masterman, 2003); however, this intervention has not been well researched. Cohen-Mansfield (2001) noted that bright light therapy is likely to be more effective for patients with dementia who have intact vision.

Social Interventions. Limited research suggests that one-to-one social interaction with patients with BPSD may reduce problematic verbal behaviors in nursing home residents (Cohen-Mansfield, 2001). It is recommended that in administering this intervention, treatment providers and caregivers consider various cultural factors, including the individual's preferred language. For example, Cohen-Mansfield (2001) reported a case study in which a female patient with dementia whose first language was Italian demonstrated less frequent abnormal verbal behaviors when one-to-one interaction was administered in her preferred language.

Simulated social interaction is another intervention with limited research. It has been reported, however, that listening to an audiotape of a relative asking conversational questions resulted in less problematic verbal behaviors during exposure; showing a videotape of a relative talking to a patient also reduced hallucinations (Cohen-Mansfield, 2001). Cohen-Mansfield also discussed that the combination of social interaction and activity engagement seems to show the best results in terms of BPSD reduction. Social stimulation and socialization interventions for dementia are discussed in detail in Chapter 4.

Environmental Modifications. The environmental vulnerability/reduced stress threshold model assumes that dementia can lead to impaired ability to cope with stress and increased reactivity to environmental stressors (Cohen-Mansfield, 2001). As the disease progresses, the individual's threshold for coping with stress is further reduced. Accordingly, by identifying and modifying the distressing environmental stimuli, the patient's resources for coping with stress should not be as taxed. Reduced stimulation environments have been associated with decreased agitation. These environments are characterized by use of quiet voices, removal of television, and decoration with neutral colors.

Cohen-Mansfield (2001) discussed a study in which access to outdoor areas and the patient's choice to go outside has led to reduced agitation. She also reported that natural environments and 'simulated home environments' in an institutional setting led to reduced wandering (Cohen-Mansfield, 2001).

Alternative Interventions. Alternative interventions, including sensory stimulation and recreation/activity therapy are discussed in Chapters 5 and 9, respectively. With regard to BPSD, recreation/activity therapy has been shown to improve mood and sleep, while sensory stimulation techniques, including massage and aromatherapy, are less well-researched in neurological populations.

Caregiver Support and Training

Research consistently notes the impact of BPSD on increasing caregiver stress. Increased stress makes caregivers more vulnerable to experiencing emotional problems and compromised functioning themselves. Masterman (2003) suggests that when caregivers are provided with better training, coping skills, and stress reduction techniques, they are more likely to remain well longer and be better able to care for patients with dementia at home, thereby delaying institutionalization. In her review of non-pharmacological treatments for BSPD, Cohen-Mansfield (2001) emphasized the need for ongoing training to help caregivers, including institutional staff, understand the meaning of behaviors, improve communication, and increase ways of meeting patient needs. The research further concluded that single training sessions were not found to demonstrate significant effects in lowering staff distress or improving patient functioning; though multiple training sessions did demonstrate a significant improvement in verbal and physical non-aggressive behaviors at three-month follow up, the effects did not hold at a six-month follow up, underscoring the need for further research in this area.

Conclusion

Chronic stress is associated with increased risk of dementia, suggesting a need for stress management to promote healthy cognitive functioning. Behavioral and psychological symptoms of stress are found in the majority of patients with a dementia diagnosis. These symptoms complicate the course of the disease and often increase stress experienced by both patients and caregivers. Successful intervention is based on proper identification and targeted treatment of these symptoms. Formal assessment measures are available to detect the presence and severity of a wide-range of commonly experienced symptoms, in addition to measures focused solely on specific types of symptoms. Thorough assessment of behavioral and psychological symptoms of dementia should include data collected from multiple sources, use of psychometrically sound assessment measures, and consideration of the patient's premorbid characteristics and level of functioning.

Non-pharmacological interventions should be attempted before pharmacological treatment is recommended. Interventions should be both person-centered and systemic. Individualized treatments can more successfully target the biological, psychosocial, and environmental factors contributing to elevated stress and problematic behaviors in patients. A rigid reliance on any one form of therapy or approach is likely not in the best interest of patients, though this is often the approach that institutions and facilities are forced to undertake given resource constraints. A dynamic and flexible approach that takes into account the responses of a patient to any given treatment modality is essential. While it is easy in this population to blame the individual for problematic symptoms or behaviors, most often failure to improve is the result of choosing the wrong intervention. Determining the function that problematic behavioral and psychological symptoms may be serving an individual (e.g., wandering as a form of stimulation) can help clinicians in designing interventions that can offer more adaptive and less distressing ways to satisfy unmet needs. Relatives, caregivers, and other treatment providers can all play important roles in successfully treating patients. It is important for those involved in caring for individuals with dementia to receive ongoing training in the identification and treatment of behavioral and psychological symptoms as well as support in managing the increased stress that can be associated with caregiving.

References

Alexopolous, G. S., Abrams, R. C., Young, R. C., & Shamoian, C. A. (1988). Cornell Scale for Depression in Dementia. *Biological Psychiatry, 23*, 271-284.

Andel, R., Crowe, M., Hahn, E. A., Mortimer, J. A., Pedersen, N. L., Fratiglioni, L., Johansson, B., & Gatz, M. (2012). Work-related stress may increase risk of vascular dementia. *Journal of the American Geriatrics Society, 60*, 60-67.

Auer, S. R., Monteiro, I. M., & Reisberg, B. (1996). The Empirical Behavioral Pathology in Alzheimer's Disease (E-BEHAVE-AD) Rating Scale. *International Geropsychiatry, 8*, 247-266.

Bird, M., Llewellyn-Jones, R. H., & Korten, A. (2009). An evaluation of the effectiveness of a case-specific approach to challenging behaviour associated with dementia. *Aging and Mental Health, 13*, 79-83.

Brommelhoff, J. A., Gatz, M., Johansson, B., McArdle, J. J., Fratiglioni, L., & Pedersen, N. L. (2009). Depression as a risk factor or prodromal feature of depression? Findings in a population-based sample of Swedish twins. *Psychology and Aging, 24*, 373-384.

Burns, A., Folstein, S., Brandt, J., & Folstein, M. (1990). Clinical assessment of irritability, aggression, and apathy in Huntington and Alzheimer disease. *Journal of Nervous and Mental Disease, 178*, 20-26.

Cohen-Mansfield, J. (2001). Nonpharmacologic interventions for inappropriate behaviors in dementia: A review, summary, and critique. *Geriatric Psychiatry, 9*, 361-381.

Cohen-Mansfield, J. (2000). Use of patient characteristics to determine non-pharmacological interventions for behavioral and psychological symptoms of dementia. *International Psychogeriatrics, 12*(Suppl. 1), 373-380.

Cohen-Mansfield, J., Taylor, L., & Werner, P. (1998). Delusions and hallucinations in an adult day care population. *American Journal of Geriatric Psychiatry, 6*, 104-121.

Cummings, J. L., Mega, M., Gray, K., Rosenberg-Thompson, S., Carusi, D. A., & Gornbein, J. (1994). The Neuropsychiatric Inventory: Comprehensive assessment of psychopathology in dementia. *Neurology, 44,* 2308-2314.

Douglas, S., James, I., & Ballard, C. (2004). Non-pharmacological interventions in dementia. *Advances in Psychiatric Treatment, 10,* 171-179.

Gruber-Baldini, A. L., Zimmerman, S., Boustani, M., Watson, L.C., Williams, C. S., & Reed, P. S. (2005). Characteristics associated with depression in long-term care residents with dementia. *The Gerontologist, 45*(Special Issue I), 50-55.

Hudon, C., Voyer, P., Tremblay, I., Tardif, S., & Carmichael, P-H. (2010). Differentiation of the pattern of cognitive impairment between depressed and non-depressed patients with dementia living in long-term care facilities. *Aging and Mental Health, 14,* 293-302.

International Psychogeriatric Association. (1998, 2002). *Behavioral and psychological symptoms of dementia (BPSD)* educational pack. Retrieved from http://www.ipa-online.net/pdfs/1BPSDfinal.pdf

Johansson, L., Guo, X., Hallstrom, T., Norton, M. C., Waern, M., Ostling, S., Bengtsson, C., & Skoong, I. (2013). Common psychosocial stressors in middle-aged women related to longstanding distress and increased risk of Alzheimer's disease: A 38-year longitudinal population study. *BMJ Open, 3,* e003142. doi: 10.1136/bmjopen-2013-003142.

Kang, S. J., Choi, S. H., Lee, B. H., Jeong, Y., Hahm, D. S., Han, I. W., Cummings, J. L., & Na, D. L. (2004). Caregiver-Administered Neuropsychiatric Inventory (CGA-NPI). *Journal of Geriatric Psychiatry and Neurology, 17,* 32-35.

Kaufer, D. I., Cummings, J. L., Ketchel, P., Smith, V., MacMillan, A., Shelley, T., Lopez, O. L., & DeKosky, S. T. (2000). Validation of the NPI-Q, a brief clinical form of the Neuropsychiatric Inventory. *Journal of Neuropsychiatry and Clinical Neuroscience, 12,* 233-239.

Kiosses, D. N., Teri, L., Velligen, D. I., & Alexopolous, G. S. (2011). A home-delivered intervention for depressed, cognitively impaired, disabled elders. *International Journal of Geriatric Psychiatry, 26*, 256-262.

LaBarge, E. (1993). A preliminary scale to measure the degree of worry among mildly demented Alzheimer disease patients. *Physical and Occupational Therapy in Geriatrics, 11*, 43-57.

Landes, A. M., Sperry, S. D., Strauss, M. E., & Geldmacher, D. S. (2001). Apathy in Alzheimer's disease. *Journal of the American Geriatric Society, 49*, 1700-1707.

Levy, M. L., Cummings, J. L., & Fairbanks, L. A. (1998). Apathy is not depression. *Journal of Neuropsychiatry and Clinical Neuroscience, 10*, 314-319.

Lykestos, C. G., Sheppard, J. M., Steinberg, M., Tschanz, J. A., Norton, M. C., Steffens, D. C., & Breitner, J. C. (2001). Neuropsychiatric disturbance in Alzheimer's disease clusters into three groups: The Cache County study. *International Journal of Geriatric Psychiatry, 16*, 1043-1053.

Lykestos, C. G., Steinberg, M., Tschanz, J. T., Norton, M. C., Steffens, D.C., & Breitner, J. C. S. (2000). Mental and behavioural disturbances in dementia: Findings from the Cache County study on memory in aging. *American Journal of Psychiatry, 157*, 708-714.

Marin, R.S., Biedrzycki, R.C., & Firinciogullari, S. (1991). Reliability and validity of the apathy evaluation scale. *Psychiatry Research, 36*, 143-162.

Masterman, D. (2003). Treatment of the neuropsychiatric symptoms in Alzheimer's disease. *Journal of the American Medical Directors Association, 4*(Suppl. 6), S146-S154.

Reisberg, B., Borenstein, J., Salob, S. P., & Ferris, S. H. (1987). Behavioral symptoms in Alzheimer's disease: Phenomenology and treatment. *Journal of Clinical Psychiatry, 48*, 9-15.

Seigournel, P. J., Kunik, M. E., Snow, L., Wilson, N., & Stanley, M. (2008). Anxiety in dementia: A critical review. *Clinical Psychology Review, 28*, 1071-1082.

Shankar, K. K., Walker, M., Frost, D., & Orrell, M. W. (1999). The development of a valid and reliable scale for rating anxiety in dementia (RAID). *Aging and Mental Health, 3*, 39-49.

Starkstein, S. E., Jorge, R., Petracca, G., & Robinson, R. G. (2007). The construct of generalized anxiety disorder in Alzheimer disease. *American Journal of Geriatric Psychiatry, 15*, 42-49.

Teri, L., & Gallagher-Thompson, D. (1991) Cognitive-behavioral interventions for treatment of depression in Alzheimer's patients. *Gerontologist, 31*, 413-416.

Teri, L., Logsdon, R. G., Uomoto, J., & McCurry, S. M. (1997). Behavioral treatment of depression in dementia patients: A controlled clinical trial. *Journal of Gerontology. Series B, Psychological Sciences and Social Sciences, 52*, 159-166.

Tiemeier, H. (2003). Biological risk factors for late life depression. *European Journal of Epidemiology, 18*, 745-750.

Ujkaj, M., Davidoff, D. A., Seiner, S. J., Ellison, J. M., Harper, D. G., & Forester, B. P. (2012). Safety and efficacy of electroconvulsive therapy for the treatment of agitation and aggression in patients with dementia. *American Journal of Geriatric Psychiatry, 20*, 61-72.

Wang, H-X., Wahlberg, M., Karp, A., Winblad, B., & Fratiglioni, L. (2012). Psychosocial stress at work is associated with increased dementia risk late in life. *Alzheimer's and Dementia, 8*, 114-120.

Weissman, M. M., Markowitz, J. C., & Klerman, G. L. (2007). *Clinician's quick guide to interpersonal psychotherapy.* New York: Oxford University Press.

Wilkins, V. M., Kiosses, D., & Ravdin, L. D. (2010). Late-life depression with comorbid cognitive impairment and disability: Nonpharmacological interventions. *Clinical Interventions in Aging, 5*, 323-331.

CHAPTER 9

The Benefits of Recreational Activities for Individuals with Dementia
Deborah Hoffnung

In the 1985 movie, Cocoon, three aging retirement home residents swim in a pool that is incubating cocooned (alien) Antareans and absorb some of the water's life force, making them feel younger and stronger (Brown, Zanuck, Zanuck, & Howard, 1985). Fortunately for adults with dementia, the beneficial effects of recreation are not simply a Hollywood fairy tale; swimming and other forms of recreation may indeed be the 'life force' that can prevent, delay, and/or moderate dementia symptoms. This book has thus far explored a number of non-pharmacological approaches to slowing the cognitive and functional declines and addressing the emotional and behavioral symptoms associated with dementia. In the present chapter, we will turn to a discussion of the cognitive, behavioral, and emotional benefits of recreational and leisure activities.

Introduction

Recreational and leisure activities, defined as "the voluntary use of free time for activities outside the daily routine" (Wang, Xu, & Pei, 2012, p. 482), have been shown to improve physical functioning, reduce depression, increase social engagement, and change the behavior of individuals with dementia. Much of the theoretical framework applied to study the benefits of recreational and leisure activities in older individuals and, specifically, those with dementia, borrows from research on locus of control, social engagement, positive psychology, and psychoneuroimmunology. Analyses by Grembowski et al. (1993) and others have noted positive health outcomes in older adults who experience a sense of mastery and fulfillment in their activities. Researchers such as Bennett (2005) and Glass, de Leon, Marottoli, and Berkman (1999) have noted similar positive health outcomes when older individuals are provided with the opportunity for meaningful social engagement during activities such as visits to restaurants and sporting events, religious event attendance, participation in social groups, gardening, and meal preparation. In their review of the benefits of physical leisure activities, Buettner and Fitzsimmons (2002) draw on Csikszentmihalyi's theory of optimal recreation experiences (1998), or flow, to explain the mechanisms by which an older individual engaged in an activity that matches his or her skill level, preferred level of challenge, and interests can reach a state of energized focus and positive mood. Individuals performing flow activities report feeling more in control of their environments, more interested and absorbed, and less aware of negative feelings and symptoms. Providing opportunities for participation in leisure activities can make these positive flow outcomes accessible to those with dementia.

In explaining the benefits of recreational and leisure activities, psychoneuroimmunologists and physiologists highlight the physical effects of recreational activities on the brain and body, including lowering of body weight, improving diet, decreasing blood pressure, and improving cardiovascular health. Others have noted specific neurochemical changes in the brains and bodies of elderly individuals enrolled in recreational programs. Kumar et al. (1999) reported that music therapy increased melatonin levels in patients with Alzheimer's disease, suggesting that specific changes in neurochemicals in the brain may be directly contributing to positive mood. Leisure activities may also act as a buffer against cognitive decline by protecting and preserving neurons; individuals with 'healthier' neurons may be better able to compensate for the effects of aging and/or dementia before deficits are manifested (Scarmeas & Stern, 2003). In his research into the neurological mechanisms underlying learning, Hebb (1949) posited that repeated brain activity contributes to the establishment and maintenance of neuronal synapses. Perhaps, recreational activities promote healthy brain functioning by encouraging the continued adaptation of neurons to new experiences. Alternatively, as Mortimer and Graves (1993) suggest, neuronal activation associated with stimulating leisure activities may spare the brain from the degenerative processes associated with dementia by improving its ability to maintain cell membranes, reducing amyloid beta protein production, and limiting the pathological degradation and aggregation of cells that occurs with aging and dementia.

Recreational Activities: Predictive of, or Protective Against, Dementia?

Multiple studies have shown an inverse relationship between participation in leisure activities and development of dementia. For example, Hall et al. (2009) determined that daily participation in leisure activities in healthy individuals delayed onset of progressive cognitive decline in patients who eventually developed dementia by 0.18 year. Scarmeas, Levy, Tang, Manly, and Stern's 2001 study of the Washington Heights-Inwood Columbia Aging Project cohort found that higher rates of intellectual and social activities were associated with lower incidences of Alzheimer's disease. Cohen et al. (2006) found that participation in a professionally-led, community-based chorale program led to improvements in self-reported overall health, increased participation in other (non-program) activities, and a decline in falls in individuals aged 65 years and older. In their study of metropolitan Washington, DC elders, Cohen and his colleagues (2006) also found that the matched controls who continued with their usual (unstructured) activities actually reported a decline in overall health, participation in fewer activities, and an increased number of falls over the same one year period as compared to their own baseline scores. Some theorists have argued that the benefits experienced by those older individuals who remain engaged in recreational activities are moderated by various pre-morbid factors, such as higher socioeconomic status, improved ability to manage stress, personality factors, and better overall health. Yet, even when educational background, prior income level, and other variables are controlled for, degree of participation in recreational activities in adulthood remains a strong predictor of development of cognitive decline as individuals age (Kolanowski, Fick, & Buettner, 2009).

These and similar findings have prompted the following question: is reduced participation in recreational activities predictive of developing dementia, or is continued engagement in leisure pastimes protective against dementia? Some authors have speculated that declines in interest and participation in leisure activities by some older adults actually reflect an early subclinical stage of dementia, with reduced participation in recreational activities a consequence of the early functional changes caused by the incipient dementia long before the cognitive deficits become apparent. Friedland et al. (2001) found that, by surrogate and retrospective report, individuals who went on to develop Alzheimer's disease were less likely to have participated in intellectual, recreational, and physical activities during early and middle adulthood (years prior to the development of dementia) than a control group; this association persisted even when age, sex, education, and income were controlled. According to odds ratios calculated by these authors, individuals who demonstrated reduced participation in intellectual, recreational, and/or physical activities over the four decades from early to middle adulthood had about a 250% increased risk of developing Alzheimer's disease. In other words, withdrawal from preferred recreational activities and interests may be a very early, and very strong, predictor of an incipient dementia, years before cognitive changes are observed.

Alternatively, Verghese et al. (2003) found that increased participation in cognitive, but not physical, leisure activities including reading, playing board games, and playing musical instruments, was associated with a reduced risk of both Alzheimer's disease and vascular dementia, even after adjustment for baseline cognitive status, verbal IQ, educational attainment, and presence of chronic medical illnesses. Statistically, a one-point increment in individuals' activities-per-day-per-week score was associated with a reduction of 7% in their risk of dementia, and individuals with scores in the highest third on the cognitive-activity scale had a risk of dementia that was 63% lower than those with scores in the lower third. Verghese and his co-authors also found that the protective benefits of recreational activities held even when they removed individuals from the analyses who developed dementia within seven years of participating in the study who, arguably, could have been showing decreased participation in activities as the very earliest symptoms of their incipient disease. Given that increased participation in leisure activities at baseline seemed to clearly predict a decreased risk of developing dementia over time, Verghese concluded that it is the recreational activities themselves that provide neuroprotective effects against dementia.

Community and Home-Based Recreational Programs

Recreational and leisure activities also hold promise for individuals with dementia and their caregivers, who typically strive to enable their loved ones to stay in their own homes and out of institutions for as long as possible. As Chabot (2013) noted in her review of community-based recreation programs for the elderly, dementia can cause significant limitations in physical and adaptive functioning and place a person at risk for isolation and withdrawal from daily activities. Individuals with dementia may also have less ability to tolerate and manage stimuli as their dementia progresses (Gitlin et al., 2009). Although aging and dementia typically bring declines in health and physical functioning, the presence and severity of dementia-related cognitive impairment and emotional and behavioral instability are the factors that most accurately predict decisions related to assisted living or nursing home placement (de Vugt et al., 2005). Similarly, studies of caregiver burden have also shown that behavioral problems (e.g., verbal outbursts, hitting, wandering) that arise in dementia may be as, or even more, distressing to caregivers than the memory impairment and other cognitive deficits that rob the person with dementia of their ability to participate meaningfully in activities of daily life (Schultz, O'Brien, Bookwala, & Fleissner, 1995). Thus, interventions that target the emotional and behavioral manifestations of dementia are likely to improve life satisfaction in both the individuals with dementia and their caregivers, and may even help to keep them in their preferred living situations longer.

In their 2012 article, Ito and Urakami described significant improvements in overall cognitive functioning and various day-to-day variables associated with quality of life, including interest level and involvement in activities, in older Japanese individuals with mild cognitive impairment or suspected dementia who participated in dementia-prevention classes. This program included classes held once per week for three months in one provincial district and once every two weeks for six months in another district. The specific content of the class was decided by each class leader and included exercise, recreation, creative activities, and/or local excursions. In their analyses, Ito and Urakami noted that more than 95% of the participants rated the classes as being either 'very effective' (59.8%) or 'slightly effective' (35.6%) in preventing dementia, and the individuals who participated in the districts where the classes included a range of activities showed more cognitive improvements on a measure of dementia severity than those who participated in programs that focused on fewer types of activities. In terms of their daily lives, participants also reported more involvement with others in their communities, improved mood and a more positive outlook, and an increased level of activity after participating in the classes, even when cognitive functioning did not improve.

Home-based activities programs, such as the Tailored Activity Program (TAP) developed by Gitlin and her colleagues (2008, 2009), also seek to improve quality of life and participation in activities of daily living by adjusting the environment of the person with dementia to better fit his or her cognitive abilities and level of tolerance for stimuli. As Gitlin et al. (2008) explain, TAP is based on the environmental vulnerability/reduced stress-threshold model, which posits that undesirable behaviors occur because individuals with dementia are less able to tolerate stimulation and also less able to shape the environment to meet their needs. A TAP-based intervention aims to reduce apathy, depressed affect, agitation, aggressiveness, and associated caregiver distress by providing the opportunity for meaningful activities matched to an individual's cognitive and functional abilities and his/her previous roles, habits, and interests. Activities fall within the six domains of reminiscence and photo activities, instrumental activities of daily living and household activities, games and recreation, arts and crafts, exercise and physical activity, and videos and music (Gitlin et al., 2009). Therapists also instruct the caregiver in cueing, rule relaxation, allowing for increased processing time, environmental set-up, and communication simplification, as well as personal stress-reduction techniques. In their pilot study of TAP efficacy, Gitlin and her co-authors (2008) noted reduced behavioral symptoms, increased engagement in activities outside of the program tasks, and improved feelings of self-efficacy among those providing care. Fitzsimmons and Buettner (2002) reviewed a less structured form of at-home recreational therapy for community dwelling adults with dementia and also noted a significant decrease in levels of passivity and agitation after two weeks of daily, individualized recreation therapy provided in the home by a recreation therapist.

Recreation and Leisure Activities in Long-Term Care Settings

As Kolanowski, Litaker, and Buettner (2005) and other authors have noted, leisure activities can also promote improved mood and quality of life, enhance appropriate and goal-directed behaviors, and reduce agitation and disruptive outbursts in residents of long-term care facilities. A number of authors refer to the Cohen-Mansfield, Marx, and Rosenthal (1989) article in citing the statistic that up to 90% of individuals with dementia exhibit problematic behaviors or symptoms, including agitation, wandering, apathy, anxiety, irritability, excessive motor behavior, and delusions and/or hallucinations at some point during the course of the disease progression. Additionally, some estimate that cognitive disorders and depression coexist in up to 15% to 24% of nursing home residents (Schumacher, Zedlick, & Frenzel, 1997). Individuals with dementia often have the added disadvantage of being unable to take specific actions or modify their ways of thinking, on which many therapeutic models rely, to improve their mood (Schreiner, Yamamoto, & Shiotani, 2005). Acute medical conditions, delirium, and/or pain are often to blame for these emotional and behavioral symptoms. However, even when physical causes are excluded, physicians are still most likely to conceptualize depression, anxiety, and problematic behaviors within the context of a medical model of disease and to choose interventions that are pharmacological in nature. Psychotropic use is common in long-term care facilities, with antidepressants, antipsychotics, benzodiazepines, and other sedatives often being the first-line agents chosen to manage depression, anxiety, agitation, hallucinations, and aggressive behaviors directed toward other residents and staff (Seitz et al., 2012). However, these medications also carry the risk of negative adverse effects, including falls, strokes, and death. Further, pharmacological treatments have been criticized for their potential to increase apathy, confusion, disorientation, and withdrawal due to sedation.

Concerns about the risks and downsides to the use of medications emphasize the need for non-pharmacological alternatives to effectively manage the behavioral symptoms of dementia. Recreational therapy and leisure activities seek to improve stimulation and reduce negative emotional and behavioral symptoms in individuals with dementia without the unwanted side effects of drugs. Such modalities typically take a person-centered approach to care that emphasizes the distinctiveness of the individual with dementia. Structured recreational programs increase stimulation, contribute to a more positive and predictable environment, and encourage more adaptive and appropriate ways for individuals with dementia to obtain positive reinforcement and meet their emotional and physical needs. Specifically, music therapy and exercise programs have been found to increase alertness in nursing home residents (Kovach & Henschel, 1996). Individuals with Alzheimer's dementia who participated in guided sensorimotor activities demonstrated less agitation and fewer uncooperative behaviors after these activities as compared to observations taken prior to the intervention (Buettner, 1999). Fitzsimmons and Buettner (2002) also described a reduction of the symptoms of depression, increased engagement with other residents, and higher levels of participation in other nursing home activities when individuals with dementia participated in an intensive two-week program of daily wheelchair biking. In an innovative study, Edwards and Beck (2002) noted increased food intake and weight gain when an aquarium was placed in the dining room of a dementia care unit.

Recreational and leisure activity programs have also shown promise in reducing the expression of negative behaviors in nursing home residents with more advanced dementia. Kolanowski et al. (2005) found that nursing home residents enrolled in activities matched to their current physical and cognitive skills and prior activity preferences exhibited decreased agitation, increased engagement, more positive affect, and less passivity than residents who were not engaged in any structured recreation activities. Schreiner et al. (2005) noted a seven-fold increase in 'happiness' behaviors (e.g., resident obviously smiling or laughing) during recreation time; further, they noted an absence of agitated, aggressive, or 'problem behaviors' that seemed to generalize to both recreation and unstructured activities when residents participated in structured recreational activities in a nursing home setting. Bober, McLellan, McBee, and Westreich (2002) observed lower levels of disturbing behaviors in residents who had participated in a 10-week program of art therapy than in those who did not participate. Koger, Chapin, and Brotons' 1999 metanalysis of 21 studies concluded that musical interventions, including dancing, creative movement, and singing led to a reduction in negative and disruptive behaviors and produced 'highly significant' effects with regard to improved social engagement, mood, and cognitive skills. Regardless of the specific activities chosen, the findings of the aforementioned researchers and others who have investigated the benefits of recreational programs in individuals with dementia using animals (Churchill, Safaoui, McCabe, & Baun, 1999), gardening (Detweiler et al., 2012), and one-on-one leisure activities including magazines, board games, and puzzles (Cohen-Mansfield, Libin, & Marx, 2007) provide support for the feasibility and efficacy of using non-pharmacological interventions in place of pharmacological treatments to manage agitation and other disruptive behaviors.

Selection of Specific Recreational and Leisure Activities for Individuals

Older individuals and those with dementia may be more prone to withdraw from and/or decline invitations to participate in recreational and leisure activities due to perceived and real limitations in their cognitive and physical abilities and their access to transportation. However, as a number of authors have pointed out, individuals with dementia do seem to remain fully capable of selecting, participating in, enjoying, and benefitting from leisure activities. Menne, Johnson, Whitlatch, and Schwartz (2012) asked the question: What specific leisure and recreational activities appeal to older adults with dementia, given that so many have physical and cognitive limitations that may make previously-enjoyed activities unfeasible and/or impractical? When Menne and colleagues conducted interviews with individuals with dementia and asked "What kinds of activities do you like to do now?", they found that responses could be coded into 18 different categories, namely, socializing, television/music/radio, exercise/recreation, cognitive/stimulation, housework/chores, yard work/garden/enjoy nature, cook/eat, religion/spirituality, volunteer/work, hobby, sleep/relax, theater/movies/concerts, shopping/errands, travel/vacation, keep busy/be at home, health maintenance, spouse/partner time, and unable to do anything. As the authors noted, the preferred activities reported as pleasant and enjoyable by persons with dementia were the very same activities chosen by those within the general older-adult population (Kelly, Steinkamp, & Kelly, 1987; Verbrugge, Gruber-Baldini, & Fozard, 1996). As will be discussed further below, other authors, including Schreiner et al. (2005) and Seitz et al. (2012), have described observable changes in facial expressions of happiness and enjoyment and reductions in agitated behaviors in individuals with more advanced stages of dementia after the introduction of recreational activities into their daily routines. Concisely put, individuals with dementia can certainly still enjoy, and benefit from, a wide array of recreational experiences and leisure activities both at home, in the community, and in long-term care settings.

In their 2002 article, Fitzsimmons and Buettner provide a helpful review of the Need-Driven Dementia-Compromised Behavior (NDB) model, originally put forth by Algase et al. (1996), which posits that agitation, verbal outbursts, withdrawal from the environment, and other disturbing behaviors are actually functional behaviors demonstrated by the cognitively-impaired individual in an attempt to fulfill certain basic needs, including the need to belong, the need to have an identity, and the need to feel capable and useful. According to Fitzsimmons and Buettner, selection of recreational and leisure activities should target specific behaviors and an individual's needs by taking into consideration the characteristics of the individual, including his/her current cognitive and physical limitations, previously preferred activities, and the situations in which the undesirable behaviors occur. Recreation therapy is not a one-size-fits-all enterprise, and selection of activities requires individualization and flexibility. In their review of an at-home recreational therapy program for community dwelling older adults with dementia presenting with disturbing behaviors, Fitzsimmons and Buettner reported an overall positive effect of individualized prescribed recreational activities, with significant reductions noted in caregiver reports of agitated behaviors on a dementia questionnaire, fewer passive behaviors and less clinging to the caregiver noted during observational periods, and desirable improvements in physiological measures, including heart rate and blood volume pulse readings. Although the selection of specific interventions should, again, be customized for the person with dementia, the caregiver and/or professional looking to incorporate recreational activities in the home might start with any of the following pursuits, which produced at least 80% engagement scores (percent of time engaged in task) in Fitzsimmons and Buettner's subjects: ambulation, bird activities, books, cards (adapted), clay/pottery, cognitive games, community outings, cooking, construction crafts, current events, exercise, feelings/discussion, flower arranging, gardening, golf (adapted), hint book (individualized notebook with names for family members, stores, doctors, and other categories), instrument playing, interior design, jewelry box (filled with costume jewelry, scarves, and fabric samples), massage, memory book, memory tea, message magnets, music (adapted), painting/drawing, photography, puzzles, reminiscing, watching fish, singing, wheelchair biking, and woodworking.

Kolanowski et al. (2009) provide additional guidance in the selection of recreational activities to reduce behavioral symptoms in individuals with dementia. These authors highlight the need to match the demands of an activity to an individual's skills and limitations by asking a number of questions, including but not limited to the following:

- What parts of the body are required?
- What level of coordination and/or strength is needed?
- How much immediate recall is necessary?
- What level of concentration is required and how many rules are there?
- What time of social interaction is involved?

Activity adaptation, or the modification of activities to meet the abilities of the individual, is also an option. The authors provide the example of the adaptation of the game of Bingo, including the use of homemade cards with fewer numbers, using only the numbers 1-20, eliminating the free space, and playing each game to 'black out', or until all of the squares are covered.

The interested reader is also directed to Gitlin and colleagues' previously mentioned TAP procedure, summarized in their 2008 and 2009 articles, which provides a framework for selecting and applying therapeutic interventions for persons with dementia. In the early TAP sessions, a trained interventionist meets with caregivers in the home to develop and introduce intervention goals, identify daily routines, and determine the previous and current interests of the cognitively-impaired person. The TAP assessment also employs neuropsychological testing and performance observations to identify the specific capacities and deficits of the individual with dementia. Activities are then developed, and a 2-3 page written plan is provided to the caregiver that catalogs the strengths of the individual with dementia and states the activity goal(s) and specific implementation techniques. The interventionist introduces one activity at a time through role-play or direct demonstration with the person with dementia, and caregivers are also instructed in stress reduction strategies to help them manage their own emotional responses. In the example given by Gitlin et al. (2008), the strengths of the individual with dementia included 'good hand skills,' 'good attention and tolerance with activities of interests,' and, 'able to distinguish between size, shape, and feel of objects'; the recommended activity was 'wood craft', and the activity goal was 'paint/stain wood boxes with familiar paintbrush for 30 minutes/one time per week'. The caregiver was provided with specific written instructions that addressed how to simplify the setting for the activity, how to simplify the activity itself, and how to enhance participation and communicate effectively, and she was also provided with stress management strategies for herself, including 'try to relax, take a few deep breaths', and 'feel good about yourself – you are doing a great job' (Appendix A). As Gitlin and colleagues concluded in their pilot study of TAP efficacy (2008), TAP-based interventions can provide clinically-relevant benefits for individuals with dementia and their caregivers and reduce behaviors that commonly trigger nursing home placement.

Conclusion

To conclude, a number of studies have shown the positive impacts of participatory recreation and leisure activities on overall health, cognition, mood, quality of life, caregiver satisfaction, and behavior in older individuals, specifically those with dementia. Limitations do include the modest number of large, high-quality, randomized trials in this area, and the heterogeneity of study designs and outcome measures makes it difficult to analyze the effectiveness of recreation therapy and leisure activity programs in real-world community and long-term care settings (Seitz et al., 2012). Nevertheless, as Fitzsimmons and Buettner (2002) note, preserving an individual's personal control, dignity, and quality of life is *an enormous and important task*, especially in individuals with dementia. Leisure activities and recreation therapy programs seem able to offer the elderly the opportunity to "attain happiness, purpose, a state of well-being, and an improved quality of life" (p. 367). The prevention and treatment of dementia has emerged as a major public health priority in the 21st century, and the studies reviewed in this chapter support the value of recreational and leisure activities as a non-pharmacological method for managing the cognitive, physical, emotional, and behavioral consequences of dementia.

References

Algase, D., Beck, C., Kolanowski, A., Whall, A., Berent, S., Richards, K., & Beattie, E. (1996). Need-driven dementia-compromised behavior: An alternative view of disruptive behavior. *American Journal of Alzheimer's Disease and Other Dementias, 6,* 10-19.

Bennett, K. M. (2005). Social engagement as a longitudinal predictor of objective and subjective health. *European Journal of Aging, 2,* 48-55.

Bober, S. J., McLellan, E., McBee, L., & Westreich, L. (2002). The feelings art group: A vehicle for personal expression in skilled nursing home residents with dementia. *Journal of Social Work in Long-Term Care, 1,* 73-86.

Brown, D., Zanuck, L.F., & Zanuck, R.D. (Producers), & Howard, R. (Director). (1985). *Cocoon* [Motion picture]. USA: 20th Century-Fox.

Buettner, L. L. (1999). Simple pleasures: A multilevel sensorimotor intervention for nursing home residents with dementia. *American Journal of Alzheimer's Disease and Other Dementias, 14,* 41-52.

Buettner, L. L., & Fitzsimmons, S. (2002). AD-venture program: Therapeutic biking for the treatment of depression in long-term care residents with dementia. *American Journal of Alzheimer's Disease and Other Dementias, 17,* 121-127.

Chabot, M. (2013). Review of programs to support engagement of older adults with mild to moderate dementia. *Gerontology, Special Interest Section Quarterly, 36,* 1-4.

Churchill, M., Safaoui, J., McCabe, B. W., & Baun, M. W. (1999). Using a therapy dog to alleviate the agitation and desocialization of people with Alzheimer's disease. *Journal of Psychosocial Nursing and Mental Health Services, 37,* 16-22.

Cohen, G. D., Perlstein, S., Chapline, J., Kelly, J., Firth, K. M., & Simmens, S. (2006). The impact of professionally conducted cultural programs on the physical health, mental health, and social functioning of older adults. *The Gerontologist, 46,* 726-734.

Cohen-Mansfield. J., Marx, M. S., & Rosenthal, A. S. (1989). A description of agitation in a nursing home. *Journal of Gerontology, 44*, M77-M84.

Cohen-Mansfield, J., Libin, A., & Marx, M. S. (2007). Nonpharmacological treatment of agitation: A controlled trial of systematic individualized intervention. *Journals of Gerontology, Series A: Medical Sciences, 62*, 908-916.

Csikszentmihalyi, M. (1998). *Flow: The psychology of optimal experience.* New York: Harper Perennial.

Detweiler, M. B., Sharma, T., Detweiler, J. G., Murphy, P. F., Lane, S., Carman, J., Chudhary, A. S., Halling, M. H., & Kim, K. Y. (2012). What is the evidence to support the use of therapeutic gardens for the elderly? *Psychiatry Investigation, 9*, 100-110.

de Vugt, M. E., Stevens, F., Aalten, P., Lousberg, R., Jaspers, N., & Verhey, F. R. J. (2005) A prospective study of the effects of behavioral symptoms on the institutionalization of patients with dementia. *International Psychogeriatrics, 17*, 577-589.

Edwards, N. E., & Beck, A. M. (2002). Animal-assisted therapy and nutrition in Alzheimer's disease. *Western Journal of Nursing Research, 24*, 697-712.

Fitzsimmons, S., & Buettner, L. L. (2002). Therapeutic recreation interventions for need-driven dementia-compromised behaviors in community-dwelling elders. *American Journal of Alzheimer's Disease and Other Dementias, 17*, 367-381.

Friedland, R. P., Fritsch, T., Smyth, K. A., Koss, E., Lerner, A. J., Chen, C. H, Petot, G. J., & Debanne, S. M. (2001). Patients with Alzheimer's disease have reduced activities in midlife as compared with healthy control-group members. *Proceedings of the National Academy of Sciences of the United States of America, 98*, 3440-3445.

Gitlin, L., Winter, L., Burke, J., Chernett, N., Dennis, M. P., & Hauck, W. W. (2008). Tailored activities to manage neuropsychiatric behaviors in persons with dementia and reduce caregiver burden: A randomized pilot study. *American Journal of Geriatric Psychiatry, 16*, 229-239.

Gitlin, L., Winter, L., Vause Earland, T., Herge, E. A., Chernett, N. L., Piersol, C. V., & Burke, J. P. (2009). The tailored activity program to reduce behavioral symptoms in individuals with dementia: Feasibility, acceptability, and replication potential. *The Gerontologist, 49*, 428-439.

Glass, T. A., de Leon, C. M., Marottoli, R. A., & Berkman, L. F. (1999). Population based study of social and productive activities as predictors of survival among elderly Americans. *BMJ, 319*, 478-483.

Grembowski, D., Patrick, D., Diehr, P., Durham, M., Beresford, S., Kay, E., & Hecht, J. (1993). Self-efficacy and health behavior among older adults. *Journal of Health and Social Behavior, 34*, 89-104.

Hall, C. B., Lipton, R. B., Sliwinski, M., Katz, M. J., Derby, C. A., & Verghese, J. (2009). Cognitive activities delay onset of memory decline in persons who develop dementia. *Neurology, 73*, 356-361.

Hebb, D. O. (1949). *The Organization of Behavior: A Neuropsychological Theory*. New York: Wiley and Sons.

Ito, Y., & Urakami, K. (2012). Evaluation of dementia-prevention classes for community-dwelling older adults with mild cognitive impairment. *Psychogeriatrics, 12*, 3-10.

Kelly, J. R., Steinkamp, M. W., & Kelly, J. R. (1987). Later-life satisfaction: Does leisure contribute? *Leisure Sciences, 9*, 189-200.

Koger, S. M., Chapin, M., & Brotons, M. (1999). Is music therapy an effective intervention for dementia? A meta-analytic review of the literature. *Journal of Music Therapy, 1*, 2-15.

Kolanowski, A., Fick, D. M., & Buettner, L. (2009). Recreational activities to reduce behavioral symptoms in dementia. *Geriatrics and Aging, 12*, 37-42. Kolanowski, A. M., Litaker, M., Buettner, L. (2005). Efficacy of theory-based activities for behavioral symptoms of dementia. *Nursing Research, 54*, 19-28.

Kovach, C. R., & Henschel, H. (1996). Planning activities for patients with dementia: A descriptive study of therapeutic activities on special care units. *Journal of Gerontological Nursing, 9*, 33-38.

Kumar, A. M, Tims, F., Cruess, D. G., Mintzer, M. J., Ironson, G., Lowenstein, D., Cattan, R., Fernandez, J. B., Eisdorfer, C., & Kumar, M. (1999). Music therapy increases serum melatonin levels in patients with Alzheimer's disease. *Alternative Therapies in Health and Medicine, 5,* 49-57.

Menne, H. L., Johnson, J. D., Whitlatch, C. J., & Schwartz, S. M. (2012). Activity preferences of persons with dementia. *Activities, Adaptation, and Aging, 36,* 195-213.

Mortimer, J. A., & Graves, A. B. (1993). Education and other socioeconomic determinants of dementia and Alzheimer's disease. *Neurology, 43*(Suppl. 4), S39-S44.

Scarmeas, N., Levy, G., Tang, M-X., Manly, J., & Stern, Y. (2001). Influence of leisure activity on the incidence of Alzheimer's disease. *Neurology, 57,* 2236-2242.

Scarmeas, N., & Stern, Y. (2003). Cognitive reserve and lifestyle. *Journal of Clinical and Experimental Neuropsychology, 25,* 625-633.

Schreiner, A. S., Yamamoto, E., & Shiotani, H. (2005). Positive affect among nursing home residents with Alzheimer's dementia: The effect of recreational activity. *Aging and Mental Health, 9,* 129-134.

Schultz, R., O'Brien, A. T., Bookwala, M.S., & Fleissner, K. (1995). Psychiatric and physical morbidity effects of dementia caregiving: Prevalence, correlates, and causes. *The Gerontologist, 35,* 771-791.

Schumacher, J., Zedlick, D. , & Frenzel, G. (1997). Depressive mood and cognitive impairment in results of old age nursing homes. *Zeitschrift fur Gerontologie und Geriatrie, 30,* 46-53.

Seitz, D. P., Brisbin, S., Herrmann, N., Rapoport, M. J., Wilson, K., Gill, S. S., Rines, J., Le Clair, K., & Conn, D. (2012). Efficacy and feasibility of nonpharmacological interventions for neuropsychiatric symptoms of dementia in long term care: A systematic review. *Journal of the American Medical Directors Association, 13,* 503-506.

Verbrugge, L. M., Gruber-Baldini, A., & Fozard, J. L. (1996). Age differences and age changes in activities: Baltimore Longitudinal Study of Aging. *Journals of Gerontology, Series B: Psychological Sciences, 51*, S30-S41.

Verghese, J., Lipton, R. B., Katz, M. J., Hall, C. B., Derby, C. A., Kuslansky, G., Ambrose, A. F., Sliwinski, M., & Buschke, H. (2003). Leisure activities and the risk of dementia in the elderly. *New England Journal Medicine, 348*, 2508-2516.

Wang, H., Xu, W., & Pei, J. (2012). Leisure activities, cognition, and dementia. *Biochimica et Biophysica Acta-Molecular Basis of Disease, 1822*, 482-491.

CHAPTER 10

Cognitive Interventions to Address Symptoms of Dementia

Aaron W. Powell and Samuel T. Gontkovsky

As discussed in the previous chapters, the engagement in certain behaviors and interventions may have a positive effect on brain health, offering neuroprotective benefits through delaying the onset of cognitive problems and/or slowing the progression of cognitive symptoms that have already developed. The non-pharmacological approaches reviewed to this point, however, are either non-specific to brain health or take a more indirect approach in attempting to improve cognitive and functional status. In other words, the previously discussed interventions are beneficial not only for the brain but for other organs and systems in the body, as well. Thus, they attempt to positively impact cognition by promoting benefits in overall functioning and general health.

As examples of non-specificity, consider that the dietary recommendations reviewed in Chapter 6 for reducing the detrimental effects on brain cells from free radical-induced, oxidative stress also apply to cells of the body outside of the brain. Therefore, a healthy diet not only benefits the brain but also the entire body. The principles of exercise and physical activity discussed in Chapter 7 are similar. Although exercise clearly functions to promote brain health, it essentially also functions to promote general bodily health. Thus, these behavioral choices and interventions can be described as non-specific to brain functioning. As an example of indirectness, recall the various social and recreational activities discussed in Chapters 4 and 9, respectively. Research suggests that engagement in activities and interventions in these domains have been shown positively influence affect, cognitive functioning, and behavior, but do so without isolating cognition, specifically.

In contrast to these approaches for promoting brain health and functioning, the cognitive activities and interventions discussed in this chapter are relatively specific to the brain and more direct in targeting specific cognitive processes (e.g., attention, memory, language, visual-spatial perception, executive functioning, etc.). In terms of directness, memory interventions specifically target the improvement of memory processes. For example, one would not necessarily expect engagement in cognitive training to lower blood glucose levels in persons with diabetes mellitus. In this light, this chapter is somewhat distinct in comparison to the previous chapters exploring interventions. Herein, we will provide an overview of the cognitive activities and interventions that can best act as a protective barrier to the onset and progression of dementia symptoms.

Cognitive functioning is a product of multiple factors, such as age, occupation, education, nature of leisure activities, and diet. Individuals, therefore, present with unique risk and protective factors and consequently differ with respect to the impact of neurological disease on their mental and physical functioning. Yet, there seems to be significant support around the hypothesis that the degree of cognitive activity during one's lifetime can act to protect against cognitive decline and dementia. In their prospective study of 724 healthy participants, Wilson et al. (2002) performed neurological evaluations every year for an average of five years, at the same time gathering data on activities labeled as cognitive in nature, such as watching television, listening to the radio, reading, or playing games. A person in the 90th percentile of frequent cognitive activity was found to be 47% less likely to develop Alzheimer's disease (AD) than a person at the 10th percentile. This effect was found to be independent of education and age.

A literature review by Valenzuela and Sachdev (2009) examined 22 studies, aggregating data from over 29,000 individuals, and found results of an overall risk reduction for dementia of 46% for high levels of cognitive activity. The researchers argue that a number of studies have demonstrated a similar protective effect from increased cognitive activity later in life; further, this effect is dose dependent (i.e., the more the better). Still, given concerns of causality given correlational methodologies of many of the studies, Valenquela and Sachdev (2009) performed a more rigorous, targeted review of seven intervention studies, representing a cumulative sample of 3,194 healthy older individuals. They found in the meta-analysis that a dose of two to three months of cognitive intervention may have long-lasting and persistent protective effects on cognition over a number of years, and training protocols appear to generalize to domains beyond those of the intervention. Also, combining cognitive interventions with physical exercise seems to have the greatest cognitive benefit.

Cognitive Reserve

The theory of cognitive reserve suggests that higher levels of cognitively stimulating activities throughout life may act as a protective mechanism following the onset of brain injury or disease. As an example, individuals who acquire higher levels of education and hold mentally stimulating occupations throughout their lives may exhibit, following the development of Alzheimer's disease, a discrepancy between the degree of pathology within the brain and the associated clinical manifestations of the disease, such that marked neuropathology may be exhibited in only subtle cognitive and behavioral difficulties. According to this theory, those with higher reserve have greater cognitive resources, which permit the optimization or maximization of functioning through differential recruitment of brain networks and/or alternative cognitive strategies.

Helzner, Scarmeas, Cosentino, Portet, and Stern (2007) examined the influence of cognitive activity on the rate of cognitive decline among those who developed AD during study follow-up, the primary outcome being rate of change in a composite measure of cognition. A complete neuropsychological battery assessed the domains of memory, abstract reasoning, visual-spatial, language, and executive speed. The primary predictor variable was self-reported type of leisure activity, classified as intellectual, social, or physical. Category-specific analysis demonstrated that lack of intellectual activity was associated with faster cognitive decline.

In support of Helzner et al. (2007), Hall et al. (2009) found upon examination of 101 participants who were cognitively normal at baseline but developed dementia at follow-up that those individuals in the upper quartile of activity had cognitive decline delayed by 1.3 years as compared with those in the lower quartile of cognitive activity. The researchers argue that engagement in cognitive activities in later life would likely maintain cognitive vitality. Verghese et al. (2003) measured cognitive activity in 469 participants over 75 years of age. The median follow up period was five years. A one-point increment in the cognitive activity outcome score was significantly associated with 7% reduction in dementia risk. Participants with scores in the highest third in measured cognitive activity had a risk of dementia that was 63% lower than that among those with scores in the lowest third.

224

Some researchers have called the generalizability of the findings of such studies into question. Park and Bischof (2013) argue the weakness of many of the findings due to their correlational nature, suggesting that it remains unclear as to whether maintaining a mentally-active lifestyle offers the protection or if those who are protected tend to also maintain a mentally-active lifestyle. They further argue that such studies have other issues that make them problematic when used in support of potentially overstated claims that older adults can improve their cognitive performance, or even prevent Alzheimer's disease and other forms of dementia, through brain-training exercises.

Nature of Research and Terms

In addition to the cognitive reserve argument, it is clear that neuronal damage is no longer considered irrecoverable. As discussed in Chapter 3, the brain is now understood to be plastic and regenerative (Yu et al., 2009), even during adulthood. Studies have shown that in animal models of dementia, neuronal stimulation and rehabilitation can be achieved through environmental enrichment, such as larger cages as well as a variety of running wheels and play tubes, all shifted on a weekly basis (Jankowsky et al., 2005). In essence, the goal in this chapter is to explore the best human versions of these running wheels and play tubes, or to determine what is currently considered the best cognitive interventions among humans. Still, Park and Bischof (2013) argue that despite the power of recent tools for examining neural function of the brain, we still do not know if changes observed are due to neural plasticity or "merely represent shifts in strategy" (p. 117).

The results from the literature are often at odds with each other, but there is also disparity in quality of the studies. There often are issues in obtaining the necessary sample sizes or developing the appropriate control groups to protect against the influences of other variables. There also is a significant lack of standardization in assessments and intervention protocols, posing challenges for replication and external validity.

Some studies and literature reviews, in fact, have found little promise with cognitive interventions significantly improving cognition. One such review (Plassman, Williams, Burke, Holsinger, & Benjamin, 2010) used very restrictive criteria for inclusion, arguably limiting their results and calling into question the manner in which this review informs future practice. The authors grouped potential mediating variables into the five categories of nutritional, medical, economic or behavioral, toxic environmental exposure, and genetic. They found that only current tobacco use, the E4 genotype, and certain other medical conditions to be significantly associated with cognitive impairment. There was limited evidence even for the role of diet. One of the reviewed studies did report positive effects of exercise after 18 months follow-up. Another study (the ACTIVE study, described further below) examined cognitive training and concluded positive domain specific effects.

Given the toll that dementia takes on the brain, however, the lack of statistically significant, positive results may arguably be of little surprise and should be considered in relation to controls. Yu et al. (2009) reported an average Mini-Mental State Examination (MMSE; Folstein, Folstein, & McHugh, 1975) improvement across studies of approximately 1.5 points, while control groups typically declined 3 points per year, a more than 4-point spread. Scores on the MMSE range from 0-30, with higher scores indicating better cognitive functioning. Therefore, contextually, one point on the MMSE is actually fairly practically significant, if not statistically significant, since a three-point decline without intervention is relatively dramatic. Furthermore, according to Yu et al. (2009), interventions are relatively simple and cost effective to disseminate and do not result in the adverse effects often associated with medications.

There also is some debate in the field as to the different forms of cognitive interventions or the use of terms to define them, further complicating interpretation and application. Herein, the three main forms outlined by Clare and Woods (2004) will be used to interpret and organize results in the literature:

- *Cognitive stimulation:* increases cognitive and social functioning more globally, using a non-specific approach. The rationale is that cognitive functions, such as memory, do not operate independently.

- *Cognitive training:* incorporates guided practice on a set of specific tasks using specific techniques to solicit particular aspects of cognitive functioning, such as language or attention. The rationale is that regular practice will improve, or at least maintain, functioning in cognitive domains and that effects of practice will generalize beyond training.

- *Cognitive rehabilitation:* individualizes the training program to the specific impairments, needs, and interests of the patient. The aim is to maintain optimal physical, psychological, and social functioning in an integrated, holistic way, thus facilitating participation in preferred activities and valued social roles in everyday contexts.

The following three studies highlight the positive results that are possible with each of these types of intervention.

Aguirre, Woods, Spector, and Orrell (2013) specifically examined cognitive stimulation in their review of the literature. Of 94 studies identified, only nine met the inclusion criteria. Six more studies were included from a previous review by some of the same authors for a total of 15 studies. For the collective total of 657 participants, treatment groups showed significant improvement over control groups across cognitive and quality-of-life measures. Furthermore, the additional positive effect of cognitive stimulation over medication was demonstrated. The authors argue that this result defends the premise that cognitive stimulation is effective independent of medications and that any association results in even better cognitive performance.

In the ACTIVE study (Willis et al., 2006), one of the more widely cited studies, a relatively large sample of 2,802 healthy participants was randomized to a control and the three cognitive training intervention groups of memory, reasoning, and speed of processing. Each intervention produced immediate and lasting improvement in the cognitive ability of training. With the booster training at 11 and 35 months, the improvements for reasoning and speed of processing still were significantly improved after five years. The reasoning group had significant impact on self-reported ADLs at five years, and the effect sizes for memory and speed of processing training were close to that of reasoning.

Werd, Boelen, Rikkert, and Kessels (2013) specifically examined errorless learning among individuals with dementia, a method of cognitive rehabilitation that involves immediate error correction, graded tasks, modeling next steps, fading cues and prompts, and spaced retrieval. Most of the studies reviewed focused on teaching participants the use of common devices, such as cell phones, microwaves, answering machines, or coffee makers. Face-name associations and orientation skills also were common

227

skills. Of the 25 studies examined, 17 demonstrated significant improvement of participant performance over control groups. Furthermore, many studies also found in follow-up assessments that effects were preserved over time.

Reviews of the Literature

Jean, Bergeron, Thivierge, & Simard (2010) closely examined 15 cognitive rehabilitation studies in individuals with mild cognitive impairment (MCI) of the amnestic type, only seven of which completed extensive neuropsychological evaluations for assessments. Number of sessions and duration of the intervention varied across the studies. Still, the authors found that 44% of the objective measures of memory revealed significant improvements. Memory interventions included errorless learning, errorful learning, spaced retrieval, method of loci, mind mapping, visual imagery, face-name associations, categorization, hierarchical organization, chunking, and cueing. Only 12% of the objective measures of other cognition scores, however, were significantly improved. An important note here is that the reviews and studies explored below find reversed outcomes for memory in relation to other cognitive domains (Gates, Sachdev, Fiatarone Singh, & Valenzuela, 2011; Martin, Clare, Altgassen, Cameron, & Zehnder, 2011). Subjective or qualitative measures in the Jean et al. (2010) study presented more positive results in that 49% of measurements of memory, quality of life, and mood were statistically improved after interventions.

A Cochrane review (Martin et al., 2011) examined studies on cognition-based interventions for healthy people and individuals with MCI. Only data on memory training could be pooled for analysis, as studies providing data on training in speed of processing, attention, and executive functioning were excluded due to lack of correspondence to the review's strict inclusion criteria. Twenty-four studies were pooled for a total of 2,229 participants. For both the healthy and MCI groups, studies showed significant improvements for the treatment group. Treatment effects were not significantly better than the no-contact controls, however, with the exception of two of the seven cognitive domains, immediate and delayed recall. Thus, the researchers concluded, "alternative interventions do just as well as cognitive interventions, and the training interventions cannot be regarded as effective because they do not improve on the effects of active control conditions" (p. 10).

In another review of the literature, Gates et al. (2011) compared outcomes between cognitive training (computerized) and memory strategy training. Mean number of sessions for memory strategies was eight, while it was much higher for cognitive exercises at 57, thus posing challenges for comparison. Overall, large effects were found for 50% of the memory outcomes in cognitive exercise trials compared to 37% of memory strategy outcomes. Cognitive training also improved mood and decreased depressive symptoms. Greater volume of cognitive training also showed greater effect. Memory strategy training was associated with decreases in objective memory performance in two trials, at three and six months. Moderate-sized effects were found on memory performance and global cognitive measures in a majority of studies, with computer-based cognitive exercise studies exhibiting an increased frequency of stronger effect sizes. Cognitive training also displayed enhanced generalization of benefits compared to memory strategy training. Therefore, the authors postulate that cognitive training involving multiple cognitive domains appears to demonstrate greater efficacy than uni-modal memory strategy training. Multi-domain exercises provide a broader range of cognitive challenges to directly stimulate plasticity and, in several studies, have resulted in improved global cognitive function.

Calleo et al. (2012) examined four intervention trials of cognitive rehabilitation and the associated impact on executive dysfunction in participants with cognitive impairments related to Parkinson's disease. In one study, a computerized cognitive rehabilitation program resulted in significantly improved verbal fluency, immediate and delayed logical memory, and visuospatial reasoning. Another study found positive, self-reported results for increased attention and enjoyment. There were two random clinical trials. In one, 12 participants in only 10 sessions of cognitive training yielded improved executive functioning and maintained working memory; the control group had decline in working memory. In the other, 18 participants demonstrated improved performance across several cognitive domains in a four-week clinical trial. The researchers found no difference in effect between those with and without MCI.

Yuill and Hollis (2011) performed a review of the literature that specifically focused on cognitive stimulation therapy (CST), through the perspective of occupational therapy. CST includes themed sessions of reality orientation or reminiscence therapy. Firstly, the authors outlined their preferred paradigm of the humanistic, client-centered approach of occupational therapy, as opposed to cognitive training, which they argued fails to consider cognition within a real-life context and is thus an insensitive experience for individuals with dementia. The authors claimed that CST is more person-centered, fostering individual strengths through structured, functionally-oriented activities that may be adapted according to needs. A common trend among study results was that CST interventions were found to have the potential to enhance cognitive function or at least slow the rate of cognitive decline. Though changes on outcome measures were relatively small, the authors claim the results are still clinically meaningful. Half of the included studies reported positive functional outcomes, including enhanced emotion regulation and interpersonal relationships. The authors noted one study that associated CST participation with enhanced quality of life, improved relationships with significant others, and increased energy levels and ability to perform chores. Another study in the review found that CST improved participant communication while reducing symptoms of apathy and irritability. Intervention descriptions were limited, according to the authors, but some positive components were observed:

- Creating a climate of acceptance and appreciation,
- Adopting a reactivation approach,
- Providing caregivers with goal-oriented home programs, and
- Implementing ongoing sessions to maintain function over time.

In their review of the literature, Sitzer, Twamley, and Jeste (2006) targeted all psychosocial interventions that had cognition as an outcome variable. They found the two basic categories of compensatory and restorative strategies. According to the authors, the aim of compensatory strategies is to teach new ways of performing cognitive tasks by working around cognitive deficits, such as organizing or visualizing information to be remembered, or environmental cues. Restorative strategies attempt to improve functioning in specific domains, with the ultimate goal of returning function to premorbid levels; examples include spaced retrieval, drills, vanishing cues, errorless learning, reality orientation, and reminiscence therapy. Since reviews by other researchers had found only a small effect size on cognitive and behavioral functioning in response to cognitive interventions, with magnitudes rarely quantified, the researches were less restrictive in this review, though they confirmed that studies rated as higher quality were less optimistic on the efficacy of cognitive interventions. Between restorative and compensatory approaches, individual versus group treatment, or placebo versus wait-list control group, there were no significant differences in effect sizes. The review found that while cognitive interventions can improve cognitive and functional abilities of AD, effect sizes are generally small. The most efficacious cognitive interventions were restorative in nature, such as general cognitive stimulation, involving prompting recall of remote memories, practicing conversation skills, problem solving, creative activities, computerized visuospatial drills, and memory drills emphasizing repetition. Four of the five reports with the most beneficial results employed general stimulation techniques, and greater effect sizes were achieved with individual treatment versus groups; the authors argued that these findings underscored "the potential role that family members might play in providing general cognitive stimulation" (p. 87). Compensatory techniques were found to be less effective; individuals with AD may forget the strategies or forget to use them. An exception, however, was that the greatest overall effect was observed on measures of performance based ADLs, from studies that used compensatory procedural memory strategies. For the specific domains of cognitive function, the authors found negative or minimal effects on visuospatial functioning and language, small effects on motor speed and visual learning, medium effects on executive functioning, and large effects on verbal and visual learning.

Cooper et al. (2012) argue that quality of life is consistently viewed by older adults to be of greater importance than outcomes specific to dementia-related disease (specific cognitive domains), yet little is known regarding the positive or negative effects of interventions on quality of life. They noted that poorer quality of life has not been associated with greater activity limitation. They reviewed the literature that has examined quality-of-life outcomes for participants living at home or in institutions and organized the studies into intervention groups:

- **At home intervention:**
    - family caregiver coping strategies
    - activity programs combined with caregiver coping
    - cognitive stimulation therapy

    o care management software
    o discussion groups
    o individual cognitive rehabilitation
    o exercise

- **Institution intervention:**
    o group cognitive stimulation therapy
    o staff training and individualized care plans
    o other (i.e. kit-based activities, aromatherapy, reminiscence)

For the care home studies, only the group receiving cognitive stimulation therapy experienced significant improvement in quality of life. Of all the intervention studies for at home participants, those that appeared effective included the customized care management or family caregiver coping support combined with tailored activities and interventions. The authors recommended that future studies examine effects of this combination on participants with professional caregivers.

The final review in this summary was quite extensive in examining the efficacy of non-pharmacological therapeutic approaches (Olazarán et al., 2010). Over 1,300 candidate studies were reduced to a selection of 179 that met inclusion criteria; of these, only 13 of the studies were considered of high quality. Seven of the 13 studies had positive results. The studies collectively examined 26 intervention categories. The multi-component intervention of education and support for the caregivers received the highest recommendation for delaying institutionalization and death of persons receiving care. As the authors described, "This important outcome in relation to both quality of life and cost was not found with any other treatment approach on the basis of high-quality evidence" (p. 171). For other outcomes, such as cognition, ADL performance, and mood, effect was similar to that with pharmacological treatment.

Generally, while the study results are conflicting, they still can provide informative recommendations. Firstly, simply by virtue of the extra attention bestowed upon control groups improvements can be found; thus, even minimal intervention may be warranted. Though, there generally seems to be a finding of dose effect, such that the more intervention, the better the outcomes. Also, interventions appear to be just as effective in individuals with mild cases of dementia, if not more so, as with those who are asymptomatic. Furthermore, while some studies may not have statistically positive results, the participants at least maintain cognition or slow the progression of impairment; qualitative data and analysis demonstrates that clients do respond positively, at minimum feeling as though they are making some progress. Involving the client in setting goals for person-centered intervention certainly would be more advantageous it seems, and individualized attention does seem more effectives than group-based interventions. Finally, the combination of cognitive stimulation and training or restorative strategies appear to be more effective than isolated memory strategies or simple, compensatory strategies. The aforementioned reviews are a worthy starting point, but further research is necessary and greater attention to optimal study design and methodology is warranted.

Cognitive Stimulation

In a single-blind, randomized controlled trial, one study evaluated a cognitive stimulation therapy piloted in three facilities and a day center for individuals with dementia (Spector et al., 2003). There were 201 total participants, with 115 in treatment and 86 serving as controls. None were on cholinesterase inhibitors (see Chapter 2). The activities of the control group were basic ADLs and, in some cases, typical games, such as bingo, music and singing, arts and crafts, and activity groups were included. The treatment group received a 14-session program, twice per week for 45 minutes for seven weeks. Sessions incorporated cognitive stimulation and reality orientation activities, including topics of using money, word games, and famous faces. At follow-up, the treatment group tested significantly higher on measures of cognition and quality of life. No difference was found between the groups for functional ability, anxiety, or depression. The center emerged as a significant covariate, with poor staff-patient relationships in some cases being too strong a negative environment to overcome. The researchers calculated that six to eight people would need treatment for one to benefit, depending on the statistical degree of benefit. Compared to the effectiveness of medications, for small improvements or simply maintaining ability, the program was deemed to be not quite as effective as rivastigmine, donepezil, and galantamine. For greater improvements, cognitive stimulation did as well as galantimine or tacrine and substantially better than rivastigmine or the 5 mg dosage of donepezil. Only the 10 mg dose of donepezil had a smaller number needed to treat. The researchers noted that the pharmacological treatments last 24-30 weeks, compared with only seven weeks of cognitive stimulation in this study. Further, they noted that the drugs do have some negative side effects.

Another randomized controlled trial (Onder et al., 2005) evaluated the effectiveness of a long-term, home-based program of reality orientation on cognitive function of 156 patients with AD taking cholinesterase inhibitors. Caregivers provided three orientation sessions per week for 25 consecutive weeks. Sessions generally lasted 30 minutes. Caregivers also were encouraged to informally stimulate patients in reality-based communication two to three times throughout the day, focusing on personal, time, and space orientation as well as discussion of news and topics of interest. The treatment group showed slight improvement in scores, while the scores of the control group declined. The effect was more powerful for the moderately impaired individuals than the mildly impaired individuals. There was no difference in other assessments, such as those assessing ADLs or depression. The authors concluded that reality orientation enhanced the effects of donepezil on cognition.

A study of reality orientation (Orrell, Spector, Thorgrimsen, & Woods, 2005), or cognitive stimulation therapy (CST), examined the effect of follow-up maintenance sessions for 201 participants with dementia recruited from 23 residential homes. Fourteen 45-minute sessions were provided twice per week in groups of five. Topics included money, word games, and famous faces. The treatment group improved significantly over the controls on the main outcome measures of cognition and quality of life. The researchers also tested whether 16 maintenance sessions improved cognition over the initial program. Thirty-five participants from the original group were examined and included eight in maintenance CST, 12 with original CST only, and 15 baseline controls who received no treatment. Changes in MMSE scores were significant between the groups. The mean improvement for the maintenance group was 1.9 points on the MMSE; there was a .7 point decline for the control group. The CST-only group with no maintenance, improved initially but then declined to one point below baseline. There were no differences in quality of life, communication, or behavioral function. The researchers suggested that longer interventions were more effective and, in fact, necessary to see improvements in measures of quality of life for people with dementia.

Another study of cognitive stimulation (Breuil et al., 1994) investigated some unique strategies that are arguably a blend of cognitive training and cognitive stimulation, such as starting with a dotted outline of an umbrella and asking patients to connect the dots and progressing to a discussion of associated words to talk about the weather in the local region. The researchers had 59 patients, 29 of whom were provided with stimulation and 27 who were not provided with stimulation. For five weeks, groups of ten patients received ten, one-hour sessions facilitated by two therapists, a physician, and a psychologist. Each group was assessed at baseline and at week six. The researchers found no change in verbal fluency, but there was significant improvement in other aspects of cognition, including memory. They conclude based on these findings that global cognitive function stimulation over a period of five weeks can have significant improvement for patients with degenerative dementia. The researchers were flexible with the implementation of the program and therefore had strong participation, but they argue that patients would likely have refused such interference over a lengthy period of time.

Mapelli, Di Rosa, Nocita, & Sava (2013) examined the effect of cognitive stimulation versus placebo and control groups for individuals with both mild and moderate dementia. The experimental and placebo groups received eight weeks of intervention consisting of five one-hour sessions per week. The placebo group received occupational therapy as well as structured creative and recreation activities. The control group continued with usual activities in the group home. The cognitive stimulation started with personal, spatial, and temporal orientation sessions and then moved into the cognitive training arena with exercises focusing on various cognitive domains, including memory, language, attention, and logic. The researchers found no difference between the mild-dementia and moderate-dementia groups. Only the experimental group exhibited improvement in cognitive performance and behavioral symptoms.

Zanetti et al. (2001) sought to investigate the effectiveness of a procedural memory intervention on the performance of ADLs. Their argument was that training of ADLs is more reality-based and should be more useful than completion of puzzles on a computer screen. All participants were women and had a diagnosis of probable AD, with 10 participating in the training group and six in the control group. The treatment group received training on 13 procedural memory tasks, such as washing hands or brushing teeth, and this group had a statistically significant decrease in the time to complete tasks. The control group showed a slight increase in time to complete tasks. The researchers argued that procedural training improved participant outcomes because participants developed greater motivation when allowed to complete tasks on their own, with caregivers taking a "hands off" approach while providing basic guidance.

Another study (Niu, Tan, Guan, Zhang, & Wang, 2010) examined the benefits of cognitive stimulation therapy on neuropsychiatric symptoms in AD, such as paranoia and hallucinations. All 16 participants had a "wash-out" period of any drugs they might have been taking, except for cholinesterase inhibitors. The intervention involved 10-weeks of bi-weekly, 45-minute individual sessions. The control group showed a slight worsening while the experimental group demonstrated significant improvement in the neuropsychiatric symptoms. Also, a general improvement in cognition was demonstrated by the experimental group. Some of the interventions involved the following:

- Reality orientation (i.e., verbal orientation as to time, place, and person)
- Verbal fluency
- Overlapping figure task (e.g., numbers, letters, animals)
- Photo-story task, using errorless learning strategy

Farina et al. (2002) compared a cognitive stimulation intervention with cognitive training. The researchers' results in a past study comparing two different cognitive-specific techniques demonstrated improved cognition and function; however, there was no improvement in behavior or caregiver distress, which the authors believed challenges the legitimacy of such interventions. Therefore, they decided to investigate whether psychotherapy and more social-oriented or group-oriented approaches would show better efficacy than cognitive-specific strategies with regard to functional and attitudinal improvements. Thirty-two patients were divided into groups of four. Some were being prescribed cholinesterase inhibitors and antidepressants during the study. Each group was assigned to one of the two treatment groups. Each treatment involved 15 sessions spread over six weeks, weighted with more sessions in the first few weeks. Each session lasted three hours and was preceded by a shared meal to provide for socialization. Global stimulation entailed various recreational activities, such as singing, dancing, party games (scrabble or bingo), and group comments on pictures/collage. All interventions were facilitated by specially trained volunteer staff who were supported by rehabilitation therapists. Cognitive-specific activities involved a combination of procedural memory training on activities of daily living and neuropsychological rehabilitation of residual functions, including attention, short-term memory, language, visuospatial perception, and categorization. Participants received a full battery of assessments at the outset of the study as well as at eight weeks and six-month follow-up. Comparing baseline with post training, a substantial reduction in behavioral disturbances was detected for global stimulation. There was also improvement in performance on functional living skills and verbal fluency. The cognitive-specific group improved on a different scale of functional improvement but did not show superior efficacy. At six months, the global groups showed improvement in behavior and caregiver distress. The researchers concluded that a global cognitive stimulation treatment can be linked to a significant improvement for behavioral and functional aspects.

Another study by Schecker, Pirnay-Dummer, Schmidtke, Hentrich-Hesse, and Borchardt, (2013) compared cognitive stimulation with cognitive training in individuals with dementia. The authors examined the four functional areas of cognition, language processing, ADLs, and quality of life. While the two treatment groups appeared initially to compare favorably overall, both with significant improvement over control groups, a closer look at specific functional areas demonstrated that the participants receiving cognitive stimulation achieved better results on all functional areas, with the exception of ADLs. Though the participants receiving cognitive training had better results for ADL performance, the other functional areas declined, though not as poorly as in the control group.

This section concludes with two studies on the predictors of the success of cognitive stimulation therapy. Aguirre et al. (2013) sought to determine whether socio-demographic characteristics or the use of medications could predict positive response to cognitive stimulation therapy. The stimulation utilized was that described by Spector et al. (2003) consisting of two 45-minute sessions per week for seven weeks. Their findings reinforce the efficacy of stimulation for benefiting cognitive performance and quality of life of individuals with dementia, and that this benefit is above and beyond the benefits from medication. They report that those who benefit most from treatment seem to be women and people over 80 years of age. Binetti et al. (2013) studied 145 participants' responses to cognitive stimulation interventions involving reality orientation (12 one-hour group sessions two times per week), global reactivation (12 one-hour group sessions three times per week), and memory training (eight individual sessions of 150 minutes each). Sixty-eight of the participants responded to these interventions with significant improvement in cognitive scores on assessments. The variables found by the authors to be the most predictive at baseline for the performance improvement among these individuals was high levels of awareness/insight, preserved functional abilities, and lack of behavioral disorders. The participants did not differ on other variables, such as age, gender, educational level, family history, medications, and functional status.

In their cognitive stimulation literature review outlined previously, Aguirre et al. (2013) found strong evidence to support the use of cognitive stimulation to improve cognitive performance and quality of life of people with dementia symptoms. They found that no differences were observed, however, for ADLs, behavior, or mood, and there were no findings with respect to type or amount of treatment. Many researchers do observe that assessments are likely not sensitive enough to gauge functional differences in response to changes in cognition.

Aquirre et al. (2013) did find that positive effects may generally last up to three months and that continued reinforcement of stimulation would be required for more long-term results. The trials explicated above generally reinforce the findings by Aquirre et al. (2013). When interventions focus particularly on non-cognitive outcomes, such as mood, behavior, or ADLs, positive results appear obtainable (Niu et al., 2010; Zanetti et al., 2001). The research on cognitive stimulation does appear more positive, overall, as compared with studies on cognitive training, and the comparison studies outlined herein reinforce this impression (Farina et al., 2002; Schecker et al., 2013). Such findings arguably hold intuitive and practical sense as well, since cognitive stimulation is more contextual, holistic, and reality-based than cognitive training. Finally, researchers seem to agree that cognitive stimulation is at least as effective as medications and combined with medications, results in positive outcomes over and above those obtained by medications alone.

Cognitive Training

Though discussed in the context of patients with schizophrenia, Kurtz, Seltzer, Shagan, Thime, and Wexler (2007) examined the effects of cognitive remediation on attention, verbal and non-verbal episodic and working memory, and language processing skills. The control group in this study received basic computer skills training and participated in the same amount of computer time with the same amount of clinician interaction as the cognitive specific-training group. Forty-two participants were divided into the two groups. After the twelve-month trial, neurocognitive testing demonstrated that function in specific cognitive domains improved for both groups. For the treatment group, only working memory improved significantly over that of the computer skills control group. Significant improvement was identified in the control group's non-specific neurocognitive abilities. Therefore, Kurtz et al. suspect that development and use of computer skills alone is a major mechanism for the results of computer-based cognitive training.

Another study (Barnes et al., 2009) tested the effects of a computer-based cognitive training program compared with more passive computer-based activities. Training was completed in the homes of participants with MCI using study-provided computers. The program involved seven exercises designed to improve processing speed and accuracy in the auditory cortex. The control group listened to audio books, read online news, and played a computer game. No significant difference was found between the groups in any of the cognitive categories, though measures of learning and delayed memory trended toward favoring the intervention group. As with the Kurtz et al. study (2007), this investigation demonstrates that general activities with a computer can perhaps be equally beneficial as much more involved and expensive cognitive training programs in certain contexts.

Gaitán et al. (2013) compared paper-based, cognitive training with combined paper-based and computer-based cognitive training for three months between 60 participants. The traditional training took place in one-hour sessions three times per week. The additional computer-based training also was delivered approximately three times per week; the duration of the sessions was dependent on user performance. The researchers found no significant difference in cognitive performance between the two groups at one year follow-up assessment. The authors suspected there may have been a ceiling effect. They did find that the addition of computer-based training had improvement in anxiety and decision making among the participants.

A study by Tárraga et al. (2006) compared computer-based cognitive training interventions with a cognitive stimulation program as a control, both as an adjunct to cholinesterase inhibitors. The multimedia system had 19 different exercises across several cognitive domains. There was a total of 72 sessions, which were administered with participants three times per week. Sessions were initially 15 minutes in duration and progressively expanded to 25 minutes. It should be noted that none of the participants had previous experience with a computer. An integrated psycho-stimulation program (IPP) acted as the control, 120 minutes in the morning and 90 minutes in the afternoon. It consisted of cognitive stimulation tasks, various recreation workshops, and reinforcement of instrumental ADLs. Forty-three patients, divided fairly equally among the three groups, completed the study. A battery of assessments was performed at entry into the study and again at 12 weeks and 24 weeks. After 12 weeks, both the IPP and experimental groups were equally superior to the drugs-only control group on the primary cognitive outcome; at 24 weeks, the experimental group performed better than both other groups on the primary cognitive outcome. Functional assessments showed no difference among groups. Findings cannot be explained simply by increased social contact, due to the nature of the IPP control. The authors explained that the lack of functional improvement may have been related to the fact that the study group was only mildly impaired, with physical and functional abilities largely intact, and did not exhibit any disruptive behaviors.

Participants receiving cognitive therapies, such as memory training, have demonstrated improvement on specific neuropsychological tests, but not on global cognitive performance or functional measures (Galante, Venturini, & Fiaccadori, 2007). Galante et al. used a program called Neuropsychological Training with one hundred exercises subdivided into six groups consisting of memory, attention, language, non-verbal intelligence, visual perception, and spatial cognition exercises. Participants were diagnosed with MCI or probable AD and on a stable dose of cholinesterase inhibitors for three months and were assigned to either a treatment or control group. The individuals in the treatment group received

12 individual 60-minute sessions of training three times per week for four weeks. The computers had touch screens, and a neuropsychologist assisted participants, choosing exercises and providing instruction. The control group received discussion on current affairs and life history. Pre-study, post-study, three-month follow-up, and nine-month follow-up assessments were completed. The participants in the active control group decreased significantly in performance at the nine-month follow-up compared to both the baseline and the three-month follow-up, while the scores of the treatment group remained stable. The researchers argued that because of the progressive cognitive decline associated with Alzheimer's disease, simply maintaining cognitive levels can be a worthy goal, as similarly argued by Viola et al. (2011) below.

Park and Bischof (2013) reinforce some of the findings described above, namely that response to cognitive training rarely transfers from the targeted areas to more global performance. These authors argued, as do other researchers, particularly those from more humanistic or holistic theoretical backgrounds, that cognitive intervention should focus on skills and abilities that have practical value in daily life, as described in several of the cognitive stimulation studies. They stressed that any effort to support people with dementia in leading more engaged lives should benefit more from activities that are intrinsically satisfying and sustained over time versus cognitive training that is temporary and removes participants from social and more purposeful activities.

With few exceptions among the studies described above (Galante et al., 2007; Tárraga et al., 2006), researchers appear to struggle in making a case for cognitive training. There are also practical issues to be considered, such as the sometimes increasingly high overhead to sustain such interventions, given the cost of the equipment and training of personnel, and issues around computer literacy that may thwart progress for some individuals.

Cognitive Rehabilitation

An important caveat for this section is that several of the studies included herein do not adhere fully to the definition of cognitive rehabilitation provided above, namely in their group treatment rather than individualized intervention prescribed by the aforementioned definition.

Yet, the programs are extensive and varied relative to the studies explicated above. Kurz, Pohl, Ramsenthaler, and Sorg (2008) examined whether their cognitive rehabilitation program improved ADLs, mood, and cognitive functioning in patients with MCI and mild dementia, and whether the potential effect was influenced by the severity of patient impairment. Forty patients participated, 30 with MCI and 10 with mild dementia. The 22-hour per week intervention was provided to fixed groups of ten participants, with waiting list controls, and was four weeks in duration. The program combined practical problem solving strategies with cognitive training, self-assertiveness training, motor exercise, relaxation techniques, and stress management. The MCI group had significant improvements on all outcome variables. Performance on ADLs increased, depression was reduced by 50%, and there were gains in verbal as well as non-verbal episodic memory. Participants with mild dementia exhibited minimal change, however. According to the researchers, the level of difficulty of some of the components likely was too high relative to participants' cognitive abilities. While their study confirms that general cognitive stimulation, recreation, and social activity can improve quality of life, mood, behavior, and general cognitive performance, the researchers argued that these strategies are less likely to produce improvements in specific cognitive abilities.

Loewenstein, Acevedo, Czaja, and Duara (2004) examined individualized rehabilitation strategies that involved spaced retrieval, dual cognitive support, and procedural memory training. Forty-four participants with possible or probable AD were randomly assigned to the cognitive rehabilitation experimental group or mental stimulation control group. All participants were taking a stable dose of cholinesterase inhibitor. A battery of neuropsychological assessments was performed at baseline, post-study, and at three-month follow-up. The treatment group received 24 training sessions, twice per week for 12 to 16 weeks. Each session lasted 45 minutes. The cognitive rehabilitation focused on face-name associations, practicing time and place orientation, activating procedural and motor memory, sustaining attention, and activating visuo-motor processing. The researchers concluded that mildly impaired AD patients on a stable dose of cholinesterase inhibitors can benefit from this cognitive-rehabilitation intervention and maintain effects over a three-month post-intervention follow-up without a maintenance session. Participants in both the treatment and control groups also experienced less depression.

Viola et al. (2011) evaluated the effects of a relatively extensive multidisciplinary rehabilitation program for individuals with AD focusing on cognition, quality of life, and neuropsychiatric symptoms. Two groups met twice per week for six and one-half hours for 12 weeks. Participants were supported by a multi-professional team on memory training, computer-assisted cognitive stimulation, expressive activities (e.g., painting, verbal expression, writing), physiotherapy, and physical training. The experimental group remained stable on scores of cognitive functioning and had significantly reduced levels of depression and other neuropsychiatric symptoms, with improved scores on measures on quality of life. Control groups displayed mild but significant worsening across outcome measures. The authors argue that their results are in line with much of the literature in that robust changes in cognition are not likely in patients with Alzheimer's disease as a consequence of cognitive training and that improvements will tend to be modest and may be best documented as a slight improvement in certain aspects of cognition.

Machado et al. (2009) sought to determine whether participation in a multidisciplinary rehabilitation center program would improve quality of life. Nineteen AD patients were divided into control and experimental groups and completed 24 sessions of group rehabilitation at a frequency of twice per week for three months. The rehabilitation included computerized cognitive stimulation, speech therapy, occupational therapy, art therapy, physical training, physiotherapy, and cognitive stimulation through reading and logic games. Support groups were offered to family, caregivers, and participants for the opportunity to exchange personal accounts and experiences. Quantitative measures of quality of life showed no significant difference pre-rehabilitation and post-rehabilitation. A qualitative measure of perceived quality of life, however, yielded a positive change among participants. Finally, there also was a significant decrease in MMSE score for the control group. The researchers argued, similar to Viola et al. (2011), that qualitative measures may be more valid assessments in this research context.

In another investigation, Carbone et al. (2013) performed a cognitive rehabilitation program in the homes of 22 participants with probable AD. Each participant received a thorough assessment and individualized program of treatment. The program consisted of individual six-hour sessions three times per week for three months. Participants received numerous therapies, emphasizing memory, reality orientation, occupational issues, reminiscence, motor rehabilitation, and supportive psychotherapy. Family members also received counseling and other supportive interventions, such as compensatory strategy training. The participants improved significantly on most measures of cognition, behavior, and ADLs. Caregivers also showed reduced physical and social burden. At three-month follow-up, however, all gains had been lost. Still, the authors argued that maintaining the status quo over a period of time may be considered a positive outcome.

The limited efficacy of cognitive training and the group rehabilitation efforts described in this chapter suggests that a more client-centered approach is warranted, specifically one that targets goals that are more meaningful to the client and the client's functioning (Clare, Evans, Parkinson, Woods, & Linden, 2011). Clare et al. refer to their method Goal Attainment Scaling (GAS), stating that, "The client plays a central role in a collaborative goal-setting process, and the client's perceptions of change serve as the primary outcome measure" (p. 222), as opposed to standardized assessments that attend to the efficacy of the program, overall. In their study, 66 participants with early-stage Alzheimer's disease who were receiving cholinesterase inhibiters participated in the intervention process. For all the goals identified, there was a mean performance rating of 4.83, and mean satisfaction of 4.97, based on a 10-point scale. Almost half the goals related to everyday memory function. Practical skills with ADLs, facility with words, and concentration were also prominent goals. A smaller number of goals focused on organization, social interaction, visual recognition, orientation, and general well-being. The cognitive rehabilitation group had eight weekly sessions that covered a client's selection of two to three goals from the set in most cases. The therapist and participant independently rated goal performance at start of the intervention, collaboratively established criteria for meeting the goal, and then rated performance at end of intervention. Analysis of participant and professional ratings prior and subsequent to the intervention resulted in significant positive indication that the goals were achieved, if not in whole (46%), in part (50%). Ratings by clients and therapists were consistent. Cognitive rehabilitation outcome ratings covered a wide range of the available 10-point scale, suggesting that participants understood the concept well and were able to identify areas in which they would like to see improvements in functioning. Though many participants tended to underestimate their memory difficulties, they were able to monitor their performance and detect problems.

There seems to be fewer studies in the area of cognitive rehabilitation relative to cognitive stimulation and cognitive training, with less consistent results. These interventions are much more involved, with considerably more variables that can complicate the research methodology. Because these interventions take substantially greater resources and can be much more expensive to implement, and because they don't seem to have any better results than cognitive stimulation, there should be considerable pause in choosing them for mainstream treatment of dementia. Of primary concern, of course, are the needs of individuals with dementia. Cognitive rehabilitation programs can be a significant burden to recipients, depending on their type, flexibility, and connections to the lives of participants. One certainly would want to avoid an outcome of reduced quality of life.

Conclusion

The lack of quality studies, variation in methodology, and conflicting results in the literature are clearly limiting and demonstrate both the challenge of research in this area and the lack of definitive evidence that exists on which to build a cognitive intervention program for individuals with dementia. The overall findings herein align with those of Calleo et al. (2012), who have observed that there exist standardized guidelines neither for the specific types of cognitive impairments or stages of cognitive decline for which treatment is most beneficial nor for the specific strategies that offer the most beneficial outcomes for patients. If there is a single conclusion to gain from this literature overview, it is that some level of cognitive intervention is better than no cognitive intervention at all, and that the more personalized and varied the program, the better the outcomes (Yu et al., 2009). Spector et al. (2003) had remarkable success simply with 14 sessions of basic group cognitive-stimulation treatment, twice per week for 45 minutes for seven weeks. They demonstrated that cognitive stimulation was more effective than most medications. The literature demonstrates that cognitive stimulation can, at minimum, enhance the effects of medication (Loewenstein et al., 2004; Yu et al., 2009).

There is significant evidence that cognitive decline can be delayed and quality of life generally improved with even a small effort at engaging individuals with dementia in activities that continue to exercise mental faculties. Much of the basic cognitive stimulation strategies can be implemented in the context of ADLs through re-orientation, conversation, and general recreation, with simply a more conscientious, person-centered caregiver approach. Indeed, of all the studies they reviewed, Sitzer et al. (2006) found that the single largest effect size was observed on measures of performance-based ADLs, resulting from compensatory procedural memory strategies. Thus, even basic interventions stand to make meaningful impacts on the lives of individuals living with dementia. In Sitzer et al.'s review, four of the five reports with the most beneficial results employed general stimulation techniques, and greater effect sizes were achieved with individualized interventions as compared to group interventions. Stimulation may include various games and puzzles, in general, or may be more specific, with engaging activities, such as reminiscent therapy and journaling with family photos. In addition to the improvements in function and quality of life that can be gained from cognitive stimulation, there is potential for significant improvement of neuropsychiatric behaviors (Niu et al., 2010). Furthermore, cognitive stimulation and its components in cognitive rehabilitation seem a more humane approach, more authentic to the lives of those living with dementia.

Cognitive training programs seem to be predominately computer-based, with some now available on mobile technologies in limited form. These programs provide very structured exercises designed to promote cognitive functioning in various domains and can be flexible and interactive with respect to a patient's level of difficulties (Galante et al., 2007). While computer-based cognitive training may provide wider accessibility and have success with the more mildly impaired individuals, the software and hardware can be expensive, the individual must have basic skills to use them properly, and treatment providers require thorough training on supporting implementation of the programs in order for them to be effective. Valenquela and Sachdev (2009) cite the ACTIVE study among others to substantiate their claim that a dose of two to three months of cognitive training may have long-lasting and persistent protective effects on cognition over a number of years, with transfer to gains in functioning as well. Plassman et al. (2010) found the ACTIVE trial to be the only study of high quality evidence, where cognitive training on processing speed or reasoning resulted in decreased risk of cognitive decline in these domains at two-year follow-up. While the ACTIVE study (Willis et al., 2006) found positive results both for the specific individual cognitive domains that were trained and for ADL function, there was some question as to the impact of such results on increased quality of life (Wolinsky et al., 2006). Still, other studies and researchers have questioned the value of cognitive training alone (Clare et al., 2011; Farina et al., 2002). While cognitive training can improve cognitive and functional abilities, the effect sizes are typically small, and there is argument that the observed benefits may largely be functions of the increased attention and interpersonal interactions received by participants (Sitzer et al., 2006). Studies on rehabilitation and stimulation, however, do appear to demonstrate greater improvements on quality of life measures than those on cognitive training.

In the context of professional in-home treatment, all of the cognitive intervention strategies discussed here are likely candidates, as many studies have had success with a combination of strategies (Galante et al., 2007). Certainly both cognitive stimulation and cognitive training can be incorporated into cognitive rehabilitation, which, in its more formal sense, also can addresses particular neuropsychological disorders (Miniussi & Vallar, 2011). Cognitive rehabilitation should include numerous assessments and an evaluation of needs based on those assessments, from which an individualized intervention program is designed to target those needs. Though not individualized, the program performed by Viola et al. (2011), for example, was rather comprehensive in its inclusion of possible interventions used; it certainly was the most inclusive of the studies reviewed herein and perhaps a model for future interventions. Yet, their outcomes were fairly flat. They interpret such results positively, however, since the degenerative nature of the associated diseases typically reduces the performance of control groups while those of the treatment groups may at least be maintained. Outcomes for their program, however, were no better than many of the less resource-intensive cognitive stimulation programs, some of which actually seemed to have better results. Also, Viola et al. (2011) actually argue for the term cognitive stimulation over rehabilitation because rehabilitation, restoring function to pre-morbid levels, simply is not possible in dementia cases.

There is a troubling lack of consistency with respect to the interventions implemented across the studies in terms of quantity, duration, quality, and type. The brevity of the timelines is particularly disturbing, especially when strategies are effective. According to Jean et al. (2010), 20 sessions over 12 weeks would suffice to be cost effective; however, they argue there is little to gain by having much more. Unfortunately, the researchers make these assessments based on a very small number of studies. More important, their context is that of clinical trials and thus already temporally limited. Some of the interventions in the studies explicated herein were completed so quickly, one may wonder how the facilitator ever had a chance to even get to know the patient, much less be effective with the intervention. At the same time, however, a number of the more extensive studies in the rehabilitation section did not seem to have any stronger outcomes than shorter-term stimulation. Based on many of the studies, continuous maintenance sessions are warranted to prevent the benefits from diminishing.

Obviously, interventions should not disrupt the life or cause undue distress to patients. Shorter sessions of 30-120 minutes (Jean et al. 2010) and longevity of the program (Orrell et al., 2005; Willis et al., 2006; Yuill & Hollis, 2011) seem the most advantageous approach. One study not discussed above (Oswald, Gunzelmann, Rupprecht, & Hagen, 2006) examined weekly, 30-minute sessions over the period of one year in six different training groups. The researchers found that the combined cognitive and physical training versus providing each independently demonstrated the greatest degree of participant improvement in cognitive and physical function, emotional status, and independent living. Also, these improvements were strongest over a five-year follow-up as compared to the other groups. Valenzuela and Sachdev (2009) corroborated the superiority of combining cognitive and physical training in their review of the literature.

Probably the most important lesson to take from this literature review is that one gold-standard approach does not yet exist for delaying onset of cognitive problems or slowing the cognitive deterioration associated with dementia. Every individual with dementia is unique, manifesting a distinct symptom picture and having a different path of progression. Therefore, each person should receive individualized assessments and treatment plans, even for the more abbreviated cognitive stimulation programs. The final study explicated in the rehabilitation section above (Carbone et al., 2013) had strong initial success with customized programs, though the improvements were not maintained at follow-up assessments. Clearly, there is an argument for sustained and lengthier interventions. Finally, Yuill and Hollis (2011) examined dementia care from an occupational therapy perspective and identified several, important person-centered themes, calling for programs to be focused on authentic, person-centered needs and goals.

References

Aguirre, E., Hoare, Z., Streater, A., Spector, A., Woods, B., Hoe, J., & Orrell, M. (2013). Cognitive stimulation therapy (CST) for people with dementia—Who benefits most? *International Journal of Geriatric Psychiatry, 28,* 284-290.

Aguirre, E., Woods, R. T., Spector, A., & Orrell, M. (2013). Cognitive stimulation for dementia: A systematic review of the evidence of effectiveness from randomised controlled trials. *Ageing Research Reviews, 12,* 253-262.

Barnes, D. E., Yaffe, K., Belfor, N., Jagust, W. J., DeCarli, C., Reed, B. R., & Kramer, J. H. (2009). Computer-based cognitive training for mild cognitive impairment: Results from a pilot randomized, controlled trial. *Alzheimer Disease and Associated Disorders, 23,* 205-210.

Binetti, G., Moretti, D. V., Scalvini, C., di Giovanni, G., Verzeletti, C., Mazzini, F., Valent, S., Ghidoni, R., & Benussi, L. (2013). Predictors of comprehensive stimulation program efficacy in patients with cognitive impairment. Clinical practice recommendations. *International Journal of Geriatric Psychiatry, 28,* 26-33.

Breuil, V., De Rotrou, J., Forette, F., Tortrat, D., Ganansia-Ganem, A., Frambourt, A., Moulin, F., & Boller, F. (1994). Cognitive stimulation of patients with dementia: Preliminary results. *International Journal of Geriatric Psychiatry, 9,* 211-217.

Calleo, J., Burrows, C., Levin, H., Marsh, L., Lai, E., & York, M. K. (2012). Cognitive rehabilitation for executive dysfunction in Parkinson's disease: Application and current directions. *Parkinson's Disease,* 512892. doi:10.1155/2012/512892

Carbone, G., Barreca, F., Mancini, G., Pauletti, G., Salvi, V., Vanacore, N., Salvitti, C., Ubaldi, F., & Sinibaldi, L. (2013). A home assistance model for dementia: Outcome in patients with mild-to-moderate Alzheimer's disease after three months. *Annali dell'Istituto Superiore di Sanità, 49,* 34-41.

Clare, L., Evans, S., Parkinson, C., Woods, R., & Linden, D. (2011). Goal-setting in cognitive rehabilitation for people with early-stage Alzheimer's disease. *Clinical Gerontologist, 34,* 220-236.

Clare, L., & Woods, R. T. (2004). Cognitive training and cognitive rehabilitation for people with early-stage Alzheimer's disease: A review. *Neuropsychological Rehabilitation, 14,* 385-401.

Cooper, C., Mukadam, N., Katona, C., Lyketsos, C. G., Ames, D., Rabins, P., Engedal, K., de Mendonça Lima C., Blazer, D., Teri, L., Brodaty, H., Livingston, G.; & World Federation of Biological Psychiatry – Old Age Taskforce. (2012). Systematic review of the effectiveness of non-pharmacological interventions to improve quality of life of people with dementia. *International Psychogeriatrics, 24,* 856-870.

de Werd, M. M., Boelen, D., Rikkert, M. G. O., & Kessels, R. P. (2013). Errorless learning of everyday tasks in people with dementia. *Clinical Interventions in Aging, 8,* 1177-1190.

Farina, E., Fioravanti, R., Chiavari, L., Imbornone, E., Alberoni, M., Pomati, S., Pinardi, G., Pignatti, R., & Mariani, C. (2002). Comparing two programs of cognitive training in Alzheimer's disease: A pilot study. Acta Neurologica Scandinavica, 105, 365-371.

Folstein, M. F., Folstein, S. E., & McHugh, P. R. (1975). "Mini-Mental State": A practical method for grading the cognitive state of outpatients for the clinician. *Journal of Psychiatric Research, 12,* 189-198.

Gaitán, A., Garolera, M., Cerulla, N., Chico, G., Rodriguez-Querol, M., & Canela-Soler, J. (2013). Efficacy of an adjunctive computer-based cognitive training program in amnestic mild cognitive impairment and Alzheimer's disease: A single-blind, randomized clinical trial. *International Journal of Geriatric Psychiatry, 28,* 91-99.

Galante, E., Venturini, G., & Fiaccadori, C. (2007). Computer-based cognitive intervention for dementia: Preliminary results of a randomized clinical trial. *Giornale Italiano di Medicina del Lavoro ed Ergonomia, 29*(3 Suppl. B), B26-32.

Gates, N., Sachdev, P., Fiatarone Singh, M., & Valenzuela, M. (2011). Cognitive and memory training in adults at risk of dementia: A systematic review. *BMC Geriatrics, 11*, 1-14.

Hall, C. B., Lipton, R. B., Sliwinski, M., Katz, M. J., Derby, C. A., & Verghese, J. (2009). Cognitive activities delay onset of memory decline in persons who develop dementia. *Neurology, 73*, 356-361.

Helzner, E. P., Scarmeas, N., Cosentino, S., Portet, F., & Stern, Y. (2007). Leisure activity and cognitive decline in incident Alzheimer disease. *Archives of Neurology, 64*, 1749-1754.

Jankowsky, J. L., Melnikova, T., Fadale, D. J., Xu, G. M., Slunt, H. H., Gonzales, V., Younkin, L. H., Younkin, S. G., Borchelt, D. R., & Savonenko, A. V. (2005). Environmental enrichment mitigates cognitive deficits in a mouse model of Alzheimer's disease. *Journal of Neuroscience, 25*, 5217-5224.

Jean, L., Bergeron, M-È., Thivierge, S., & Simard, M. (2010). Cognitive intervention programs for individuals with mild cognitive impairment: Systematic review of the literature. *American Journal of Geriatric Psychiatry, 18*, 281-296.

Kurtz, M. M., Seltzer, J. C., Shagan, D. S., Thime, W. R., & Wexler, B. E. (2007). Computer-assisted cognitive remediation in schizophrenia: What is the active ingredient? *Schizophrenia Research, 89*, 251-260.

Kurz, A., Pohl, C., Ramsenthaler, M., & Sorg, C. (2008). Cognitive rehabilitation in patients with mild cognitive impairment. *International Journal of Geriatric Psychiatry, 24*, 163-168.

Loewenstein, D. A., Acevedo, A., Czaja, S. J., & Duara, R. (2004). Cognitive rehabilitation of mildly impaired Alzheimer disease patients on cholinesterase inhibitors. *American Journal of Geriatric Psychiatry, 12*, 395-402.

Machado, F., Nunes, P. V., Viola, L. F., Santos, F. S., Forlenza, O. V., & Yassuda, M. S. (2009). Quality of life and Alzheimer's disease: Influence of participation at a rehabilitation center. *Dementia and Neuropsychologia, 3,* 241-247.

Mapelli, D., Di Rosa, E., Nocita, R., & Sava, D. (2013). Cognitive stimulation in patients with dementia: Randomized controlled trial. *Dementia and Geriatric Cognitive Disorders Extra, 3,* 263-271.

Martin, M., Clare, L., Altgassen, A. M., Cameron, M. H., & Zehnder, F. (2011). Cognition-based interventions for healthy older people and people with mild cognitive impairment. *Cochrane Database of Systematic Reviews,* (1): CD006220. doi: 10.1002/14651858.CD006220.pub2.

Miniussi, C., & Vallar, G. (2011). Brain stimulation and behavioural cognitive rehabilitation: A new tool for neurorehabilitation? *Neuropsychological Rehabilitation, 21,* 553-559.

Niu, Y.-X., Tan, J.-P., Guan, J-Q., Zhang, Z-Q., & Wang, L-N. (2010). Cognitive stimulation therapy in the treatment of neuropsychiatric symptoms in Alzheimer's disease: A randomized controlled trial. *Clinical Rehabilitation, 24,* 1102-1111.

Olazarán, J., Reisberg, B., Clare, L., Cruz, I., Peña-Casanova, J., del Ser, T., Woods, B., Beck, C., Auer, S., Lai, C., Spector, A., Fazio, S., Bond, J., Kivipelto, M., Brodaty, H., Rojo, J. M., Collins, H., Teri, L., Mittelman, M., Orrell, M., Feldman, H. H., & Muñiz, R. (2010). Nonpharmacological therapies in Alzheimer's disease: A systematic review of efficacy. *Dementia and Geriatric Cognitive Disorders, 30,* 161-178.

Onder, G., Zanetti, O., Giacobini, E., Frisoni, G. B., Bartorelli, L., Carbone, G., Lambertucci, P., Caterina Silveri, M., & Bernabei, R.. (2005). Reality orientation therapy combined with cholinesterase inhibitors in Alzheimer's disease: Randomised controlled trial. *British Journal of Psychiatry, 187,* 450-455.

Orrell, M., Spector, A., Thorgrimsen, L., & Woods, B. (2005). A pilot study examining the effectiveness of maintenance cognitive stimulation therapy (MCST) for people with dementia. *International Journal of Geriatric Psychiatry, 20*, 446-451.

Oswald, W., Gunzelmann, T., Rupprecht, R., & Hagen, B. (2006). Differential effects of single versus combined cognitive and physical training with older adults: The SimA study in a 5-year perspective. *European Journal of Ageing, 3*, 179-192.

Park, D. C., & Bischof, G. N. (2013). The aging mind: Neuroplasticity in response to cognitive training. *Dialogues in Clinical Neuroscience, 15*, 109-119.

Plassman, B. L., Williams, J. W., Burke, J. R., Holsinger, T., & Benjamin, S. (2010). Systematic review: Factors associated with risk for and possible prevention of cognitive decline in later life. *Annals of Internal Medicine, 153*, 182-193.

Schecker, M., Pirnay-Dummer, P., Schmidtke, K., Hentrich-Hesse, T., & Borchardt, D. (2013). Cognitive interventions in mild Alzheimer's disease: A therapy-evaluation study on the interaction of medication and cognitive treatment. *Dementia and Geriatric Cognitive Disorders Extra, 3*, 301-311.

Sitzer, D. I., Twamley, E. W., & Jeste, D. V. (2006). Cognitive training in Alzheimer's disease: A meta-analysis of the literature. *Acta Psychiatrica Scandinavica, 114*, 75-90.

Spector, A., Thorgrimsen, L., Woods, B., Royan, L., Davies, S., Butterworth, M., & Orrell, M. (2003). Efficacy of an evidence-based cognitive stimulation therapy programme for people with dementia randomised controlled trial. *British Journal of Psychiatry, 183*, 248-254.

Tárraga, L., Boada, M., Modinos, G., Espinosa, A., Diego, S., Morera, A., Guitart, M., Balcells, J., Lopez, O. L., & Becker, J. T. (2006). A randomised pilot study to assess the efficacy of an interactive, multimedia tool of cognitive stimulation in Alzheimer's disease. *Journal of Neurology, Neurosurgery and Psychiatry, 77*, 1116-1121.

Valenzuela, M., & Sachdev, P. (2009). Can cognitive exercise prevent the onset of dementia? Systematic review of randomized clinical trials with longitudinal follow-up. *American Journal of Geriatric Psychiatry, 17*, 179-187.

Verghese, J., Lipton, R. B., Katz, M. J., Hall, C. B., Derby, C. A., Kuslansky, G., Ambrose, A. F., Sliwinski, M., & Buschke, H. (2003). Leisure activities and the risk of dementia in the elderly. *New England Journal of Medicine, 348*, 2508-2516.

Viola, L. F., Nunes, P. V., Yassuda, M. S., Aprahamian, I., Santos, F. S., Santos, G. D., Brum, P. S., Borges, S. M., Oliveira, A. M., Chaves, G. F. S., Ciasca, E. C., Ferreira, R. C. R., de Paula, V. J. R., Takeda, O. H., Mirandez, R. M., Watari, R., Falcao, D. V. S., Cachioni, M., & Forlenza, O. V. (2011). Effects of a multidisciplinar cognitive rehabilitation program for patients with mild Alzheimer's disease. *Clinics, 66*, 1395-1400.

Willis, S. L., Tennstedt, S. L., Marsiske, M., Ball, K., Elias, J., Koepke, K. M., Morris, J. N., Rebok, G. W., Unverzagt, F. W., Stoddard, A. M., & Wright, E., for the ACTIVE Study Group. (2006). Long-term effects of cognitive training on everyday functional outcomes in older adults. *JAMA, 296*, 2805-2814.

Wilson, R. S., Mendes De Leon, C. F., Barnes, L. L., Schneider, J. A., Bienias, J. L., Evans, D. A., & Bennett, D. A. (2002). Participation in cognitively stimulating activities and risk of incident Alzheimer disease. *JAMA, 287*, 742-748.

Wolinsky, F. D., Unverzagt, F. W., Smith, D. M., Jones, R., Wright, E., & Tennstedt, S. L. (2006). The effects of the ACTIVE cognitive training trial on clinically relevant declines in health-related quality of life. *Journals of Gerontology, Series B: Psychological Sciences, 61*, S281-S287.

Yu, F., Rose, K. M., Burgener, S. C., Cunningham, C., Buettner, L. L., Beattie, E., Bossen, A. L., Buckwalter, K. C., Fick, D. M., Fitzsimmons, S., Kolanowski, A., Janet, K., Specht, P., Richeson, N. E., Testad, I., & McKenzie, S. E. (2009). Cognitive training for early-stage Alzheimer's disease and dementia. *Journal of Gerontological Nursing, 35*, 23-29.

Yuill, N., & Hollis, V. (2011). A systematic review of cognitive stimulation therapy for older adults with mild to moderate dementia: An occupational therapy perspective. *Occupational Therapy International, 18*, 163-186.

Zanetti, O., Zanieri, G., Giovanni, G. D., De Vreese, L. P., Pezzini, A., Metitieri, T., & Trabucchi, M. (2001). Effectiveness of procedural memory stimulation in mild Alzheimer's disease patients: A controlled study. *Neuropsychological Rehabilitation, 11*, 263-272.

CHAPTER 11

Treatment of Dementia: Past, Present, and Future

Samuel T. Gontkovsky

The history of dementia likely is as old as humankind itself (Boller & Forbes, 1998). The term dementia is dervied from Latin, translating to "without mind," underscoring the devestating cognitive impacts that the syndrome can have on the lives of those it touches. In their historical overview concerning the conceptualization of dementia and Alzheimer's disease from the Greco-Roman period through the 1960s, Berchtold and Cotman (1998) cite the Greek physician, Pythagoras, of the 7th century B.C. as making one of the earliest references to age-related mental deficiency. Viewing the life cycle as five distinct stages, commencing respectively at ages 7, 21, 49, 63, and 81, the last two were designated by Pythagoras as the *senium*, or old age, and were characterized by the decline and decay of the human body and the regression of mental capacities. Based on the writings of Pythagoras, Becrchtold and Cotman conclude that such extreme regressions in mental capacities with age must have been observed fairly frequently during this time period, and were seriously enough to be incorporated into lawmaking and storytelling.

In today's world, despite the increasing public attention given to Alzheimer's disease and dementia, the use of these terms in discussions with family members who may be experiencing cognitive problems still can pose discomfort and a sense of stigma. According to figures provided by the Alzheimer's Association (2013), more than five million Americans presently are living with Alzheimer's disease, and one in three seniors will die with Alzheimer's disease or some other form of dementia. In 2012, 15.4 million caregivers provided more than 17.5 billion hours of unpaid care to individuals with dementia valued at $216 billion. Further, in 2013, Alzheimer's disease will cost the United States $203 billion, and this number is projected to rise to $1.2 trillion by the year 2050. Further, it has been estimated by Larrabee and Crook (1994) that for every person diagnosed with dementia, several other individuals suffer from undiagnosed cognitive impairments that significantly affect their quality of life. These figures very clearly demonstrate the overwhelming societal cost and burden of dementia and the associated need for more effective treatments.

Treatment of Dementia

Past

A comprehensive review of the history of dementia and its treatment is beyond the scope of this chapter, but I will begin with a short overview of the management and treatment of dementia prior to the late 20th century before moving on to discuss the current treatment approaches for dementia. Until the late 19th century, dementia often was conceptualized much more broadly relative to the present time, and essentially described individuals who had lost the capability to reason. The term therefore described nearly any and all forms of mental illness and associated psychosocial incapacity, whether psychiatric or organic in origin. Both Plato and Aristotle comment in their writings during the 4th century B.C. on mental failure in old age, with the conviction that old age is inseparable from mental failure. During the 2nd century A.D., the Roman physician, Galen, included morosis in his list of mental diseases and cited old age as one of the factors leading to its development, going on to describe old age as an unnatural and inevitable infection of the body (Berchtold & Cotman, 1998).

During the 13th century, Roger Bacon described old age as being characterized by forgetfulness as well as by problems with reasoning and imagination, each of which he attributed to damage in specific regions of the brain. Various literary figures in the 14th through the 16th centuries, including Chaucer and Shakespeare, also made reference in their works to the mental deterioration associated with aging, which gradually became known as senility. During the 17th century, varying forms of dementia became better characterized from a behavioral perspective and were shaped into more defined and distinct concepts. In addition, as dissection of the human body became tolerated, there was an increasing trend by anatomists toward searching for underlying physiological changes in the brain that might be the source of mental disorders (Berchtold & Cotman, 1998). It was not until the 19th century, however, that physicians, such as James Parkinson, Alois Alzheimer, and Otto Binswanger, began to more clearly describe and distinguish the various forms of dementia recognized in contemporary science and medicine.

In terms of the historical approaches for treating symptoms of dementia, it likely will come as no surprise, given the limited efficacy of today's medications in producing meaningful improvement in patient functioning, that historically, little, if anything, was available to alleviate the suffering of those with substantial cognitive and functional deficits. It is likely that some patients were treated with bloodletting, a practice used in some ancient cultures to release demons and bad energy as well as to restore the body's balance of fluids. Even during medieval and Renaissance Europe, individuals frequently were bled to reduce inflammation, which was thought to be the basis of most, if not all, diseases.

Prior to the 19th century, mentally insane individuals, including those with senile dementia, generally were incarcerated in prisons. It was not until the humanitarian efforts of Phillippe Pinel, French professor and consulting physician to Napolean, in establishing "madness" as a disease rather than a crime that conditions for individuals with dementia began to change (Berchtold & Cotman, 1998). Nevertheless, separation from mainstream society remained the foremost outcome for individuals with dementia. Those persons incapable of being managed appropriately within the home by family or other caregivers often were institutionalized within state psychiatric facilities or nursing homes.

Present

As discussed in Chapter 1, the present conceptualization of dementia is that of a non-specific syndrome, consisting of a clinical presentation characterized by a range of signs and symptoms related to neurocognition and functional status, the specific etiology of which must be determined through a comprehensive examination process in order to formulate a plan of treatment. The advent in the late 20th century of pharmacological agents to potentially address the symptoms associated with Alzheimer's disease and other forms of dementia represented the first major breakthrough in terms of medical treatment.

Medications presently remain the primary form of medical intervention for dementia, yet a cure remains elusive. As noted in Chapter 2, the goal of current pharmacological agents is to slow the cognitive and functional decline associated with dementia, but the efficacy of these drugs is quite limited. As individuals with dementia experience ongoing deterioration of functioning over time, institutionalization continues to be a common eventual outcome. Although there certainly exist many quality facilities for the placement of individuals with dementia, the ideal situation is for the patient to remain in the familiar environment of home for as long as possible. Power (2010) discusses in detail the multitude of problematic issues with the traditional nursing home model, which often includes the use of sedative medications as a means for managing the disruptive behavioral issues of patients. In such instances, the institutional setting serves merely as a warehouse for holding individuals until their eventual demise.

Given that individuals are living longer in conjunction with the fact that rates of individuals developing dementia continues to rise, many skilled nursing and assisted living facilities have begun establishing specialty care units for residents with dementia, the rationale generally being to provide a higher degree of patient care and safety as well as tailored activities specifically for those with cognitive impairments. Unfortunately, early research revealed that individuals with dementia placed in nursing home special care units experience no significant difference in the rate of functional decline compared with those residing in traditional units (Phillips et al., 1997). More recent research revealed that individuals with dementia placed in specialty care units were significantly less likely to use bed rails, which have been implicated in falls and injuries, and feeding tubes but were more likely to have received psychotropic medications, primarily antipsychotics (Gruneir, Lapane, Miller, & Mor, 2007), which, as discussed in Chapter 2, can be unsafe from a medical standpoint. Gruneir, Miller, Intrator, and Mor (2007) also reported findings suggesting that directed management of chronic conditions in patients with cognitive impairment, as indicated by facilities' investment in special care units, reduces the risk of hospitalization. They noted, however, that fragmentation in the financing system, as illustrated by the effect of bed-hold policies, often impedes these efforts.

A study by Thomas et al. (2004) examined reasons for the institutionalization of individuals with dementia who previously were residing at home. Dependence was the primary problem identified as ultimately resulting in the institutionalization of the person with dementia. Other patient issues that emerged as posing challenges for caregivers included incontinence, inappropriate motor behaviors, agitation/violence, and poor motivation associated with opposition to care. In addition, it was found that caregivers often required respite from care as well as assistance in coping with the burden of providing care. Based on these findings, the authors recommended efforts to better utilize in-home care for patients with dementia, with greater emphasis directed toward preventing loss of autonomy and its consequences.

In this light and based on, 1) the limited clinical effectiveness of medications in treating dementia, as discussed in Chapter 2, 2) the concepts of neuroplasticity and brain reorganization described in Chapter 3, and 3) the promising empirical research supporting non-pharmacological approaches in promoting brain health, delaying onset of cognitive symptoms, and slowing the cognitive and functional decline in individuals diagnosed with mild cognitive impairment or dementia reviewed in Chapters 4-10, Home Care Assistance, one of the leading providers of home care in North America, established in 2012 a scientific division, known as Dementia Therapeutics, dedicated to furthering research and development related to cognitive issues in the elderly.

During the late spring of 2013, Home Care Assistance launched its newly established Cognitive Therapeutics intervention program. Developed by the interdisciplinary team of professionals comprising the Dementia Therapeutics division and based on the latest scientific research, this program offered an innovative approach to care through individually tailored, non-pharmacological interventions for persons with Alzheimer's disease and other forms of dementia and cognitive impairments within the home environment. Clients in the program are provided with a range of interventions across the various domains described in Chapters 4-10, with services being administered through one-to-one interactions with staff members multiple times per week. Intervention plans not only are uniquely tailored to each individual client, but also are dynamic, as they are modified and adapted based on client performance and preferences as well as changes in functioning. Thus, the program remains new, relevant, challenging, exciting, and enjoyable.

Although a number of companies are promoting cognitive enhancement programs, technologies, and games for promoting brain health and functioning, most are targeted to individuals without significant cognitive impairment. Programs and interventions developed for individuals with dementia rarely offer individually-tailored intervention plans and one-to-one staff interaction within the home environment.

Power (2010) states that current non-pharmacological alternatives to medication often fall short of meeting their intended outcomes in practice because they are too brief in duration and do not exert influence required to facilitate a meaningful change in the underlying environment of the individual with dementia. Cognitive Therapeutics generally is regarded as an ongoing program of intervention, and can be considered parallal to other lifestyle changes promoting improved health, such as healthy diet and physical exercise. Thus, the intervention represents a lifestyle change for healthy cognitive and functional longevity. Indeed, lifestyle choices may represent the largest influence in preventing Alzheimer's disease and dementia, as noted in Chapter 1, and may be the most efficacious and promising solution for slowing neurocognitive and functional decline at the present time.

Future

Of course, the future of dementia treatment is uncertain. Without question, incredible resources are being allocated to the development of more effective and efficient strategies for diagnosing and treating Alzheimer's disease and other forms of dementia. Research efforts targeted at identifying disease biomarkers should help in diagnosis as well as in tracking progression, which ideally will assist in the development of new treatments. Pharmaceutical companies continue to explore routes for drug targeting; however, recent trials essentially have been failures, so it is difficult to remain optimistic in this regard, at least with respect to the near future. Several of the more promising pharmacological avenues for treatment were discussed in Chapter 2. In closing I will provide a brief overview of just a few of the promising non-pharmacological medical interventions presently being explored for the treatment of Alzheimer's disease and other forms of dementia.

Laser Treatment. A collaborative group of researchers from Chalmers University of Technology in Sweden and the Institute of Physical and Theoretical Chemistry in Poland recently proposed that the enhanced multi-photon absorption of insulin and lysozyme amyloid beta as well as α-synuclein fibers is due to a cooperative mechanism involving through-space dipolar coupling between excited states of aromatic amino acids densely packed in the fibrous structures. Further, they suggest that this finding will provide the opportunity to develop non-linear optical techniques to detect and study amyloid structures and that new protein-based materials with sizable multi-photon absorption could be designed for specific applications in nanotechnology, photonics, and optoelectronics (Hanczyc, Samoc, & Norden, 2013). Simply stated, it may be possible to treat Alzheimer's disease, Parkinson's disease, and other forms of dementia by using a multi-photon laser, or photo acoustic therapy, to remove the malfunctioning proteins associated with these conditions.

Hyperbaric Oxygen Therapy. As discussed in Chapter 1, vascular dementia may be developed secondary to a stroke, or cerebrovascular accident. In the rehabilitation process of individuals who have suffered a stroke, the greatest benefit from treatment generally is thought to occur soon after injury (i.e., within the first six months), at which time rehabilitation efforts can capitalize on the short time window of neuroplasticity that has been demonstrated to occur. In a recent prospective, randomized, controlled trial, Efrati et al. (2013) investigated whether increasing the level of dissolved oxygen by hyperbaric oxygen therapy (HBOT) could activate neuroplasticity in patients with chronic neurologic deficiencies due to stroke suffered 6-36 months prior to participation in the study. Patients were randomly assigned to either a treatment group or cross control group. Brain activity was assessed by single-photon emission computed tomography (SPECT) imaging. Patients in the treatment group were evaluated at baseline and following 40 HBOT sessions; those in the cross control group were evaluated at baseline, after a two-month control period of no treatment, and after subsequent two-months of 40 HBOT sessions. The HBOT protocol consisted of 40 90-minute sessions, administered five days per week over a two-month span at 100% oxygen at two ATA. Findings revealed that the neurological functions and quality of life for all patients in both groups were significantly improved following the HBOT sessions, while no improvement was found during the control period of those in the cross control group. Results of SPECT imaging also were correlated with clinical improvement. Elevated brain activity was detected primarily in regions of live cells, as confirmed by computed tomography (CT), with low activity based on SPECT. Based on these findings, it appears that HBOT can lead to significant neurological improvements in post-stroke patients, even at chronic stages, implying that neuroplasticity still can be activated long after onset of damage in regions where there is a brain CT/SPECT, anatomy/physiology, mismatch.

Transcranial Magnetic Stimulation. Transcranial magnetic stimulation (TMS) is a non-invasive technique for producing depolarization or hyperpolarization of neurons using electromagnetic induction to induce weak electric currents, which results in activity in the brain allowing for the study of interconnections and functioning. TMS has demonstrated neuroplastic effects analogous to long-term potentiation and long-term depression (see Chapter 3 for a discussion of these concepts), and therapeutic applications presently are being explored for post-stroke recovery as well as treatment of Alzheimer's disease (Luber, McClintock, & Lisanby, (2013). Although still in the early stages of investigation, TMS, whether used alone or in combination with pharmacologic intervention, shows promise in treating cognitive deficits post-stroke and in dementia (Smith, 2013).

Genetic Paths. Eleven new genes linked to late-onset Alzheimer's disease recently were found following a two-stage, meta-analysis of genome-wide association studies in individuals of European ancestry, which included genetic data from more than 25,500 individuals with Alzheimer's disease and more than 48,000 persons without the disease from 15 countries (Lambert et al., 2013). Some of these newly discovered genes are tied to immune response and inflammation, while others are related to cell migration and brain pathways (see Chapter 3 for a discussion of these concepts). Discovery of these new genes doubles the number now known to be associated with Alzheimer's disease and provides the opportunity for more precise drug therapy targets and allows for additional opportunities to explore potential common mechanisms that may underlie Alzheimer's disease and other neurological diseases causing dementia.

Conclusion

As this chapter illustrates, we have certainly advanced in our understanding of dementia, but still have so far to go. Technological advances continue to expand our understanding of the correlates of various disease processes and potentially enable us to more accurately identify those who may be at increased risk for development of dementia. Although a cure for Alzheimer's disease and other forms of dementia remains elusive, the growing base of knowledge hopefully will translate into more effective treatments and interventions. The small number of promising avenues of investigation discussed in this chapter only touches upon the expansive volume of research being conducted in this area. Although the lines of investigation mentioned herein clearly offer hope, much more research is needed before firm conclusions can be made and effective treatment protocols developed. At the present time and for the foreseeable immediate future, it appears that existing pharmacological agents will remain the first-line treatment for Alzheimer's disease and other forms of dementia. Given their limited efficacy, however, the non-pharmacological approaches discussed in this text appear to offer the best means at the present time for promoting brain health, delaying the onset of neurocognitive impairment, and slowing the progression of the cognitive and functional decline associated with chronic and progressive dementias.

To learn more about Home Care Assistance, please visit **www.HomeCareAssistance.com**. To learn more about The Cognitive Therapeutics Method, please visit **www.CognitiveTherapeutics.com**

References

Alzheimer's Association. (2013). Alzheimer's disease facts and figures. *Alzheimer's and Dementia, 9*, 208-245.

Berchtold, N. C., & Cotman, C. W. (1998). Evolution in the conceptualization of dementia and Alzheimer's disease: Greco-Roman period to the 1960s. *Neurobiology of Aging, 19*, 173-189.

Boller, F., & Forbes, M. M. (1998). History of dementia and dementia in history: An overview. *Journal of the Neurological Sciences, 158*, 125-133.

Efrati, S., Fishlev, G., Bechor, Y., Volkov, O., Bergan, J., Kliakhandler, K., Kamiager, I., Gal, N., Friedman, M., Ben-Jacob, E., & Golan, H. (2013). Hyperbaric oxygen induces late neuroplasticity in post stroke patients - Randomized, prospective trial. *PLoS ONE 8, e*53716. doi:10.1371/journal.pone.0053716

Gruneir, A., Lapane, K. L., Miller, S. C., & Mor, V. (2007). Is dementia special care really special? A new look at an old question. *Journal of the American Geriatrics Society, 56*, 199-205.

Gruneir, A., Miller, S. C., Intrator, O., & Mor, V. (2007). Hospitalization of nursing home residents with cognitive impairments: The influence of organizational features and state policies. *The Gerontologist, 47*, 447-456.

Hanczyc, P., Samoc, M., & Norden, B. (2013). Multiphoton absorption in amyloid protein fibres. *Nature Photonics*, doi:10.1038/nphoton.2013.282

Lambert, J-C., Ibrahim-Verbaas, C. A., Harold, D., Naj, A. C., Sims, R., Bellenguez, C., Jun, G., De Stefano, A. L., Bis, J. C., Beecham, G. W., Grenier-Boley, B., Russo, G.,Thornton-Wells, T. A., Jones, N., Smith, A. V., Chouraki, V., Thomas, C., Ikram, M. A., Zelenika, D., Vardarajan, B. N., Kamatani, Y., Lin, C-F., Gerrish, A., Schmidt, H., Kunkle, B., et al. (2013). Meta-analysis of 74,046 individuals identifies 11 new susceptibility loci for Alzheimer's disease. *Nature Genetics*, doi:10.1038/ng.2802

Larrabee, G. J., & Crook, T. H. (1994). Estimated prevalence of age-related memory impairment derived from standardized tests of memory function. *International Psychogeriatrics, 6,* 95-104.

Luber, B., McClintock, S., & Lisanby, S. H. (2013). Applications of transcranial magnetic stimulation and magnetic seizure therapy in the study and treatment of disorders related to cerebral aging. *Dialogues in Clinical Neuroscience, 15,* 87-98.

Phillips, C. D., Sloane, P. D., Hawes, C., Koch, G., Han, J., Spry, K., Dunteman, G., Williams, R. L. (1997). Effects of residence in Alzheimer disease special care units on functional outcomes. *JAMA, 278,* 1340-1344.

Power, G. A. (2010). Dementia beyond drugs: Changing the culture of care. Baltimore, MD: Health Professions Press. Smith, G. S. (2013). Aging and neuroplasticity. *Dialogues in Clinical Neuroscience, 15,* 3-5.

Thomas, P., Ingrand, P., Lalloue, F., Hazif-Thomas, C., Billon, R., Viéban, F., & Clément, J. P. (2004). Reasons of informal caregivers for institutionalizing dementia patients previously living at home: The Pixel study. *International Journal of Geriatric Psychiatry, 19,* 127-135.